Atlantic Tales

Shiner saw a fish leap from the midst of the most broken turmoil —
a curve of white and tarnished silver (p. 94)

Atlantic Tales

Contributions to
The Atlantic Monthly
1927 – 1947

Henry Williamson

THE HENRY WILLIAMSON SOCIETY

This collection first published 2007

The Henry Williamson Society
14 Nether Grove
Longstanton
Cambs

Standard edition ISBN 978-1-873507-26-1
Limited edition ISBN 978-1-873507-27-8

Typesetting and design by John Gregory
Printed and bound by RPM Reprographics (Chichester) Ltd

CONTENTS

INTRODUCTION

THESE ARE STORIES GOOD enough to be read many times, as one might listen to a Chopin nocturne or a Schubert song. They can become as dear to the listener. In your several moods from time to time they fill the same need for the familiar: the peace of understanding, the admiration for ability, the star point of brilliance which is found nowhere else. These are among the best of my father's words. I grew up with them, for they tell of the lost time of my boyhood. But they tell a much wider story than the landscape I with my own eyes saw. Several more layers have been peeled back in the telling. This exposed world is new country that my childish eyes never saw. I am as startled now as I was when I first read them years ago, at the depth to which the author saw and the experiences he had to have to see so much. Some (perhaps most) have appeared elsewhere but, like Beethoven, Father was very canny at changing details to maintain his sales and there are several little nuances of difference in the versions here that give them a freshness worth exploring. Besides in their very collectiveness they take on a new meaning: these are *The Atlantic Monthly* tales – the tales the editors on the other side of the water chose for their readership. That alone gives them a special cachet – a piquancy of flavour.

I would like to share with you my thoughts about my own favourites: starting with 'The Crow Starver'. Note first the clever device of placing innocence with anger in the first sentence. This intrigues us, for it is unexpected. He has our attention. He persuades us to continue, by entering the boy's personality. Father absorbed half the raw material for his writing life as a boy. It remained fresh and was often re-used in the later novels. Then there is the persuasive cadence of the rhythm. The short sentences fall continually in almost equal lengths like pentameters in steep curves from left to right. It becomes mesmeric, like watching continual white plumes of a waterfall dropping. I could go on – but will give just one last example of the unexpected among the dozens here. 'He made tea in an old marmalade pot.' Subconsciously, one is expecting an old teapot – but that would be a forbidden cliché.

'Strange Birds' shows the proximity of Jefferies and it is quite pleasant to enjoy briefly the ambience of ancient sunlight. But 'Night Music of Birds' is the new voice that brought *Tarka*. This is almost interchangeable with those unearthly moments of rapture. Here again is the spirit of poetry with again almost its classical rhythms in the prose. It also shows the unhappy user of words longing to have the power of music which seems far more beguiling.

'Linhay on the Downs' is an adventure much loved by the readership. It is a fable, an allegory, a haunting memory of times past. Partly it is the writer's look back in anguish to the mainspring of his energy – the battlefields: the suffering is borne by a rabbit but more especially a wounded fox. Here again is the familiar alter ego of the damaged psyche and the attempts to mend the wounds. We see this continually throughout the writer's career. Death is often allowed in the stories – Tarka, Willie Maddison, Manfred, Chee-kai. Here we must remember that this is a fable, can be contrived, has all the artefacts of the romantic drama, and with as upstaged a plot as might be found in the genre, be it Schubert lieder or a Sherlock Holmes' adventure. Accept this and you may enter an underworld brilliantly utilised by Goethe, Pope, Milton, and all religions. Perhaps this story of the fox is not entirely true. But perhaps it is. Little matter. Story-telling, whether from Ancient Egyptians, Shamans, Gospels or Sagas, is heavily embroidered. The human mind demands such medicine for its arousal, understanding, and quiescence. The story is certainly clearly a catharsis for the author.

Another theme that returns again and again in his career is the storm. As always, it is lovingly described. It appears finally in *The Gale of the World*, where another animal shares much the same majestic scenery, even as the Fool shares King Lear's misery on the heath near Dover.

'Muggy' is akin to those stories sold to Fleet Street in the Twenties and onwards for the next forty years up to those in the *Daily Express* in the Sixties. It is pure reportage, with facts, for the reader's curiosity. But what lifts it above all the later tales are the additions of dialogue and personal detail. These are casual and apparently effortless, but they are as telling as the daubed chairs in the Van Gogh paintings. Both would be too parochial and naïve if placed as if lifted from a tape recorder or a camera. The dialogue is stitched into those facts with the same skill to highlight as the brush is used to show shadows and moods and isolation that give the simple scenes inside the house at Arles that tragic drama.

This leads us to another display of story-telling at its best in 'The Heller'. I love this story. Here again is the perfect understanding and word painting of the marsh; the tide moving, the thorn hedge, the frightened dog, all building onwards to an unknown drama. A useful device to capture attention is description of inconsequential detail we all record during dramas. The marshman's book *The History of the Jews* is as unexpected a juxtaposition as it is possible to imagine, yet willy-nilly it somehow focuses us on him and fascinates with ambiguity. To remove the book would be to remove the brief jokes in a Beethoven piano sonata that scared the pants off contemporary critics. In this story the mind seizes on these trite details giving what psychiatrists call obsessional defence mechanism – which is to cling wildly to escape, or normality. It is that story-telling technique of minutiae that pulls us through *Tarka* (Tarka playing with an empty cocoa tin), or Richard Maddison in his youthful tennis togs feeling the distant tremors of the artillery barrage through the calm summer air of England.

'Swagdagger' is another apparently simple story. The idea seems to have come from an adventure Henry's father-in-law Charles Hibbert recounted which happened to him. A family of stoats, travelling as they will in single file in rippling line astern, were so intent on getting safely across a field they climbed up the stationary figure, aware more of danger from the sky than of my tweed-clad grandfather.

'Christmas' is my father at his best as a man, as he always hoped to be and sometimes was. It was no real matter that sometimes he was not. He knew the faults in himself and a story is usually so much better than real life anyway. If it was not we would have no need for them. They give escape for both listener and teller. In this thumbnail sketch are all the ingredients for the social plum pudding: Yule log and reindeer, enough human contact in the bright eyes and fantasies of the children to stitch the thing together – almost as good as 'The Crow Starver'.

'Moonlight' is an adventure we all know well: the moon haunts with a promise of escape. Is it dream, or reality? It is not an unhappy story of 'unhappy me – see how I suffer and nobody cares'. It is everyone's story, told with clever simile and reassurance that in fact all will be well if you learn not to fight yourself as well as all the rest of the world. The more we read into these stories we see how the writer is learning to cope with horrid reality, and the advice is free to us. Thoreau said: 'The majority of people live lives of quiet desperation.' As with horror movies, it is good to see that our lives are not alone. *The Pathway* was for a large and untethered generation almost a blueprint for survival. Father's stories give the same camaraderie. In the Thirties there were few totems for lost generations in England and America as there are today with the present mass industry of pop and blog. Sins, guilt and despair are common to all and these *Atlantic Monthly* stories speak as well for modern culture as for the time they were written.

Similarly – the confession in 'A Night on Salisbury Plain' give a reassurance to our own incompetence. 'Foolishly I had relied on my petrol gauge, knowing it to be faulty.' Father recounted the story of Achilles to me when I was eight. Many readers have told me that his admission of weakness is one of the big attractions in his writing for them. The weakness leads cleverly on into the jaws of the story's equation: sacrifice. Stonehenge was the ancient altar of sacrifice, a very convenient backdrop. Father was certainly well aware that Thomas Hardy had used the same scenery for his sacrifice of Tess. It all gives as cold a shudder as the thrill upon mention of the Great Grimpen Mire. The story is enlarged to the Great War; diminished to a mouse: a microcosm of the macrocosm. It has much of the sustained drama as learned from reading Conrad, especially his story *Youth*.

'The Dear One' is another adroit parable with all the ingredients for communication: small children, harassed parent, the complexities of reason and religion all released by a morsel of mischance.

'A Crown of Life' may make you weep – I did. Not just because of the true sadness and utter hopelessness of Clibbit's weaknesses or because of the one true friend – Ship the dog – but also because the power of the writing that carries you into these dark corners. Father used to tell us the ancient story of a king's faithful hound which guarded his children and killed a wolf which attacked them, only to be slain by the king who, on returning, wrongly translated blood and chaos as the doings of his faithful hound. Drama in Father's story is unprovoked. It occurs quite naturally. The apparent simplicity is worthy of anything by Turgenev.

Henry explains how he feels about the act of writing in the essay on 'Richard Jefferies', much of which is a description of himself. It is a useful document. Jefferies, like many other writers, artists, and composers of the time, had tragic circumstances. It is interesting for me, having grown up with so many of the later *Atlantic* stories, either second hand from my brothers, or first hand in my own childhood of the last four stories, to see how Father tried really quite valiantly to overcome his own loneliness and neurosis by presenting to the world a happier and more balanced side of affairs.

It was quite often this rising of spirit that gives a heroic legacy of output that succeeding generations can admire. 'The Snipe's Nest', for instance, describes a most terrible time on the Norfolk farm, which made all of us feel very unhappy. The Ayrshire cow (hardly a heifer as he describes since it had had a calf) was one of the most pitiful sights for me of that farm. It stood in the glow of a fine evening sun, its udder pristine and pink, except for that dull red hole. It was said to have been shot deliberately and we could feel gaunt horror at the presence of such a person who could do that. Father was distraught. But the story rises over the ashes and I remember the terrific relief on being shown the shiny magazine from America that had arrived that morning with my picture that Father proudly showed me. It was a lighted candle in a darkened room.

So shone these articles, these good deeds in a naughty world. They were always brave yet competent gestures against complacency, anger, stupidity and greed in the world around us. They were lifelines for our family too. They are beautiful examples of story-telling and we should treasure their existence, back from the brink of being lost for ever: grateful thanks to the Henry Williamson Society and in particular John Gregory.

Richard Williamson

ENGLISH IDYLLS

I

THE CROW STARVER

THE LITTLE BOY SPOKE angrily to the dead stick he was dragging; his teeth were white as a weasel's. The stick was a fallen branch of a pine, and he could just drag it; but when the brambles caught in a stump he tugged and heaved in vain. He threw all his weight on the stick, frowning fiercely at it and making a growling sound in his throat. The brambles gave and he staggered backward, then tugged the stick toward his fire, crying, 'Ah, ee would, would ee? He-aa-eh! Ee would, would ee?'

I had walked to the spinney along the right of way through the cornfield. The island of hornbeam and pine rose in the middle of the field's ridge, lapped around by a gentle green sea, for the wheat was raising slender blades in the sunlight. Seeing me, the boy leaped up from beside his fire, seized a clapper, and whirled it round his head. The noise caused a rook three hundred yards away to float into the wind again and drift into the next field.

The boy's face was thin, his cheek bones high. His long hair fell over the collar of his loose coat – he had robbed an odd-me-dod, or scarecrow, of that coat. It hung to his knees. His head turned quickly at my footfall. His eyes were bright and keen as a bird's. He had left school a year before; now he was a crow starver. He liked the job, for he was a peculiar child. I remember seeing him one day, when he was about six years old, dart out of his grannie's cottage and pounce upon a girl carrying a basket of butter. 'Give it to me!' he had screeched, hanging to the basket and making angry growling noises. He had seen an orange in the basket. He hung on until the girl, with a laugh, gave it to the urchin, who ran into his cottage and hid it in the dark corner under the table, his hiding place.

1

A domed heap of turfs and sticks roughly piled and pleached, with a hole in the side facing northeast, away from the gales, was the crow starver's abode. Into the earth floor stakes had been driven, supporting crosspieces on which rested withies from the brook and bracken from the covert beyond. Two sacks kept him warm.

At dawn he came up from his grannie's cottage and lit his fire. When the daws and rooks came to plunder the sprouting grain, his voice and his engines of alarm drove them away.

'Ulloo-oo-oo-a! Ulloo-oo-oo-a!' His cries floated forlorn with the wailing of the lapwings wheeling and diving above the flinty field. The sound of old tins and baths being walloped came with them, and then his shrill voice and the rattle of his clappers. A length of iron rail hung from a low hornbeam branch, and he beat it with a hammer made from a holly stick pushed through the hole in a flint.

He had a store of birch bark pushed in a niche within his dugout. It burned with a sooty flame, for birch bark is full of oil. A sooty flame of orange bit the twigs – much better kindling than paper, which absorbed the damp. He made tea in an old marmalade pot and drank it without milk. Sometimes he had a little milk – there were goats in the vicarage garden and cows in the water meadow. In the embers he baked potatoes; sweet brown turnip he ate in slices. No one missed a 'tettie' or a 'root,' and no one saw him take them.

I used to visit him at night, when he lay in the opening of his shelter. The fire cast flame-light and shadow on his grinning squirrel-like face, as skits of wind rested and sped onward, rolling the bright sparks over the ground. He was happy in the spinney. One must not look too closely among the embers of his fire – after all, there were many rabbits, and an occasional one found with puffed face in a pegged noose of brass wire was anyone's property. 'A didden till the snare; a only found 'n in 'n.'

Sixpence a day, from dawn till sunset, banging the rusty tins and whirling the clapper. A mind unformed, a nature without pity, a brain experienced in artfulness. He had never known a father. Probably his mother, who rarely saw him, did not know who was his father. He was already formed into a solitary, living with the wind that was never silent in the pines. Sometimes, in dry weather, he slept there, in dreamless sleep as the brilliant stars of early spring swept westward, and the owls flew to the trees, hooted to their mates in the covert below, listened for mice and young rabbits, and flew on again. He knew few names, but he knew where the birds nested and when the flowers came in the hedgerows.

He looks up and listens to a singing lark; and yet I know, if he finds a nest, he will suck the eggs like a crow.

No – he does not feel the cold at night. A quick grin. No, he 'didden' want to live in a cottage; but the policeman must n't know that.

'Ess, a wull tend to craw starvin' long as a can, a wull, forever, a wull.'

A mixed flock of rooks and jackdaws fly down to dig the grain. The crow starver springs up; the ragged trousers flap round his thin legs. (When they became entirely disgraceful he would beg a new pair from 'his reverence,' and give his own to a scarecrow.)

'Ulloo-oo-oo-a! Ulloo-oo-oo-a!'

Bang, clang, on bath and rail. Rattle of walnut wood on oaken cogs of the clapper. Up rise the birds. The crow starver grins, and suddenly squats by his fire.

'A made 'n spark, didden a, you?'

The spinney stands on the ridge of the wheat field to-day, but the dugout is fallen in and covered with brambles. The bath and tins are rust in the earth; the clapper is probably an antique in a dealer's shop, or hanging on a wall somewhere, a relic of old England. When I walk along the right of way now, I walk in a smaller field; hedges, flints, the brook and the covert below, all have shrunken. The pines are not so tall – the pines where every spring a sparrow hawk used to nest. Once the illusion of boyhood arose out of the wheat and the trees and the birds in the sky, a living thing, brilliant as the sun up through the hornbeam leaves.

Other eyes may be finding it there now; my little boy may see it when he is older; but for me it is lost forever, though sometimes a smell of burning wood or a forlorn far cry may bring a glimpse in the mind. For between that vision of green wheat and singing larks and sunshine and the present lies an immense darkness and corruption, a vast negation of all beauty, as of life broken and moving backward to the original void. Its viewless shadow lies over the spinney to-day, and somewhere in that shadow wanders the ghost of the crow starver, dead in the war, with that old wraith of myself in the well-loved places.

Still the beautiful clouds lie over the downs, the larks are singing, the wheat rising green. There is hope in the wide and open sky.

II

STRANGE BIRDS

Standing by the parapet of London Bridge as it shuddered under the wheels of omnibuses, my feet cold on the pavement, I could imagine the wild eyes of an ancient Briton, suddenly brought back to life, filling with terror that the stars had fallen by the river, their vast flickering glares casting shadows about strange cliffs arisen where the forest was. The sun and the moon had fallen, too, and lay shattered and gleaming on the water; the whole sky hung with a haze of fire. And then out of this strange and dreadful scene arose a wild sweet note, startlingly near, passing in the night; another followed, and the spirit flew up with the familiar voices, away from this place where the grass had been dead so long and no trees grew.

I leaned on the cold stone of the parapet. The arc lamps blazed over the ships alongside the wharves, casting a coppery dust of life on cranes and rigging and burdened men. It was a usual night scene in the world's greatest port. The beautiful cries were gone, beaten under by the gigantic meaningless roar coming out of the stone and iron of the city.

London is old, but the spirit of the earth is older, and its wild birds sometimes return to their ancient river haunts. There used to be a kingfisher flying over the reservoir by Hammersmith Bridge, to perch on a snag before the house of William Morris. I saw it twice in 1920, but I have not been there since. I dare say the bird is gone with the black branch in the mud. In flight over the tidal water it drew such a bright line, brilliant blue in the sunlight as it flew away and ruddy brown as it returned. If thought could give it life, it would be there now, fishing the water's verge for sticklebacks and beetles and shrimps, for all the children to see.

London is the less confining for me when I know that brown owls nest every year in the elms of Hyde Park. Last spring, as I was wandering under one of the great old trees, my hat was struck off my head by the talons of a hen bird whose nest was in the hollow of a branch above. She flew out in the brightest sunlight with her eyes fully opened, alighted halfway up another tree, and uttered her sharp cries of *te-jick, te-jick*. As I lingered under her nest, she flew down again in a swooping curve and would have struck my face if I had not turned my back and ducked. In her frenzy of protection she struck with her whole body, throwing herself at me behind the spread claws of her feet and falling to the ground with the shock.

I have seen woodpeckers in the Park, both the green and the greater-spotted birds; but I have never heard the yaffling laugh of the one or the beak drumming of the other – the mating calls. Perhaps the birds were solitary, or visitants from outlying woods. I searched many of the trees, failing to find any nesting hole or litter of gouged chips beneath.

The little owl (*Athene noctua*) has now strayed into London. Early one morning I saw a bird on the rim of the plash around the eastern fountain of Trafalgar Square; it was staring at the sparrows under the pedestal of the Nelson Column. It flew quickly toward them, snatched one in its claws, and bore it off squealing in the direction of St. Martin's-in-the-Fields. It is quite possible that many of these owls nest in spring on the roofs of London houses. They appear to adapt themselves anywhere, and to live on any food: pigeons, their eggs, the squabs in the nests, might now be among these things – the swift snipe included – known to nourish these little alien pests, who are in England what rabbits are in Australia.

I have seen kestrel hawks in Greater London, hovering over the waste ground of the gravel pit by the Mazawattee tea factory in New Cross. And every year cuckoos return to the big cemetery at Brockley, flying among the tombstones which fill the fields that half a century ago were under the plough. During a rare space in the rumble of motor transport and drone of tramcars, their calls float faintly to the highroad like an echo of olden summer happiness stealing from that place now set apart for stones and silence.

III

NIGHT MUSIC OF BIRDS

Those restless and wild-piping birds, the waders, are sent wandering by frost to the estuary sand banks, and in the night a thousand cries come through the darkness. The curlews' notes are more distinct, sounding like a chain of gold bubbles rising in a pool vast and starry. As the tide carries its froth up the channels, the cries increase. There are gulls and plover with them, redshank, dunlin, little stint, and shelduck, and the night is a maze of sweet sounds. The curlew is a shy, nervous bird, and in winter he cannot bear to be separated from his fellows. Sometimes by day a flock goes inland, flying high over the ploughlands, with their tossing wake of gulls and rooks and starlings. They stalk in the marshy fields afar off, rising like many eyelashes, dull brown, and scattered at the sight of a man walking two fields away.

One frosty night, as I listened to the lap and gurgle of the sea racing past the gravel ridges, a faint clamor, like staghounds laid on to the line of a deer far away, came down from the stars. The clamor changed to a trumpeting; the water shook in a net of stars. The night was filled with the rush of vast wings; *Honk! Honk!* from stretched necks; a sudden uprising of frail cries from bank to bank, traveling far down into the distance; the harsh *krark!* of an uneasy heron. The wild geese were down from the north.

For an hour, as I stamped on the foreshore to keep warm, I heard other birds joining them: mallard, heard half a mile away by the quick whistle of wings from which pinion feathers were missing; green plover, soughing and calling forlornly, *See-o-weet see-o-weet!*

Listening to the slur and trickle and 'bubble-link' in the starlight, I wished I had the power to reproduce in music the variant night cries. Interwoven and continued, they glorified the night. Debussy could have caught and rendered them. Stravinsky could do it; no one knowing the natural life and hearing his original version of 'The Nightingale' could doubt his power and his feeling. The same spirit is in Shelley's poetry. The composer of 'The Immortal Hour' could change into music the flare and flicker of Sirius; the dry hiss of wind in the rimed shore grasses; the tiny glitter, as of black spiders' eyes, of the Pleiads; the blue lights of unseen ships lying off

6

Bideford Bay; the luminous smear of star-lit mist over the Pebble Ridge; the myriad cries of the birds; the hollow roar of the breakers on the bar. Not only the translation of actual sight and sound into music, but the purest feeling of man who in moments of freedom – of the earth unearthy – becomes one in spirit with the birds, sharing their joyous lives, and hopes arising in their hearts, to be loosed in wildest song when spring comes on the south wind and the earth grows green in the sunshine.

August 1927

THE LINHAY ON THE DOWNS

ON THE HIGH DOWN above the sea, in the corner of the last rough grazing field, stands a linhay, half fallen into ruin. It is built of boles of spruce fir, unhewn but barked, and boarded with rough wooden boards. It has a roof of corrugated iron. The roof is intact, but many of the wooden boards have fallen with the rusted nails. Those boards remaining are green and damp, and shaggy with gray lichens.

The linhay had been built with its eastern end open for bullocks to shelter in stormy weather; but the gentleman farmer had sold the down with his other land after the Great War, and the new owner had let it fall ruinous. Battering winds and rain straight from off the Atlantic, and the hot sun of summer, had warped and rotted the boards, and opened two other walls to the weather.

On windy days buzzard hawks lie over the down on crooked wings, watching for rabbits in the heather slope below, or turn and glide over the line of the hill. It is a beautiful and desolate place, where the spirit can spread itself wide and airy as the sea and the sky.

One morning I set out for the linhay with a companion. As we climbed the road to Windwhistle Cross the wind blew harder, and found cold places in our clothes. Past the spinney the way lay over fields, cutting across the broad and rushing gale. I was more hardened than my companion, who covered her face with her gloved hands and walked with bowed head. After a while we reached a wall of stone and earth, tunneled by rabbits and lying broken in gaps. The wind, seeking to level all things, was whipping up bits of stone and earth over the wall, and we had to shield our eyes. Plants growing on the crumbling riband of earth remaining on the top of the stones were pressed tightly down, guarding their leaves among the mosses from the stripping storms. White splashes marked the stones, where in still weather the buzzards had waited and watched for rabbits to lollop out of their buries.

We reached the ruined linhay, and realized it would give no shelter for a fire, as in other expeditions. The hollow was frigid in shadow, and scoured by the wind. The last stone wall before the heather and brambles of the wild seaward slope stood a few strides away, and behind this we sat down and rested. An easy matter to break the old boards with a fifty-pound slab of ironstone fallen from the wall, but not so easy to make a fire. Half a box of matches and chips sliced with a knife, however, changed the acrid smoke of deal wood into flame, and the flame into red and black brittle embers, which wasted in sparks over the grass.

While we were munching our sandwiches in the sunshine my companion, who had been staring into the shadow-cut interior of the linhay ten yards away, asked me if I saw anything above a stone against the inner wall. Yes, I saw a pair of ears upraised, and a dark brown eye below them. I stood up, and the ears went flat; but the brown eye continued to watch. A rabbit was squatting there.

I sat down out of the wind, and soon afterward the ears were raised again. The wind tore at the flames, and rocked a loose stone on the wall behind us. It was blowing harder. We moved away, spreading a raincoat before a derelict plough which old grasses had partly covered. Seagulls, shifting and slanting in swift, uneven gliding, began to appear above our heads, first in pairs, and then in many numbers. The sunlight was put out, and it was instantly chilly. I got up and looked over the wall.

I saw a grand and terrible sight. The headland, which lay out into the bay, dark and puny under the vastness of sky that seemed to begin just beyond my feet, was blurred and lost. Beyond a mile or two from the extended sands below, where hundreds of gulls were standing, still and tiny as scattered whitish seeds, all was chaos. It was as though the sky was falling; as though a monstrous spectre had risen out of the vast sea and was moving to overthrow the land.

We picked up our raincoats, gathered them back from the wind, and allowed ourselves to be billowed into the linhay. The air blows thudded against the boards of the intact side – the shippen was open west, south, and east, except for the round support posts, gnawn with damp at the base, which remained upright. Wind, rebounding from the single wall, flung over us like a comber, dropping dust and straw specks in our ears and the corners

9

of our eyes. It was cold on the rough trodden floor, whereon lay flakes of board, and dried dung of bullocks. The slabs of stone lay against the wall, about six inches from the bottom board, and in the space the rabbit was crouching, its ears pressed on its shoulders, its life quivering behind the staring dark eyes.

The headland was gone; the sky was falling. Beyond the forming ridges of distant waves the sea seemed to be taking on a wrinkled dull gray skin, like molten lead in a trough; and as we watched, the falling blackness was riven, and in the rift a snout arose, and spread upward into the shape of a funnel as it traveled over the surf to the shore. We saw the tiny white seeds sprout with wings, and settle on the sands again. The open linhay trembled, and we buttoned our coats to the neck.

A ladder was fixed to the middle post of one side of the linhay, leading to the tallat, or loft, through an open trapdoor seven feet above our heads. We climbed up, and were in an open space crossed by beams under slanting corrugated iron sheets, lit at the seaward end by a window frame without glass. The floor was rotten in places. Wooden pegs of snares, some with tarnished brass-wire loops, were thrown in one corner, with a sack. The skull of a mouse, with brittle bones interlocked in grayish fur, lay on one beam, where an owl had roosted. I looked through a break in the floor; the rabbit was still beside the stone.

Wind noises ran through the bleak tallat, coming in at the eaves, the floor cracks, the window frame stripped of putty and paint, where owls had perched. They filled the loft, like the hollow and curious voices of straying things, never of the earth or its life. The light drained from the rafters, the floor, each other's face. The plaining voices were lost in the buffets of the iron roof. The skull of the mouse rolled on the beam, and the bones fell aslant, joining a trickle of broken straws along the floor. My companion wrapped her coat closer round her legs. I peered through an empty square of the window, and saw grayness rushing up the heather slope of the down. I saw the fire by the wall, already gutted of embers, kicked as though by an invisible foot. The charred lengths of board, flecked with yellow and red points of flame, rose up and flew yards, and fell flat, smoking violently in the grass.

The voices wailed and shrieked, seeming to dissolve the substance of the tallat in a pallor of darkness. Straw specks and mice bones whirled on the floor, suddenly to rise up and scatter. The linhay was shuddering in the wind. Would the inner core of its uprights hold in the storm? I trod a careful way to the trapdoor, and the wind threw up the wide skirt of the raincoat into my face.

We waited, our backs to the screaming drafts racing up the corrugations of the iron roof. Suddenly a hatch in the walled angle above the trapdoor burst its wooden latch and flung half open, before wedging against the floor and shaking on the ragged grass background of the field below. An amazing object moved slowly across the grassy rectangle cut by the lichen-frayed door. My companion saw it and clutched my arm.

The object moved on three thin legs, threw its head up and down with a roll and a flop. It paused, got its hind legs under it, and took another hop forward, dragging something on the ground. Each forward movement, which needed about five seconds to prepare, took it perhaps six inches nearer shelter. By its head and tail it was a fox – but was it a fox? The tail hung like a piece of old rope, the small head was almost without hair, the ribs showed under creases of skin muddy and stuck with tufts, through which the sharp points of shoulders and hips seemed about to break with the weight of the swelled body. I had just turned my glass into focus and seen that it was a vixen, dragging the chain and iron peg of a rusty rabbit gin clamped on its foreleg, when the first hail smote the roof with an immense clattering crash, and the linhay rocked with the hollow thunder of the wind. I feared it would turn over, crumple, and be carried through the stone wall immediately behind. The field space below the door was a gray blank; the day was torn up and hurtling past us. Jets of icy air were driven through the floor, and up between body and clothes. The sack slid over the green and rotting floor boards, reached the square of the trapdoor, jumped to the rafters, on which it moulded itself before falling. It was snatched through the hatch. I yelled in my companion's ear that it would be best to stand by that hatch, to jump clear when the linhay should buckle and rise. I took her hand, cold as stone, and guided her along one of the joists, lest the floor break under our shoes.

We had reached the eastern end when the black of the storm fell on the down. Immediately we were under a torrent. I saw alarm with the misery in the dim face beside mine. The linhay was lurching under the falling flood. Skits blown in from the open window tasted salt on my lips. And the sea

11

ATLANTIC TALES

was a mile away, at the end of a downward slant of fifteen degrees! It must
have been a waterspout we saw rising in the rift.

The earth under the linhay was awash. The water ran in wrinkled sheets
prickled with rain. I could see nothing of fox or rabbit. The smashing of
wood for the fire had given me warmth, but this warmth was used and gone
after five more minutes in the tallat. My companion was rigid, as though
being enclosed in an icicle; her teeth chattered. The wind pushed thorns
under our nails and in our jawbones, and drew its brambles down our ears
and cheeks. Our toes were broken in glacial gins.

There was no grandeur in the elements now; imagination was disharmon-
ized from the sun. Nature was indifferent to the sufferings of all life. I
could bear the screeching icy jets with fortitude, but my companion suffered,
having no dolorous background in memory to make the present ineffectual.
In that background for me were days and nights in water and clay-marn to
the waist, with death above the leafless winter hedge shot stooping-high;
days and nights without sleep, weeks and months without hope, without
liberty – life with neither present nor future, worse than death, for death was
a release; life more terrible than being in a gin, for God has blessed man with
the power to reason, and I knew that if I sought release and failed, or
escaped from killing men I did not hate nor had ever seen before, I should
be caught and shot before sunrise in peace-time clothes, with a bandage over
my eyes and a white paper mark pinned opposite my heart, still joined in
spirit to the mother who bore me in pain and after-joy, and my name and my
regiment would be read out on three successive parades to every soldier in
the British Army in that alien country. These memories of 1914, and later
ones far, far worse, made a background in endurance for the human spirit
that had suffered and survived them. The pain as of thorns pushed under
finger nails was nothing – it would pass.

The linhay withstood the storm, as it had others, held by the stout cores
of its upright posts. The day began to grow again in the glacial twilight of
the loft. Old boards grew swiftly green; the battering on the roof suddenly
ceased with a few lingering taps against the iron sheets. Drops falling by the
empty squares of the window were white; they glittered! – and blue and
white sea and sky were beyond.

Kneeling down, and moving my face to a crack between the floor boards,
I looked for rabbit and fox. Sight was limited so I crawled stiffly – some-

12

times blowing through my half-clenched hands for warmth – to the trap, and peered over. The floor of the shippen was like the Salient in the winter of 1917 seen from a low-flying aeroplane. Hoof holes, shapeless and trodden into one another, were filled with water to their broken edges. Wind wrinkled the sky gleams by the posts. Against the inner wall the vixen sat, on one of the slabs of ironstone. Her back and neck were curved like a snail shell, and her nose touched the mud. She was shivering with every breath. The foot of the broken foreleg, and the gin that gripped it, were in the mud. Beside her on the other slab, about eighteen inches away, sat the rabbit. It looked about it with the relaxed movements and expression of an animal at ease. I had heard of timid and preying animals sheltering together innocently during a storm, but this was the only time I had witnessed such a pleasing sight.

A sound from above, from my companion, made vixen and rabbit look up together. We kept still, and they relaxed. I saw the vixen turn her mangy head toward the rabbit, which continued to nibble its forepaw. The narrow head began to droop, and a voice above me begged to be allowed to get down. I had forgotten those bluish hands, rough with chilblains. The field was a brilliant green, and steaming in the hot rays of the sun.

As I climbed down the ladder I saw, from the tail of my eye, the rabbit in a series of splashes crossing to the grass beyond the round posts. It disappeared. The vixen had risen on the stone. Her mouth was open, showing her teeth. She stood on three legs placed close together, swaying to keep balance, her brush pressed against the wall. She tried to stay herself with her broken leg, but it gave no support, and each time she nearly tipped into the mud.

There used to live in the village an old trapper who nearly died of the effects of a fox's bite, which festered and made his hand swell, and his joints to be painful with inner corruption. This animal must have been feeding on slugs, beetles, and carrion left by magpies and buzzards – rats thrown out of gins in cornfields, broken carcasses of rabbits – and its teeth were probably more dirty than those of a healthy fox. How else had it survived, limping for weeks or months (long before clicketing time, perhaps), dragging the gin clanking on every stone, and rattling on the hard ground? I was afraid of its bite, having seen, some years before, a fox dead in a gin with lockjaw. Better to kill it, and so put myself out of my misery, for it was a woeful sight; and,

13

although the poor beast might have been used to its slow and crippled ways, there were the cubs, soon to be born. Better to knock the 'viccy' on the nose with my stick, and bury her under a heap of stones.

My companion and I ran over the grass in the wind and the sunshine, swinging our arms, and laughing at each other with the pain in toes and fingers. We had a warm dry cottage in the valley over the down, a garden filled with vegetables, fruit trees, stores of apples, potatoes, and wood for firing; shelves of books to read, clothes to wear, and flowers to tend in the coming spring and summer; we had a merry little babe with six teeth, who watched the rooks flying over the roof with sticks for their nests, and shouted 'Duka duk!' to them. So when we were warm again we returned with the sack to the linhay and, putting it over the head of the vixen, held her easily in her weak struggles, carried her into the field, trod on the steel spring to open the creaking iron jaws of the gin, and lifted out the paw. An easy matter to snick with a knife the frayed tendons, and to bind the stump with my tie, securing it with string. Then the sack was pulled away, rolling over the vixen. She kicked and scrambled on her three and a half feet, and faced us, snarling, with arched back and ears laid flat. I tapped the gin beside her with my stick and she snapped at it. Pushing the end through the spring, I drew it away; she lifted the stump and made the other foreleg rigid, as though to resist. Slowly we walked backward, drawing the gin over the wet grass. She whined, holding out a quivering stump. Five yards, ten yards, twenty yards – slowly we drew away from her, while she watched with raised ears and shifting feet.

We stood still. She arose and hobbled away, as though still dragging the iron. We watched her to the grass-tied plough under the wall. Here she smelt food, and down went her nose, searching for scraps of bread and boiled bacon left by us for the birds. We saw her rolling on her back in the sunlight before she disappeared through the gateway to the slope of furze and heather.

The daffodils in the garden broke yellow, and danced for weeks in the wind until their blooms were frayed; the sand martins and the chiffchaffs came back to the village. We saw the first swallows flitting over the seaward slope of the down. A trapper called to us from the bank, stopping his work to tell us of what he thought was a very strange thing. He had found something in one of his rabbit gins in the sand hills below. The sand had been laid by rain after he had tilled the gins the afternoon before, and visiting them that morning he had seen the prints of a walking fox, the marks of scurry round the gin it had sprung, and the trail leading away. How the bit of raggedy stuff had got in the gin he could n't think. Had he got it? No, he had 'throwed it away, not thinking much of it at the time; 't was a bit of old raggedy black stuff, with yaller stripes on 'n. Aiy, like a wasp!'

I knew that regimental tie.

October 1927

'MUGGY,' THE RABBIT AGENT

FROM THE HIGH GROUND of Windwhistle Cross many hundreds of fields are seen, covering the slopes of the hills like a far-lying patchwork of irregular green and brown pieces stitched together with thick dark wool; some fields bright with sunlight, others dull under distant clouds. Most of these fields, varying in extent from a rood to fifty acres, are enclosed by wide banks of earth and stone, topped with hedges of beech, ash, thorn, elm, furze, and bramble.

In every one of these banks are many holes; they are tunneled from gate to gate. Few of the tunnels are straight or level. They rise and fall and twist round inner pieces of rock. Each system has several outlet and inlet holes, with one or more bolt holes used only in panic, hidden by the grass and the plants on the bank.

Sometimes the rabbits, which scratch out these systems, called 'buries,' cause the earth and stones of the banks to fall down, when sheep and cattle tread the breaks into gaps and wander from their rightful pasture. The rabbits nibble the roots of turnip, mangel, and rape; they eat the young corn, the clover, the cabbages, the peas; they dig for potatoes, and rasp the bark of fruit trees. They multiply rapidly – a doe having five or six litters a year, with five or six young to each litter.

Part of the area of these fields seen from Windwhistle Cross, which come by gates to narrow lanes leading past farms and hamlets to the roadways, is traversed from October to February by a Ford van loaded with rectangular wicker baskets, each bearing two stout hazel-wood bars on which are strung the crossed hind legs of dead rabbits – a hind leg being thrust between the bone and sinew of the other. The van stops at the cottages of trappers, and other places where rabbits are collected. The collector gets down from beside the driver, examines the rabbits, selects what he will take, weighs them on a spring balance, and buys them by weight. The price in a normal season varies from 5½d. to 7d. a pound, including the skin.

In his round the buyer is regular and punctual, and if he knows he will change his time he sends postcards to the trappers, who are busy men. The rabbits, which are sent by train to one of the largest Midland factory cities, must be scarcely injured – that is, caught by the forepaws only. A rabbit trapped by the hind legs often strips the flesh in its struggles, and is not marketable. In five months the van carries rabbits to the value of £6000; that is, between 120,000 and 150,000 rabbits are sent away in the wicker baskets. Actually double the number may be caught during this period, but buzzards and crows 'break abroad' some of them by day, the fox and the badger take them by night. Many are trapped lightly by the forepaw and escape. Indeed, one rabbit in five packed in the baskets has a forepaw already missing.

In our village there are several trappers. One of them pays for the trapping rights of a farm by giving so many weeks' labor to the farmer in summer. A good trapper visits his gins at daybreak and in the evening, but some go along their banks only three times in a week, having other work to do. During the first hours of its agony of struggling, a rabbit fills the night with crying; but terror and pain, long borne with hunger and perhaps the beating of rain and wind, bring the ease of little-knowing.

Besides the regular trappers, there are farmers who hold from seven to ten or twenty acres of land and keep two or three cows, besides a sow and her farrow. Sometimes they bring home a couple of rabbits, taken in their half-dozen rusty gins tilled for rat or rabbit, or shot in the early morning, or caught by the dog at dimmit. The 'bad ones' they eat themselves; others may be offered at the doors of one or the other of the bungalows or small modern houses built since the Great War in and around the village. The unsold rabbits are hung up until an old man called 'Muggy' knocks with his stick on the door, standing there with a basket.

'Good morning to you, ma'm. Any rabbuts to-day, please? Thank you very much.' It may be: 'Good morning, midear. I hope you 'm very well. Will you please to ask your mother if she has any rabbut skins? I'm paying three ha'pence to-day – rabbut skins is come back.' Or: 'Rabbut skins is gone up – I'm giving tuppence to-day, if you please. That's right, ma'm, thank you very much.'

Between the two villages he walks slowly, giving a cheery 'good day' to all he meets on the way. Sometimes he has a joke to tell, or a riddle to ask. 'Now, sir, let me ask you a question, please. Can you tell me what it is that is longer when cut off at both ends? I am asking you a plain question, if you please. Just listen to what I be asking, if you please. What is it that grows longer when cut off at the ends? That's it, if you can answer me.'

The riddle may have been asked before, and Muggy forgotten; but no matter. As with his other riddle (Why did Gladstone wear yellow braces? 'To keep his trousers up, if you please, sir. That's it!'), the answer is not known.

''T is a grave,' says Muggy, moving away, and stopping to explain that in his 'kid days' he saw a coffin lowered in Ham churchyard but coming to rest on the eastern and western edges, so that the grave had to be dug longer while the mourners waited around the pit. 'Yes, sir. That be the explanation. Good day, sir.'

He has no remarks or comments to offer on the actions of other people, and is not concerned with your own. 'I don't want to know your own business, midear. No, sir. 'T is no concern of mine what other volks be doing of. I don't want to know their business.'

Muggy was born at the inn called the Manor House, which is opposite the clubroom steps where now he rests, perched above the stream; but as a young man he sold the inn and went to America, coming back to end his days in the village. For some years, when first I knew him, he had a shanty in the corner of a hillside field, which he reached by climbing the 'ditched' wall on juts of stone. The shanty was as tall as himself, but not much longer or wider than a coffin. His bed was a shelf, and he cooked on an oil stove covered with soot as the stones of the 'ditch' outside were covered with moss. His larder was a box on a post, beside his letter box. In the shanty he shaved and washed and ate, kept his accounts with the rabbit collector, wrote his occasional letters, stored his rabbit skins; until the local sanitary authorities found and condemned it. He migrated to the village up the valley, renting in Ham a two-roomed cot for three pounds a year. But after a year the landlord had a grandson time-expired in the Army and coming home from Malta with a wife and a baby; so he 'rose the rent' another pound; and Muggy, whose income from rabbits and their skins, telegram tips, watercress and crabs in summer, could not meet this increase, came out and made a room in a cottage opposite, long since disused as a dwelling, wherein sacks of artificial manure, faggots, and garden tools were kept by the landlord of the Rock Inn.

His journeys between the two villages begin to take longer, his jokes and riddles are rarer; but his cheerful courtesy still brightens the wayside. Everyone knows Muggy, and is sure of him – no casting of eyes on the road or the hedge, awaiting the unsure and awkward moment of glancing up and acknowledging that it is a fine day, or what dirty weather we're having, or that it looks like more rain. Muggy is plain as a field is plain, plough, arrish, or pasture; a rare and simple being, warped to no property, true to itself, and, therefore, to all men. Shakespeare would have loved him.

November 1927

THE HELLER

I

IN MARCH THE HIGH spring tides lap with their ragged and undulating riband of flotsam the grasses near the flat top of the sea wall; and once in a score of years the southwest gale piles the sea so high that it lops over and rushes down into the reclaimed grazing marsh within. The landlocked water returns on the ebb by way of the reedy dikes, and the culverts under the wall with their one-way hinged wooden doors, and through the muddy channels to the sea again.

I was unfortunate enough to miss seeing such a flood this year, but, hearing of it, I went down to the marsh the next afternoon before the time of high tide, hoping to see it happen again. I wandered along the sea wall with its hoof-holed path of clay still holding salt water, as far as the black hospital ship, and then I returned. The gale had blown itself out, and a blue sky lay beyond Hartland promontory, and far out over the calm Atlantic.

There is a slanting path leading to the road below by the marshman's cottage, and by this I left the wide prospect of sand hills, sea, and sky, seen from the sea wall, and as I was descending I noticed that the grasses down the inner slope were washed flat and straggly by a heavy overflooding of the day before.

The marshman was standing on the porch of the cottage, looking at his ducklings which had hatched about a fortnight before. He wore his spectacles and had a book in his hands. We greeted each other, and I stopped to talk.

I always enjoyed talking with the marshman. His face pleased me. I liked his kind brown eyes, his gray hair, his small and intelligent sea-browned face. In a soft voice he began telling me about the book in his hands, which he said was 'wonderful and most interesting.' It was thick and heavy, and printed in small close-set type. It was called *The History of the Jews*, and the marshman had read it with the same care and patience with which, year after year, he had cut the reeds in the dikes and scythed the thistles in the rank grass. For years he had been reading that book, and he had not yet reached the middle pages. Appalling labor!

Would I like to take the book home with me and have a read of it? He was a bit busy just now and could easily spare it for a day or two. I was quite welcome to take it, if —

I was saved from a reply by the sudden change in the marshman's face. He was staring intently beyond the gate by which we stood. His spectacles were pushed back from his eyes. I looked in the direction of his stare, and saw the usual scene — fowls on the stony and feathery road, and a couple of pigs nosing amid them; the down-hanging branches of the willow tree over the leat; the green pointed leaves of the flag iris rising thickly along both banks; the sky-gleams between them. On the water a brood of yellowish-white ducklings were paddling, watched anxiously from the road by the hen that had hatched them.

'The heller!'

At the muttered angry words the marshman's dog, which had assumed a stiff attitude from the moment of his master's fixed interest in something as yet unsmelled, unseen, and unheard by itself, whined and crouched and sprang over the gate. It had gone forward a few yards, sending the hens clucking and flying in all directions, when the marshman shouted. Seeing its master's arm flung to the left, the dog promptly turned in that direction. I saw its hackles rise.

The narrow leat, which brought fresh drinking water to the grazing marsh, was crossed under the willow tree by a clammer, or single heavy plank of elm wood. As the dog ran on to the clammer I saw something at the farther end slide into the water. I had a fleeting impression of the vanishing hind quarters of a squat and slender dog, dark brown as a bulrush, and with the palms of its feet widely webbed as a duck's. It had a long tail, tapering to a point. The brown tail slid over the plank flatly yet swiftly, and disappeared without splash into the slight ripple made by the submerging animal.

"'T is that darned old mousy-colored fitch,' grumbled the marshman, opening the gate. 'It be after my ducklings. It took one just about this time yesterday. Yurr, Ship!' – to the dog – 'Fetch un, Ship!' The dog sprang around barking raucously, and trotted along the plank again, nose between paws, and whining with excitement where the 'heller' had stood. Then it looked at its master, and barked at the water.

While it was barking, the ducklings, about fifteen yards away, began to run on the water, beating their little fluky stumps of wings and stretching out their necks. 'Queep! Queep! Queep!' they cried. The foster hen on the bank was clucking and jerking her comb about in agitation.

'Ah, you heller, you!' cried the marshman, as a duckling was drawn under by invisible jaws. The other ducklings waddled out by the brimming edge of the road, made for the hen in two files of uniform and tiny yellowish bodies aslant with straining to reach the cover of wings. Very red and jerky about the comb and cheek pendules, with flickering eyes, this motherly fowl squatted on the stones and lowered her wings till they rested on her useless pinion shafts, and fluffed out her feathers to make room for the eight mites which, in spite of her constant calls and entreaties, would persist in walking on that cold and unwalkable place, which was only for supping from at the edge.

'Peep, peep, peep; quip, pip; queep weep,' whistled the ducklings drowsily, in their sweet and feeble voices. The marshman came out of his cottage with a gun.

'The heller,' he said. 'The withering beast, it ought to be kicked to flames.'

We waited five minutes, watching the leat where the duckling had gone down.

Parallel lines of ripples, wavering with infirm and milk-white sky, rode along the brimming water. The tide was still rising. Twenty yards away the strong young leaves of the flag-irises began to quiver. The marshman lifted the gun and curled a finger round the trigger. The leaves were still. We waited. The pee-peeps of the happy ducklings ceased.

Water began to run, in sudden starts, around the smoothed stones in the roadway. The tide was rising fast. A feather was carried twirling on a runnel that stopped by my left toe; and after a pause it ran on a few inches, leaving dry specks of dust and bud-sheaths tacked to the welt.

The outline of the leat was lost in the overbrimming of the water. Grasses began to float and stray at its edges. The runnels of the tide explored the least hollow, running forward, pausing, turning sideways or backward, and blending, as though gladly, with one another.

'It be gone,' said the marshman, lowering the gun, to my relief; for its double barrels had been near my cheek, and they were rusty, thin as an eggshell at the muzzle, and loaded with an assortment of broken screw-heads, nuts, and odd bits of iron. He was as economical with his shooting as he was with his reading. Originally the gun had been a flintlock, owned by his great-grandfather; and his father had had it converted into a percussion cap. Its walnut stock was riddled with worm-holes; and even as I was examining it I heard the sound like the ticking of a watch, which ceased after nine ticks. The death-watch beetle. It was doubtful which would go first – the stock 'falling abroad' in its tunneled brittleness, or the barrels, bursting from frail old age.

'It's a high tide,' I said, stepping further back. 'I suppose the otter came up on it and down the leat?'

Then the marshman told me about the 'heller.' We stood with our backs to the deep and ancient thorn hedge that borders the road to the east, a hedge double-sheared by wind and man, six feet high and eight feet thick and so matted that a man could walk along it without his boots sinking. It was gray and gold with lichens. I had always admired the hedge by the marsh toll-gate. I leaned gingerly against it while the marshman told me that he had seen the otter on the two afternoons previously, and both times when the tide was nearly on the top of the flood. No, it did not come up the leat; it was a bold beast, and came over the sea wall where the tide had poured over two afternoons agone. 'My wife zeed 'n rinning over the wall, like a little brown dog. I reckon myself th' heller comes from the duckponds over in Heanton marsh, and sleeps by day in th' daggers [reeds]. Artters [otters] be always travelin' up the pill [creek] vor to get to the duckponds, or goin' on up to the pill-head, and over the basin [weir] into fresh water, after trout. Never before have I heard tell of an artter going time after time, and by day too, after the same ducklings.

'T is most unusual, zur, vor an artter will always take fish when he can get fish, eels particularly, and there be plenty of eels all over the marsh. An artter loveth an eel; 't is its most natural food, in a manner of speaking.

'T is what is called an ambulance [amphibious] baste, the artter be; yes 't is, like a crab, that can live in both land and water. A most interestin' baste vor those that possess th' education vor to study up all that sort of thing. Now can ee tell me how an artter serves an eel different from another fish?

Other fish – leastways those I've zin with my own eyes – are ate head downwards; but an eel be ate tail vust, and the head an' shoulders be left. I've a zin scores of 'n, and all ate tail vust!'

While the old fellow was speaking, the water, in irregular pourings and innocent twirls, was stealing right across the road. It reached the hen, who, to judge from the downward pose of her head, regarded it as a nuisance. A runnel slipped stealthily between her cane-colored feet, wetting the claws worn with faithful scratching for the young. She arose and strutted away in the lee of the hedge, calling her brood; and 'Wock! Wock! Wet!' she cried, for with tiny notes of glee they had headed straight for the wide water, gleaming with the early sunset.

The marshman said, 'Darn the flood!' for *The History of the Jews*, container of future years' laborious pleasure, lay in a plash by the gate, ten strides away. He picked it up, regarding ruefully the dripping cover. He was saying that it was n't no odds, a bit of damp on the outside, when I noticed a small traveling ripple in the shape of an arrow moving out from the plank, now almost awash. It continued steadily for about three yards from the plank, and beyond the ripples a line of little bubbles like shot began to rise and lie still. The line, increasing steadily by lengths varying from two or three to a dozen inches, drew out towards the ducklings.

I took long strides forward beside the marshman. Our footfalls splashed in the shallow water. The dog trotted at his heels, quivering, its ears cocked. A swirl arose in the leat and rocked the ducklings; they cried and struck out for the grass; but one stayed still, trying to rise on weeny wings, and then it went under.

'The *heller!*' cried the marshman, raising his gun.

For about twenty seconds we waited.

A brown whiskered head, flat and seal-like, with short rough hairs and beady black eyes, looked out of the water. *Bang!* It dived at the flash, and although we peered and waited for at least a minute after the whining of a screw-head ricocheting away over the marsh had ceased, I saw only our spectral faces shaking in the water.

II

The next afternoon I went down by the eastern sea wall and lay on the flat grassy ridge, with a view of the lower horn of the Ram's-horn duck pond. Wild fowl were flying round the marsh, and settling on the open water hidden between the thick green reeds. Many scores had their nests in the preserve. Why did the otter, I wondered, come all the way to the leat, when it could take all the ducklings it wanted in the pond? Perhaps in my reasoning I was falling into the old error of ascribing to a wild beast something of human reasoning; for, had I been an otter after ducklings, I should certainly have stayed where they were most numerous.

The tide flowed past me, with its usual straggle of froth covering the flotsam of corks, bottles, clinker, spruce bark from the Bideford shipyards, tins, cabbage leaves, and sticks. The murky water moved wide and deep between the muddy glidders. Two ketches rode up on the flood, the exhausts of their oil engines echoing with hollow thuds over the mud and water. I wondered why they were wasting oil, when the current was so swift to carry them; but when they made fast to their mooring buoys, and the bows swung round, I realized the use of the engines – to keep them in the fairway. Of course!

Gulls screamed as they floated around the masts and cordage of the black craft, awaiting the dumping overboard of garbage. I waited for an hour, but saw nothing of the otter.

'Did ee see 'n?' asked the marshman when I went back. His gun lay on the table, and Ship the dog was crouched over the threshold, its nose on its paws, pointing to the clammer bridge over the leat.

'He's took another duckling, the heller!' he growled.

The otter must have made an early crossing, while I was lazing on the bank. Perhaps he had come through a culvert, squeezing past the sodden wooden trap; and then, either seeing or winding me, he had crossed under water. The marshman, happening to come to the door, had seen the duckling going under, and, although he had waited ten minutes, nothing had come up.

'Ship here went nosing among the daggers, but could n't even get wind of 'n. I reckon that ambulance baste can lie on the bottom and go to sleep if it has a mind to.'

By 'ambulance' he meant amphibious, I imagined. The otter had no gills; it breathed in the ordinary way, being an animal that had learned to swim under water.

'Did n't you even see a bubble?'

'Not one!'

It seemed strange. Also, it had seemed strange that the engines of the ketches were 'wasting' oil. That had a perfectly ordinary explanation – when one realized it!

'And it took a duck in just the same way as before?'

'That's it! In a wink, that duck was down under.'

'But did n't the ducklings see the otter?'

'Noomye! The poor li'l beauty was took quick as a wink.' He was much upset by it.

'Now I'll tell ee what I'll do,' he said. 'I'll till a gin vor a rat, I will, and if I trap an artter, well, 't will be a pity, as the artter-'unting gentry would say; but there 't is!'

Otters were not generally trapped in the country of the Taw and Torridge rivers, as most of the water owners subscribed to the otter hounds. There were often occasions, however, when a gin was 'tilled,' or set, on a submerged rock where an otter was known to touch, or on a sunken post driven into the river bed near its holt. About once in a season the pack drew the brackish waters of the Ram's-horn duckpond, but an otter was never killed there, as there was impregnable 'holding' among the thick reeds.

I looked at the marshman's face, filled with grim thoughts about the 'heller' (had he got the term from the *History of the Jews*?), and remembered how, only the year before, when an otter had been killed near Branton church, he had confided to me that he did n't care much for 'artter-'unting'; that it was 'not much sport with all they girt dogs agin one small baste.'

'I've got some old rabbit gins,' said the marshman. 'And I'll till them on the clammer, and get that heller, I will.'

I went away to watch the mating flight of the golden plover over the marsh, and the sun had gone down behind the low line of the sand hills to the west when I returned along the sea wall. Three rabbit gins – rusty affairs of open iron teeth and flat iron springs ready to snap up and hold anything that trod on them – lay on the plank. The marshman had bound lengths of twisted brass rabbit wire around the plank and through the ends of the chains, so that, dragged into the leat, the weight of the three gins would drown the struggling otter.

My road home lay along the edge of the leat, which was immediately under the sea wall. Old upturned boats, rusty anchors, rotting bollards of tree trunks, and other gear lay on the wall and its inner grassy slope. Near the pill-head the brown ribs of a ketch, almost broken up, lay above the wall. I came to the hump where the road goes over the culvert; and, leaning on the stone parapet, I watched the water of the little river moving with dark eddies under the fender into the leat, and the overflow tumbling into the concrete basin of the weir and sliding down the short length of the weedy fish-pass into the dull and placid level of the rising tide. It barely rippled. The air was still, silvery with eve-star and crescent moon.

The last cart had left the Great Field, the faint cries of lambs arose under the moon, men were all home to their cottages or playing skittles in the village inns. Resting the weight of my body on the stone, I stared vaguely at the water, thinking how many strange impulses and feelings came helter-skelter out of a man, and how easy it was to judge him falsely by any one act or word. The marshman had pitied a hunted otter; he had raged against a hunting otter; he felt tenderly and protectively towards the ducklings; he would complacently ring their necks when the peas ripened, and sell them for as much money as he could get for them. In the future he would not think otter-hunting a cruel sport. And if the otter-hunters heard that he had trapped and drowned an otter, they would be sincerely upset that it had suffered such a cruel and, as it were, an unfair death. Perhaps the only difference between animal and man was that the animal had fewer notions . . .

I was musing in this idle manner, my thoughts slipping away as water, when I heard a sound somewhere behind me. It was a thin piercing whistle, the cry of an otter. Slowly I moved back my head, till only a part of my face would be visible in silhouette from the water below.

I watched for a bubble, a sinuous shadow, an arrowy ripple, a swirl; I certainly did not expect to see a fat old dog-otter come drifting down on his back, swishing with his rudder and bringing it down with great thwacking splashes on the water while he chewed a half-pound trout held in his short forepaws. My breath ceased; my eyes held from blinking. I had a perfect view of his sturdy body, the yellowish-white patch of fur on his belly below his ribs, his sweeping whiskers, his dark beady eyes. Still chewing, he

27

bumped head-on into the sill, kicked himself upright, walked on the concrete, and stood there crunching, while the five pools running from his legs and rudder ran into one. He did not chew, as I had read in books of otters chewing; he just stood there on his four legs, the tail half of the trout sticking out of his mouth, and gulping down the bits. That trout had disappeared in about ten seconds. Then the otter leaned down to the water, and lapped as a cat does.

He was old, slow, coarse-haired, and about thirty pounds in weight – the biggest otter I had seen, with the broadest head.

After quenching his thirst he put his head and shoulders under water, holding himself from falling in by his stumpy webbed forefeet, and his rudder, eighteen inches long, pressing down straight behind. He was watching for fish. As though any fish remained in the water-flow after that dreaded apparition had come splashing under the culvert!

With the least ripple he slid into the water. I breathed and blinked with relief, but dared not move otherwise. A head looked up almost immediately, and two dark eyes stared at me. The otter sneezed, shook the water out of his small ears, and sank away under. I expected it to be my last sight of the beast, and, leaning over to see if an arrowy ripple pointed upstream, I knocked a piece of loose stone off the parapet. To my amazement he came up near the sill again with something in his mouth. He swung over on his back, and bit it in play. He climbed on to the sill and dropped it there, and slipped back into the water. It was the stone that had dropped from the parapet!

I kept still. The otter reappeared with something white in his mouth. He dropped it with a tinkle beside the stone, and the tinkle must have pleased him, for he picked up the china sherd – it looked like part of a teacup, with the handle – and rolled over with it in his paws.

As in other Devon waters, the stream was a pitching place for cottage rubbish, and during the time I was standing by the parapet watching the otter at his play he had collected about a dozen objects – rusty salmon tins, bits of broken glass, sherds of clome pitchers and jam jars, and one half of a sheep's jaw. He ranged them on the sill of the weir, tapping the more musical with a paw, as a cat does, until they fell into the water, when he would dive for and retrieve them.

At the end of about half an hour the sea was lapping over the top of the sill and pressing under the fender. Soon the leat began to brim. The taste of salt water must have made the otter hungry again, or perhaps he had been waiting for the tide, for he left his playthings and, dropping into the water, went down the leat towards the marshman's cottage. I crept stealthily along the grassy border of the road, watching the arrowy ripple, gleaming with silver, of the thin curved moon. The hillside under the ruined chapel above the village of Branton began to show yellow speckles of light in the distant houses. The leat being deserted (for the brood of ducklings with their hen had been shut up for the night), why, then, that sudden swirl and commotion in the water by the flag irises, just where the ducklings had been taken before?

Bubbles broke on the water in strings – big bubbles. Then something heaved glimmering out of the leat, flapping and splashing violently. The noises ceased, and more bubbles came up; the water rocked. Suddenly the splashing increased, and seemed to be moving up and down the leat, breaking the surface of the water. Splashes wetted my face. A big struggle was going on there. After a minute there was a new noise – the noise of sappy stalks of the flags being broken. Slap, slap, slap, on the water. I saw streaks and spots of phosphorescence, or moon gleams, by the end of the plank. The flapping went on in the meadow beyond the flags, with a sound of biting.

I stood without moving for some minutes, while the biting and squirming went on steadily. My shoes filled with water. The tide had spread silently half across the road. Then the noises ceased. I heard a dull rap, as of something striking the heavy wooden plank under water; a strange noise of blowing, a jangle of iron and a heavy splash, and many bubbles and faint knocking sounds. The otter had stepped on the plank to drink, and was trapped.

III

At last the marshman, having closed *The History of the Jews*, placed his spectacles in their case, drawn on his boots, put on his coat, taken his gun off the nails on the ceiling beam and put it back for a fluke-spearing pronged fork in the corner, and lit the hurricane lamp, said with grim triumph, 'Now us will go vor to see something!' He was highly pleased that he had outwitted the otter.

'There be no hurry, midear,' he said. 'Give 'n plenty of time vor to see the water for the last occasion in his skin.'

We stood for a while by the clammer under the dark and softly shivering leaves of the willow looming over us in the lamplight.

The water had receded from the plank when the last feeble tug had come along the brass wire. The marshman, watched by his dog, hopping round and round on its wooden leg in immense excitement, pulled up the bundle of gins, and the sagging beast held to them by a forepaw. It was quite dead; but the marshman decided to leave it there all night, to make certain.

'I see in the paper,' he said, 'that a chap up to Lunnon be giving good money vor the best arttur skins' – tapping the spearing handle significantly with his hand.

When it had been dropped in the water again we went a few paces into the meadow with the lamp, and there we saw a conger eel, about four feet long, bitten through the head by the otter. It was thick as a man's arm. Suddenly I thought that it must have come with the high spring tide over the sea wall; and soon afterward the keen-nosed otter, following eagerly its scent where it had squirmed and writhed its way in the grass. The conger had stayed in the leat, hiding in a drain by the flag irises, and coming out when the colder salt water had drifted down.

The marshman carried it back to his cottage and cut it open, and then stared into my face with amazement and sadness, for within the great eel were the remains of his ducklings.

May 1928

30

SWAGDAGGER CROSSES A FIELD

I

THERE IS SOMETHING IN the nature of most men, arising on certain uneasy occasions, which has a basis so universal that everywhere it commands the sympathetic understanding of reasonable folk – an attitude of which the commonest vocal expression is 'Why do you want to interfere with me? I don't want to interfere with you! But if you're looking for trouble you'll —— well find it!' (The usual intensifying word, here omitted for the sake of those ideas of civilized culture which Mr. Ovey self-righteously upholds, is entirely apt in the case of Swagdagger.) And as with men, so with animals who live the life, wild and free and pitiless, that men have quitted.

This attitude in the wild is liable to instant reverse; the trouble seeker of one moment may be the troubled of the next. The rights and wrongs – many of them as old as life itself – of Swagdagger happily crossing a field on a certain morning in early June cannot be discussed in this story, which is able only to hold an account of all the trouble which began when Mr. Ovey, of London, looked over a bank.

His large round head, rising out of a starched collar, moved across the gap in the western bank of the field below Windwhistle Cross, and vanished; but it came back immediately – pomaded hair, waxed moustache, pince-nez rimless glasses, new shiny teeth. Mr. Ovey, a short, stout little man halfway through life, stood on his toes and peered over, preparing an indignant glance. Someone must be in the farther field! There the evidence was – a long strip of paper, blowing across the grass! Mr. Ovey pushed himself higher with his toes, and looked round to see who had dropped the paper. It had not been there a moment before, when he had been in the field. But, seeing no one, he got down from his uncomfortable position, and brushed the earth from his finger tips.

Mr. Ovey, standing in the sunken lane, looked at the gap again and thought how unprotected his property was. The sooner that notice board was up, the better! The paint ought to be dry enough; it could go up to-day. He must see that the gap in the bank – made by bullocks, so the farmer had said – was filled with thorn branches pegged down. Anyone could get over there! A padlock for the five-barred gate, and a strand or two of barbed wire twisted round the top bar. And, his head full of thoughts of boards and thorns and wire and paper, Mr. Ovey got into his car and drove down the hill to the village in the valley below.

Recently Mr. Ovey, a business man on holiday from London ('Ovey's Liver Salts – Get That Athlete's Zest for a Farthing a Day'), had bought three fields in a district adjoining Exmoor in North Devon, in the belief that a few years would see more than double his money back in building sites, as he told his wife. Not that he would want to live there himself! Mr. Ovey thought the country a dull place to live in, where there was nothing to see except views like picture postcards, and where nothing ever happened.

Three red lanes, metaled with iron-stone, – one of them already bearing much motor traffic in the summer, – met at the southwestern corner of the field, near the gate. Just above this gate was a small spinney of beech trees called Windwhistle Cross. The motor road divided the spinney, and led on over the down to Ilfracombe. It was toward these trees that Mr. Ovey had looked when he passed the gap in the bank. Mr. Ovey had always lived in London, and he considered himself both shrewd and observant; but, had the eyes of Mr. Ovey been of wider use to him, he would have noticed that the long white strip, rippling as paper in the wind, was moving in a direction contrary to that in which the wind was blowing.

Less than half a minute after the departure of Mr. Ovey, the white rippling object had reached the middle of the field. It was moving on a track it had run along many times before, a track belonging to itself. Indeed, it owned the entire field, with every other field it ran in. Its sense of ownership was similar to that of Mr. Ovey, but more elemental; its angry defiance of any intrusion was coupled with a raging desire to break with teeth the neck of its enemy. Nearly everything was its enemy, and nearly everything ran from it; for it was Swagdagger the stoat. Swagdagger lived a life harder and more eventful than any other stoat in the West Country, for he had been born without color, except for his eyes, which were pink, and the tip of his tail, which was black. Swagdagger's hairy coat, covering a long and sinuous body, was white as the snow which so seldom fell in the fields. Nearly everything saw Swagdagger as he ran prowling, low and swift and sniffing the air, over green pasture and brown ploughland, and through the thorns and brambles growing on the banks dividing the fields.

Swagdagger was hurrying, but he was not hunting. Many times a day he ran with eagerness across his fields into Windwhistle Cross, to play with the five stoats who lived under a wood stack at the foot of a beech tree. Such rough-and-tumble games they played together – Swagdagger, his mate, and their cubs.

He had reached the middle of the field when a dark brown bird, with a wing span of more than four feet, wheeled in the sky a quarter of a mile away, and slanted down over the wind-sheared tree tops of the spinney. Swagdagger saw it coming, and ran faster. It was a buzzard hawk, whose wailing cry often came down from the sky. It fed on rabbits, moles, and snakes, which it dropped on from above and clutched in its yellow feet, piercing with black talons, and tearing with its hooked beak. The hawk was stronger and much heavier than the stoat, who saw its eyes and beak and hanging legs, under the line of its outspread wings, growing larger and larger as it glided upon him. Swagdagger stopped, his forepaws on the ground, his head and neck raised and pointing at the buzzard. He crouched until it lifted great wings to drop on him, and then he stood on his hind legs. The buzzard, who had meant to grip him across the back, saw a small white flattened circle, set with whiskers, that broke across with sharp clicking teeth.

The stoat stood like a lean mushroom stalk; the hawk seemed to bounce off its angry pointed nose. It flapped its broad wings, to keep itself safely above the furious pale eyes. It flapped heavily over the stoat toward the spinney, but rippling white movement lured it back again. It turned and swept down on the stoat, spreading yellow toes for the attack. The white ripple stopped, becoming fixed and upright under the snatch of talons. Again the buzzard quailed before the snapping teeth, and, beating into the air, sent a wailing cry down the wind. *Whee-ee-i-oo!*

Another bird, black from bristled beak to toe, that was perching on the highest bough of an elderberry tree, stunted and lichen-crusted, at the southwestern point of the spinney, heard the cry, and started out of its reverie – for it was contemplating the old nest from which it had driven the

33

last of its grown winglings that morning. Immediately it stretched its head higher. Every black feather tightened when it saw the buzzard. Its craw swelled, its tail dipped, its beak opened, and *Scarl! Scarl! Scarl!* it called, harshly and rapidly.

Another carrion crow heard the call, and left the broken carcass it had been eating – rabbit in snare set by laborer – and flew toward the elderberry. The crows built their nest in one or other of the trees of Windwhistle Cross every year; they owned the spinney, and the fields around it, and whenever they saw a winged or four-legged intruder they drove it away from their property.

Krok! Krok! – Hawk! Hawk! said the first crow, flying up to meet her mate. Together they flew, silently, just above the green slope of the wind-sheared tree tops. They appeared suddenly over the spinney, seeing the field below. *Krok! Krok!* said the crow again, and flew faster toward the buzzard, meaning to peck out its feathers – a thing which the crows tried to do whenever they flew near a buzzard, not liking its face.

Before its beak had closed again, the male crow saw the stoat. The crow's name was Scarl. Scarl had seen Swagdagger many times before. *Krarr! Krarr!* cried Scarl and his mate together, turning across the wind, and slanting over the red lane and the bramble-grown bank.

Swagdagger was not far from Windwhistle Cross when the crows dived at him. He recognized the voice of Scarl, and ground his teeth. With open beak Scarl dived, but a yard from the ground the crow flattened his wings and with a jeering *Krarr!* passed over him. Scarl alighted two yards behind Swagdagger, while his mate flapped above and in front of him. The stoat stood up to meet the peck of the crow, and Scarl, hopping quickly over the grass from behind, nipped the black tip of his tail.

In this way they teased Swagdagger for more than a minute, while he grew more and more angry. Every time he attempted to run forward he was poked and jabbed from behind by one or another of the crows, and at last he was not very far from the bank whence he had started.

Meanwhile the buzzard was soaring higher, watching the shifting white streak. It soared two fields away, stared at by a bird perched on a thorn growing out of the bank near a gate. This bird was the size of a crow, but more huddled-looking; and it had a whity-gray face of bare skin. The buzzard saw it looking up, and wailed for its mate again. The gray-faced bird launched itself off the thorn, and with leisured beat of wings climbed into the air to look around. It was a sentinel rook, and the buzzard was scared of rooks, for often they mobbed him.

It flew under the hawk, and cried *Caa! Caa-r!* Hearing the summons, the rooks looked up from the earth where they were digging potatoes. Buzzard never harmed, and potatoes were good. They went on digging again, knowing that old sentinel could easily drive buzzard away.

Now Scarl the carrion crow saw the rook flying under the buzzard, and began to think. First one eye was cocked at them, then the other – for a crow cannot reason until he has taken a double squint. His beak lifted higher, his craw swelled, he dipped, and *Krok-krok-krok-krok!* he cried. The stoat bounded upon him, but the crow, still looking at the sky, hopped over his head, alighted behind him, and gave four more croaks. *Caa-r!* answered the sentinel rook, leaving the buzzard, and flying over the field to find out why the crow had called him. He saw, turned, and flew back quickly, in silence.

Usually rooks flew wide of crows, whom they distrusted, for crows had been known to chase the little red mousehawks, or kestrels, over their rookery in spring, and, in the general uproar that greeted the hawk, to sneak into the trees and suck rooks' eggs. But against Swagdagger every bird's beak and wing was raised. *Krok-krok-krok-krok!* cried the rook, wheeling over the edge of the potato field, and calling them in a voice like a crow's. This time every rook flew up. The potato diggers (Mr. Ovey's potatoes) glided and swooped down to the grass of the three-acre field as soon as they saw the white ripple. They filled the air with cawing and the sound of wings. They alighted on the grass, making around the stoat a rough excited circle, which broke wherever Swagdagger ran in his grinding rage.

Each rook urged his neighbor to hop forward and dab him one on the head. Each rook was determined not to be the one to dab first. Their wide and simple eyes, filled with scared thoughts, looked from stoat to crow, from crow to each other. Scarl and his mate hopped about in the ring, feeling safe with so many beaks near them, and enjoying the game of peck and jump. And all the while they were playing the crows were watching their chance to peck out Swagdagger's eyes.

Sometimes nervous rooks would fly up with squawks of alarm, but the croaks of the bolder crows were reassuring, and they alighted in the circle again. Jackdaws passing over the spinney dropped among them, like flakes

35

of burnt paper out of the blue sky, and croaked with deep voices, for they too belonged to the powerful family of the crows, and shared ownership of all the fields and woods. They poked their gray polls and hard azure eyes between the disheveled shoulders of the rooks, and cursed Swagdagger, who in hot rage was giving off a most penetrating stench, which in itself was almost enough to keep them at a distance. Then came four magpies, sloping over the field, their wings flickering black and white as they made slow way against the wind. They scolded loudly when they saw Swagdagger. After them came a pair of missel thrushes, who flew down boldly, the smallest birds present, and screamed in the face of Swagdagger as he stood, with swishing tail, with bared teeth, with blazing eyes, in a green space enclosed by the black and shifting mass. Suddenly every bird looked up into the air, and remained motionless, as though frozen.

Three miles westward, on his pitch two thousand feet above the sea, Chakchek the Backbreaker, the peregrine falcon, had seen the commotion of wings in the field, and a white speck in the centre. He owned the air of the world; even the eagle shifted under his stoop. Across the sky on level pinions he had glided, cutting round into the wind above Windwhistle Cross. He saw upheld beaks and eyes watching him anxiously. Crows and a stoat! He turned, and swept away.

II

The sentinel rook, sire of many birds of the rookery, in the village below, an old bird whose life was set in duty to others, watched the Backbreaker an eye-blink longer than the other rooks watched. He forgot Swagdagger as he stared at the pointed wings, which often he had heard hissing in the dreaded stoop. Then a whiteness flashed, and the old rook was on his back, his feathers were flying, his legs were kicking. He tried to screech a warning, but as his beak opened he shuddered; and Swagdagger, red on teeth and whiskers, ran at the next rook. The grass was flattened by the draught of beating wings.

Cra! cried Scarl, who had flown a yard, but returned again. *Cra!* as he hopped to the stricken rook, and pecked out its eyes.

As soon as the rooks and daws had flown up, Swagdagger started to run toward the spinney, carrying his head high. He had gone one third of the way along his track when the rooks, flying at him with open beaks, but swerving a save distance off, checked him again. Other birds came to the field – tomtits and wagtails, sparrows, finches, and stonechats. They perched on the brambles of the banks, each one adding his tick or squall or stitter to the general outcry. Some of them had lost mates or fledglings when last they had seen the white horror.

Kron-n-n-n-n-n-k!

The sound, prolonged and deep, was audible through the screeching and cawing. It came from the spinney, the sound as of the trunk of a strong and living beech tree beginning to split in the frost. Swagdagger suddenly stopped, sniffing the air. Only one thing had such an acrid smell, and whenever he encountered it Swagdagger got out of the daylight into the nearest rabbit hole.

The owner of the deep and penetrating voice had flown inland when he had seen Chakchek the Backbreaker slip off his pitch; for sometimes he robbed the falcon of what he had struck down. He alighted on a branch at the top of a tree, which bowed to his weight. Scarl the crow saw him, – he was perching on Scarl's own lookout branch, which commanded nearly all the ground around the spinney, – but Scarl said nothing. For the new-comer was Kronk, King of the Crows, the powerful and aged owner of seven miles of coast – from Pencil Rock to the Morte Stone, where the realm of his great-grandson, the Gaping Raven, began – and of thousands of acres of forest, heath, field, spinney, and down. *Kron-n-n-k!*

The raven, looking blacker than any crow, he was so big, jumped off the lookout branch, and climbed almost vertically into the air. When about twenty feet above the tree tops he rolled on one wing, dropped a yard, and rolled level again. Then, his playful movement over, he pointed his great black beak at the stoat, and glided down to kill him.

But Swagdagger did not wait while Kronk was growing bigger in his downward glide. He turned, and galloped back along the track he had started to follow more than ten minutes before. *Whee-oo!* cried the buzzard from the sky, soaring on still, cleaver-shaped wings, as he watched Swagdagger fleeing before more than fifty clamorous birds, almost to be overtaken by the fast raven.

Swagdagger rippled up the bank, and got among the top cover. The withering sword grasses, and tough strings of bindweed tying brambles and briars, and dry thorn branches laid lengthways across old bullock-broken gaps, moved and rustled as he drew his lean body under them. Crows and rooks followed him, flapping to where patches of white showed in the long net of grasses, and trying to perch on stalks of tansy, dock, and hogweed. Three times he was pecked as he traveled along the southern bank, but he reached the corner safely, and turned up the western bank toward Windwhistle Cross.

He pushed his sharp way among the brambles and grasses to the break made by the feet of bullocks scrambling over into the sunken lane below – where Mr. Ovey had peered. The gap of earth and stone was bare for two yards. On a stone bedded in the dry earth stood the great raven.

Now stoats – and their smaller relations, the weasels – possess strength and determination which last in fullness unto the moment of death; and the mind of Swagdagger was set upon getting to Windwhistle Cross. His small flat head, sharp as a white fang, pushed out of the grasses, moved up and down, swung sideways, while the nostrils worked nervously at all the hostile scents. The quick movements wove a hole in the grasses, which set around the thin neck like a collar. The gaze of the eyes wandered, then it rested on Kronk, standing a yard away.

Raven and stoat remained still, brown and pink eyes fixed in the same stare. All the lithe furious power of Swagdagger blazed in his eyes, for he dared not run forward. His tail swished the grasses behind him; fumes of anger drove the rooks into the upper air. And then, suddenly, at a new short *Kra!* from Scarl the crow, the clamor ceased, and the air over Swagdagger's head emptied of wings. Raven, crows, rooks, daws, pies, thrushes, finches, tits, all flew away silently, big birds over the field, little birds along the hedge, leaving Swagdagger alone.

The stoat stepped through his grassy collar, smelled only furze bloom and foxglove in the air, saw the birds flying away, and forgot them. Without hesitation he ran down the bank and across the grass to his track; for he had never entered Windwhistle Cross any other way.

He was near the northern bank when the noise of wings made him stop and throw up his head. The buzzard, who had been sitting on the bank by the far corner, watching in curiosity the behavior of the birds, had been alarmed when they had suddenly flown away; but not having heard what they had seen in the sunken lane beyond, and being fearful of taking the air when raven and crow were about, it had continued to sit there. The white moving lure of Swagdagger was too strong for its caution; it forgot the general alarm, and flew over to the stoat.

On broad brown wings it sank upon Swagdagger, flapping to check its glide and stiffening its legs for the clutch. Swagdagger stood up to meet it with his teeth, but, as the buzzard was about to strike, it looked away, startled by an object appearing in the opening of the five-barred gate by the road. It was a black and white object, and a man moved behind it.

Windwhistle Cross Estate
Trespassers Will Be Prosecuted

The buzzard's wings beat violently in alarm; and instantly they beat wildly, for Swagdagger's teeth had pierced one of its legs above the knee. It rose up above the level of the bank, and tumbled sideways, the weight of the stoat struggling and twisting under it.

The buzzard unclenched its feet to be free, but they were clutched on nothing. It dived and tumbled, but could not shake off the jerking weight on its leg. It dropped toward the field again, meaning to stand on the stoat and rip it up with its hooked beak, as it had ripped up many rats and rabbits, but the shout of the man made it rise again.

Many feathers floated away in the wind over the spinney, as the hawk swooped and tumbled and recovered. The rooks, back at their potato digging (Mr. Ovey's potatoes), looked up at the struggle. Some flew around the buzzard as it zigzagged overhead, and added their cawing to the wailing whistle of the hawk. Swagdagger held to the leg with his teeth and the long claws of his forepaws, and whenever the buzzard's beak came forward to cut open his head he loosened his bite and snapped at the throat. Sometimes his tail was over his head, as he swung to the turns and somersaults of his enemy.

The flight took them away from the field, which was now distant by four lines of banks. After five minutes the wings of the buzzard flapped more heavily, and its tumblings were slower. Two claws of its right uninjured foot had pierced the loose skin of Swagdagger's neck, and were clenched tightly. It flew as before, in and out of the cawing rooks, until its bitten leg began to give it pain, when it twirled and wailed toward the ground.

A final frenzied tumble in the air flung Swagdagger's head near its own, and the buzzard's beak opened to break his skull; but Swagdagger was quicker, and his teeth, like two rows of bone thorns, snapped in the feathers of the buzzard's throat. The feathers sailed away, and he snapped again, but his teeth did not click. Hanging there, he steadily changed color, his head and neck and back and dripping tail, from white to dark red.

The banks grew larger, the field below wider, as he sank down to the earth. Near the earth the hawk began to strike with its feet and buffet with its wings, and to snap its beak; but Swagdagger held on, his eyes closed as he drew warm strength from his enemy.

The dying hawk thumped on the ground, Swagdagger riding on its back. The stoat rippled away, leaving a trail of small feathers sticking to the grasses. The idea of getting to his mate was still firmly fixed in his mind. He galloped gleefully, licking his jaws as he thought of the game he would play with his cubs.

He reached the three-acre field, and ran along his track. Halfway across he stopped, his nose working at the air that came in swirls from the bank. There was the smell of fresh-turned earth, blown with a strange and puzzling taint. He left his track, making a loop to avoid the unseen danger; for everything strange was dangerous to Swagdagger. Ten yards off the north bank he seemed to freeze, for his nostrils had dipped into a stream of strong, familiar scent – Man.

Mr. Ovey stood by his newly painted notice board, which leaned on the five-barred gate. He was mopping his big face with a handkerchief, his hat pushed back from his pale forehead. A spade was stuck in a heap of earth at his feet. Mr. Ovey saw Swagdagger, and his eyes behind his glasses bulged. He started after him, shouting 'Hi!' when Swagdagger ran up the bank. When he got to the place where Swagdagger had climbed, Mr. Ovey said 'D——!' behind his teeth, for he saw nothing there.

Picking up a stick, Mr. Ovey hurried back through the gate, and round the outside corner of the lane. He was just in time to see a tail, tipped with black, disappear over the low bank at the edge of the spinney. He scrambled through the brambles, holding out an arm to ward off low branches from knocking off his eyeglasses. Grasping the stick firmly, and with head held tense, Mr. Ovey walked warily through the beech trees, peering left and right.

He came to a woodpile, and had a glimpse of a smaller animal, with white patches on its light brown body, before it diappeared. Mr. Ovey, warm with excitement, crept forward, and waited for it to run out again. It came out by his feet, but ran in again before the blow fell. Mr. Ovey saw another peep out, and then another. The whole place was full of the little animals!

He began to pull at a branch on the top of the pile. He felt strong as he levered it up, and with a vigorous turning movement threw it down. Lovely white skins: they must be valuable ermines! Mr. Ovey imagined himself returning to London with a dozen or more pelts, to be made into a lining for his motor coat. He saw himself in the midst of wondering villagers, but swiftly thought, as he levered another heavy bough off the top of the pile, 'No, keep it quiet! There might be money in it!' Mr. Ovey was enjoying himself immensely. An expression was on his face familiar to many townsfolk who glanced at the advertisements of 'Ovey's Liver Salts – Get That Athlete's Zest for a Farthing a Day.' (For, although Mr. Ovey took the farthings rather than the salts, a certain vanity had made him pose for the senescent and fatuous individual depicted as leaping tables, sprinting after motor buses, and running on air, whose bounding vitality was asserted and reasserted to be due to Ovey's Liver Salts.)

Mr. Ovey had thrown down four boughs when Swagdagger ran out of the pile. Swagdagger was in the greatest rage. He had been pestered and thwarted nearly all the morning, his play was interrupted (four cubs rolling him over and biting him with their milk teeth), and now his mate and cubs were threatened. He stood still, uttering whiny, champing noises – for a translation of which see the first paragraph of this story. When Mr. Ovey moved forward with uplifted stick, Swagdagger also moved forward. His harsh chakkering cry rattled in the spinney. He continued to approach Mr. Ovey – fourteen inches of warning and aggression – who said, '*Grrr!* Get out of it, you beast!' as he struck with his stick, and missed.

Hak! Hak! Hak! Hak! Hak! Hak!

Now Mr. Ovey's knowledge of and regard for the countrywide were almost totally confined to its money-making possibilities, and he had not the least idea that birds and animals were very near in instincts and feelings to men and women, being of the original flesh and spirit; and he did not know that Swagdagger's forefathers had run in Windwhistle Cross since the first beech tree, whose roots were long since crumbled in the ground, had sprung

41

from a single seed planted by a rook, and founded the spinney. Mr. Ovey therefore was most surprised when, immediately after he had tried to hit another stoat with his stick, Swagdagger ran forward and started to climb up his trousers. Mr. Ovey shouted when the sharp claws pricked his knee, and struck at the animal with his hand; but so quick was Swagdagger, and so sure his eye, that he bit through the tip of a finger before the blow knocked him off.

Mr. Ovey turned to leave the spinney. He shouted for help when he saw other little animals running out of the woodpile. He blundered through the low branches to the bank, brambles clawing his clothes, and filling him with fear. He stopped in the lane, and to his horror saw that he was being followed.

Hak! Hak! Hak! Hak! Hak!

Wheeling high over Windwhistle Cross, above the rooks and the crows, Kronk the raven watched Mr. Ovey running to the gate, pulling it open, and nearly falling over the strange black and white object that had been puzzling the wary Kronk. Mr. Ovey closed the gate, and, breathing heavily behind his notice board, felt safe on his own property.

'Dangerous brutes,' he puffed. 'Poison . . . traps . . . what local author-ities doing . . . permit it . . . *phoo!*'

He was pulling his handkerchief out of his cuff, where one had been tucked for many years, when the piebald family of Swagdagger ran round the corner.

Hak! Chakker! Hak!

Mr. Ovey ran as far as the middle of the field, then turned, and stared at the pack. He felt a dreadful desire to remain standing still. He gave an auto-matic glance round for a policeman.

High in the air the raven, who also had felt the fascination of being approached by a pack of hunting stoats, watched the man standing still until the white threads were almost to him. Only then did he turn and run to the lower bank. He scrambled up, and stood among the brambles, until the white threads reached the bank. He jumped down, with head turned to see if they were following.

Hak! Hak! Chakker-hak!

Wheeling on firm wings, the raven watched the man plodding across the next field, and the plunging canter of bullocks down wind when they got the musky cent of stoat. He watched him across another field, and so to the road.

Mr. Ovey ran on, slower and slower, groaning that if only he got out of this he would sell the beastly place, and give up smoking. He was chased almost to the farmhouse at the bottom of the hill, where a cattle dog, which had been lying in the roadway, got up and loped forward to see what the trouble was; and made off at full speed when it smelled and saw.

Swagdagger forgot Mr. Ovey, and went under a gate into a field at the top of which was one of his playgrounds, a quarry, in which ironstone had been blasted for the widening of the motor road, and which the brambles were always trying to reclaim. Here they played awhile, and hunted rabbits, and washed themselves after their meal, imitating Swagdagger, who was busy with his tongue on ribs and back and tail. When they had played again, the white leader led the way back to Windwhistle Cross, running along the track, and crossing the field for the first time with that season's jolly cubs.

July 1929

CHRISTMAS

SINCE MICHAELMAS MY YULE log has been propped against the walling of the hump-backed bridge over the river, which runs less than a hundred yards away from my cottage door. A small spate brought the log down one day, and the boys and I hauled it out with a lasso. It weighs about one and a half hundredweight, and is of yew.

Many times I have wondered if it were not too good for burning: if that salmon-pink wood, stronger than oak, should not be cut up for table legs.

A crack running by a twist in the 'stick' finally decided me. There stands the Yule log, which we shall drag into the sitting room on Christmas Eve.

The small children are excited, and have been rehearsing in make-believe for days. Only this morning Charlie the black cat ate three-year-old Margaret's 'yoolug' – a piece of bacon rind on a string.

It is difficult to remember all the Christmastides of the past few years. There was one up in Rhode Island, when we skated on the lakes where herrings had spawned; another in the mess of the Navvies' Battalion in Halton Park, Buckinghamshire, when the P.M.C., a major recently a sergeant major, gave us roast beef, saying it was good enough for anyone, and turkeys were only for fops, and he made his subalterns eat the fat, too, also he knocked down defaulting privates in the guardroom – but that was long ago; and then that flat and lifeless Christmas after the Armistice, when color and movement had gone from the only world we knew.

Best of all was that strange and beautiful Christmas of 1914, when we made friends with the Saxons of the 133rd Regiment opposite us under Messines Hill; when in the frosty moonlight of Christmas Eve we strolled about in No Man's Land, talking and listening to the carols sung in German, only forty yards away, and later watching with indescribable feelings the candle-lit Christmas tree they planted on their parapet. And the great white star rising from the east, over their lines, which some of us thought must be a light on a pole, it was so bright!

That time had a dream quality for my eighteen-year-old self. Many of us, German and English, longed, and even prayed voicelessly, that its good will and kindness should extend and deepen, until no war spirit remained. Alas! it was not realizable – then.

Why should not this Christmas be the best one has known?

The children are beginning to be human beings, with their own personalities, and therefore as companions they are stimulating. Also, we are looking forward as eagerly to our guests' coming as, we hope, they are eagerly anticipating their arrival. It has been fun arranging the bedrooms, and finding odd corners for camp beds.

And the walks we shall have, whatever the weather, on the high ground of Exmoor and in the lanes, with their tall beechen hedges! The blazing of wood fires on open hearths shall greet us when we return, pleasantly tired, to sip tea made from the black iron kettle hanging on its lapping crook from the chimney bar.

I have got a spruce fir, with all its roots; it is set in an oak tub, for later planting-out in the hilltop field. The sapling shall not be murdered; it shall, after Christmas, join the company of its brethren below Windwhistle Spinney. Late on Christmas Eve, when the children are lying excitedly awake upstairs, or breathing sweetly in sleep, we and our friends will deck its branches with shimmering delights. Then into the cupboard under the stairs, until the afternoon party!

Of course everyone will hang out a stocking. And of course Father Christmas will fill each stocking, and everyone will sit at the long refectory table for breakfast. On one side the children, graded according to size, from the gypsy-dark Margaret to the blue-eyed Ann; on the other ourselves, the so-called adults, watching the happy faces over the table.

Afterward a two-mile walk across the park and fields to church. On the way we shall peer over the parapet of the bridge to see if any of the spawning salmon are visible.

And I shall show my friends the ant hill beside the river where every traveling otter scratches and rolls, a small hillock very green in spring with the many fishbone fragments that nourish the root grasses.

Before the church service everyone greets everyone else in voices that are neither loud nor yet too subdued. Contrast is the salt of life; and, after the singing of the good old hymns, we shall return in an amazingly short time to see the turkey turning slowly on the jack-spit by the hearth. And what a fire! The wood for it has been selected and matured for several years. Pine for the resinous scents; oak for body; elm for its majestic white ash; alder for its charcoal – the flames of these woods will blend and be thrown out by the bulk of the yew-wood back brand.

The twin rows of human cormorants will perch themselves along our table, I shall refuse to carve, corks will pop with bubble of grape and ginger; the lighted pudding, set with holly sprigs, will come in, with the mince pies, to be eyed with lessening enthusiasm except by the row of brighter faces. Who will want figs, dates, or nuts? Then for the crackers!

There will be ping-pong, skittles, bagatelle, lead-horse-racing, crown-and-anchor, and maybe (since Harold is of the party) the three-card trick. And those of us who have realized the poise and harmony between life and death will meet in my writing room, to listen and to think as the voice of the King, symbol of our hopes for our brother men and neighbors, speaks around the earth.

Yes – this Christmas, I hope, will be 'proper.' Windles, the eldest boy, has just come in to tell me that he has seen Father Christmas's reindeer! They were going up the path to Bremridge Wood . . . or else they were the red deer from Exmoor, driven down by the hard weather. Which were they, Dad?

Quick, Windles, tell the others what you've seen! Christmas! Christmas!!

December 1934

MOONLIGHT

THE OTHER NIGHT, HAVING some letters for London which must be collected by the van at 7 a.m. the following morning, I took cap and stick, meaning to walk to the roadside group of thatched cottages a mile away. It was a few minutes before midnight. I was tired, and the thought of the walk seemed wearisome. Equally wearisome appeared the idea of unlocking the garage and taking out the car. As I hesitated, the moon's horn showed by the top of a fir tree on the hillside opposite. Well, it was the same sort of thing one had seen for years and years. An owl cried somewhere among the dark trees. So they had always cried. One had heard them so many times that they made no more impression on the mind than the noise of an exhaust made on the mind of a London bus driver.

Well, the letters must be posted, and, after the hours of enforced sitting still at the desk, perhaps it would be best to walk. One did n't take enough exercise. Ah, if one could only feel about stars, moon, trees, grass, sea, as one felt about them years ago! Wordsworth, it was recalled, had felt an identical regret, almost remorse, for the passing of similar enthusiasms.

I walked down the garden path, across the lane, and into the deer park. The air was soft and still. I passed under the great lime trees, among whose leaves, in the past summer, hundreds of thousands of bees had murmured, in whose thickets around the trunks wood pigeons and jackdaws had nested. How many years since one had climbed to a bird's nest? In a few moments I was on the bridge, looking down at the Bray water.

The moon was making the usual bright and broken lights on the three streams pouring from the three arches. Near the tail of the pool, where the water thinned and quickened, sudden tremulous strips of silver showed where a trout had risen. That was pleasing. Shadows of alders looked blacker than the trees themselves. The thought of that fact was wearisome, until

47

I told myself it was not necessary to remember it for the purposes of writing it.

Surely, I said to myself, this is a beautiful and restful scene. It is interesting, too, for see! That glimmer, just under the fall of the middle arch, was surely the big trout turning over to take something – a 'mullhead,' perhaps, that had gone down with the stream.

Your trouble, or feeling of weariness, is only that you have got into the habit of using yourself as a receiving apparatus for natural impressions, for the purpose of rendering them into words, and thus obtaining money. You feel that you can never relax, become thoughtless in the sense of letting the inner nature rise up through the enslaved mind. There are nearly a dozen people entirely dependent on you, and unless you work all the time you will get into debt.

The camera of your mind is tired, abused by a demoniacal photographer. You have, in your need to rest, almost thought yourself into a nature hater. Man does not change, – Wordsworth was wrong, – but a man needs change. For a change, try and do what you really want to do.

So I sat on the bridge, and shut my eyes, and thought of nothing, breathing deeply and slowly, and as slowly respiring. The night was warm for October, and after a while I thought I would lie on the grass. What mattered if it were dew-damp? Rheumatism, so-called, came from ill feeding and drinking. I would lie on the grass. It was fine to lie on the grass, while the distant stable clock tolled midnight.

It seemed, as I rested there, that the stars had not been seen for years. The first frost would sharpen and make them glitter; but now they shone softly, as though very peacefully.

Closing my eyes again, I let the sounds of the river flow through me until I began to feel again a serenity of earth which no conscious thought could give. How often did the activities of the brain force one away from one's true or inner or natural self! Damn the brain – a good servant, but a bad master.

I lay there until the clock tolled one, then I arose and walked happily, thoughtlessly, to the main road and the post box. Clearly the moon revealed the hour of collection, and I had brought an electric torch to make sure! Years ago the sight of anyone taking a torch for a night walk would have filled me with scornful protest. No sight – no insight.

And why go home? I was actually enjoying the walk. The windows of the cottages were all blank. The nose of the painted grotesque wooden stag's head on one of the walls gleamed where a hibernating snail had crawled. Everything was so still and quiet. My body was non-apparent. The moonlight was in me and through me. I marveled at the cottage folk who, with one exception, had shut out this lovely air from their bedrooms. I would walk up to the moor and sleep in the heather if I wanted to, or walk on if I wanted to.

Certainly I would. I went home to get my coat. Having got it, I hesitated. Tomorrow those book reviews must go off, and if one were tired – my breast seemed filled with the loveliness of the night, and this was the time to sleep. So I pulled my bed to the window and lay there happy, while the moon climbed far over the fir trees, until serrated by the silver fringe of thatch, and I fell away from myself in sleep.

January 1935

A NIGHT ON SALISBURY PLAIN

UNSEEN PEEWITS WERE CRYING their wild cries in the mist somewhere. The sounds were part of the gray silence of the Plain. I could hear the last of the hot oil dripping into the engine sump, from the overhead camshaft gear. Ten yards away, the long low length of the black car was part dissolved. I could feel mist condensing on my eyelashes.

It was late afternoon. The last twenty miles had taken me two hours and a quarter. Foolishly I had relied on my petrol gauge, although I had known it was faulty; and now I was on my reserve tank, enough for sixteen miles in ordinary traveling, but only one half or a third of that distance in second or low gear. One could not see more than five yards ahead.

By the ruins of brickwork and concrete overgrown by grasses I recognized my whereabouts: I was close to Stonehenge. This place had been an encampment for airmen and their craft during the war. Afterward there had been what is called an agitation in the press for the removal of the buildings. They were demolished; and once again the great circle of Stonehenge was seen from the road in outline against the northern sky, relict from the age of mammoths, sabre-toothed tigers, and skin-clad men of small stature, short age, inferior teeth, and ideas of salvation through the blood sacrifice of men other than themselves.

Stonehenge was clearly seen again, but no longer in solitude, for the hutments and hangars were broken down at the time when motor cars were beginning to increase almost in geometrical progression. A barbed-wire fence was erected with a tea house, and approach to the Sun Temple cost each visitor one shilling.

It was no use going on; the night must be spent here. Fortunately I wore my black leather flying coat, and there was a rug in the car. It was pleasant to sit down, to suspend oneself in the silence of Hardy's Great Plain.

What was Stonehenge? Men asked one another. How came it to be built here? And whence these mighty slabs of stone, weighing hundreds of tons? And why were they set thus and thus?

Likewise, when the sunshine and starlight of centuries have rolled away from this age and civilization, which may indeed become traceless like other civilizations save for things such as bones, shards, fragments of walling, aluminium pistons, and phosphor-bronze carburetor floats, men may wonder on the scars in the chalk of Salisbury Plain which were practice trenches for firing, bombing, and bayonet fighting; on the curious traces in the distant downs of designs which probably had some religious signifi-cance, possibly connected with the then-universally sanctified idea or ideal of blood sacrifice.

Night shut down through the grayness, and the peewits ceased to call. My footfalls among the flattened heaps of broken bricks and iron and rotting wood seemed strange and unreal to me. I felt myself to be another person. I determined to prolong the strange feeling of being strangely alone in a silent world. I collected fragments of deal wood which had been doorposts, lintels, and window frames, and made a fire. My car was off the main road, and I could sleep under its tonneau cover when so I wished. I had food and a vacuum flask of hot coffee. There was enough wood for the fires of a bivouacking battalion.

Flames speared the mist, which gave way before the bright thrusts. I ate, drank, took strength and comfort from the fire. A mouse ran over the cracked concrete whereon I sat. It took a crumb, fled away, returned for more, fled away, came back, sat upright, stared at me, and then crouched to a more serious feeding. It looked to be a very old mouse, and I wondered if it could possibly have known the time when the soldiers were here. No; but it was strange how it accepted me and the fire.

All over England were memorials to men who had not come home from the war, most of them made to the ideas of elderly noncombatants. Will the antiquarians of the future deduce from these memorials, with their chaste and sometimes angelic figures holding aloft righteous swords, torches, and lamps, that what to soldiers of the line was generally tedium was to the memorial builders generally Te Deum? That the memorials had no relation, even symbolically, to reality? That they helped by the fostering of illusion to perpetuate things as they were?

The mouse departed with a swelled belly, probably to sleep in its slightly mouldy bed of gnawn grasses under a pile of bricks somewhere. I threw more wood on the fire.

What of those designs, their regimental badges, cut by soldiers in the swarded slopes of the downs near Shaftesbury? Have the grasses, the trefoils, the cinquefoils, and other wild flowers – dove's-foot, crane's-bill, harebell – have they crept over the chalk again?

The White Horse, its origin lost beyond memory, is still the White Horse, for all to see and meditate; but where are the badges of those Australians, Londoners, County men, and the keen youths from the North? Of those youths who went from the Great Plain to the rolling chalk lands of the Somme, after cutting their own memorials in the English sunshine of 1915 and early 1916 (such things could only be done before idealism was shattered by reality, before July the First, 1916, when the New Army found its grave in Picardy) – of those singing, cheering, single-minded civilian-soldiers none returned; not one of the returning survivors was the same man. What would the future antiquarian see, then, as their true memorial, I wondered to myself, lying on my back, wrapped in the leather flying coat and strangely serene to feel the ancient gray earth beneath me. Which would the unborn antiquarian accept – the idealistic interpretation of those who stayed at home and imagined vain things, or these old scars and cuts and brick heaps in the chalk?

I lay there, between dozing and waking, until the sun peered red just above the road winding over the eastern plain. The fog was gone, the plovers were calling to one another forlornly, and a laden milk van was rolling along toward London. It was very cold. As I walked away there was a small shrill screeching, and a weasel bounded over the rubble, a large mouse in its jaws.

February 1935

'THE DEAR ONE'

WHEN I CAME DOWN the valley after trouting, the boys cried out that they had a baby Tarka. They had found it outside a field drain in the deer park, and had carried it home in a handkerchief.

A glance showed that the small, sinuous, brave-sly-eyed animal was no otter, but a stoat. The tip of its inch-long tail was dark brown, distinguishing it from a weasel. It was scarcely weaned. Its milk teeth were not yet hard. It made a shrill, chattering cry. Probably its mother had been trapped by one of the keepers, and it had wandered out in its hunger.

The boys declared it was an otter cub. Mother had said so. Farmer had said so. Their minds resisted readjustment. I said I thought it was a stoat; a little Swagdagger, not a baby Tarka.

'Oh, I love it!' cried the elder boy, aged seven, ecstatically.

'Better put it back where you found it,' I retorted, irritable with too much to think about, which in turn had been caused by my own indolence.

'Oh, I do love it!' said the boy.

Half seriously I gave it the worst character: a bloodsucker, bird strangler, gnawer of rabbits' eyes, eater of living flesh only.

'But God made it,' retorted the seven-year-old.

'His religion,' I explained to a friend, 'comes entirely from his schooling, his parents having been impartial, noncommittal, even evasive about this profound problem.' And turning to the boy, 'How do you know God made it?'

'You told me when I was four that God made trout and otters, so I thought God must have made this too,' he replied. When sure that we were not laughing at him, but at me, he dared (being a very sensitive child) to ask again if he might keep it. Might he, please? Certainly, if he wanted to. He could always do what he liked.

It became for them 'the dear one.' After their bath (tepid) they came down in pyjamas to peer into the barrel and say good-night to it, where it lay curled in cotton wool beside a saucer of milk and bread. Such a darling little thing, was n't it, Dad? Such sweet little paws and face, had n't it, Mum? The elder boy hugged himself with joy. The next night it nipped his finger; he looked bewildered, then he scowled with mortification at the betrayal of his benevolent feelings, and gave the stoat to his brother, aged five.

The beast did not thrive. Occasionally I saw it trying to eat. It chittered much, calling its parents. It was ill. Obviously it had been injured when they brought it home. I thought it would die soon of peritonitis; unless the Parson Jack Russell terrier, expert mouse snapper, secret-sly chicken slayer, got it first. The terrier, at every opportunity, and despite threats and thwacks of every kind, dashed to the barrel whenever he saw a chance.

Hearing or smelling the dog, the infant stoat would raise its long flat head, the shape of a hawk's skull, and remain poised. It showed no fear (although it had fear). Weak, starved, soon to die, it did not cower or flinch, but waited with head upheld in the enemy's direction.

Seeing its plight, the elder boy reclaimed it. We fed it on warm milk from an old fountain-pen filler. We wrapped it in cotton wool. He was heard praying at night for its recovery. Secretly, in the tenderest tones, while leaning cautiously over the barrel rim, he exhorted Swagdagger to live.

The fourth evening the terrier, whom no threat could daunt, got into the barrel. We hurried to the sounds of thumping, shoving, scrambling, chittering. He was lugged out and hurled away. There by the overturned saucer and crushed box stood the stoat, its head still upheld, but swaying on its neck.

In the morning it was curled on its side, a mite hardly big enough to fill the palm of the hand, languid with the chills of approaching death. I carried it in my trouser pocket, but soon 'it was a-go,' as the old people say of death in the West Country.

The seven-year-old appeared round the door, cheeks red, eyes wet with unhappiness. He would kill the dog. But why? God also made the dog. Oh, did God? The boy ran away and hid; was observed shaking his fist at the sky; told his mother he would say no more prayers.

Later, when we buried 'the dear one' under a rose tree, the boy became tranquil when it was suggested that he would perhaps see his friend again in a different form, but under the same sky. And the next day all was forgotten.

May 1935

1935

SALAR,
THE LEAPER

A Story of
Atlantic Salmon

by

HENRY
WILLIAMSON

London
FABER AND FABER LIMITED
24 Russell Square

*C. F. Tunnicliffe's pencil sketch for the title-page decoration, drawn on
an early proof sheet, still bearing the original title, provided by Faber*

SALAR THE SALMON

I. Tideways

I

A T FULL MOON THE tides swirling over the Island Race carry the feelings of many rivers to the schools of fish which have come in from their feeding ledges of the deep Atlantic. The returning salmon are excited and confused. Opalescent is the moon's glimmer under broken waters; the fish swim up from ocean's bed and leap to meet the sparkling silver which lures and ever eludes them, and which startles them by its strange shape as they curve in the air and see, during the moment of rest before falling, a thrilling liquescence of light on the waves beneath.

The Island Race is a meeting place of currents over a sunken reef, or chain of reefs. The sea is never still there. Twice every day and twice every night the tide rips over the ledges and pinnacles of the reef, streaming the seaweed under its white surges and mingling the layers of river waters in its green massive drifts.

Salmon feed in the Atlantic and return to the fresh-water rivers to spawn, and, by this arduous and pleasurable act, give of themselves to the immortality of salmon. For two years after hatching, the samlet lives and feeds in the river, and, having survived many dangers, in the month of May drops down to the estuary in a new silver sea coat, slender little fish no longer than a man's hand, bewildered and brave, venturing with others of its school the thickening salt waters beyond the known river water of its birth. It feels its way by the link of nerves, sensitive to the least pressure or density, along its sides from gill covers to tail. The samlet – or smolt, as it is called in its first armor of bright sea scales – feeds eagerly on the new food moving on and stirring the sandy shore of ocean, shrimps and other small crustaceans and fish. In fresh-water life it was always head to stream, poised in eddy or by stone; thus it breathed through mouth and gill, thus it waited and watched for food moving or floating before and above its eyes. In the sea it drove itself forward, a sideway sinuating movement, boring into the unknown and deepening densities of ocean. Always it was traveling farther from the shallow coast, yet following the weakening stream of fresh water beyond the last ribs of sand.

It came to a dark wall of rock from which ribbon weed was unrolling and swaying. The green water moved as in the river, but with greater press, and there the smolt waited in the race of tides, feeding on small fish which drifted past.

The tide took the smolts south of the Island, to where beyond rocks the water deepened and was quiet below the lift and roll of waves. So they began a far sea journey, their rivers forgotten. As the different schools found their food easily or hardly, so they grew quickly or slowly; thus salmon were returning to their rivers flowing into the North Atlantic at all months of the year, in varying tapers or sea mouldings. Nevertheless the salmon's cycle of renewal is fixed in the orbits of the sun, served by the moon; its spawning time is the end of the year, when days are short and rivers run high with wild rains.

II

The Romans, sailing in their galleys between the Island and the mainland of Damnonia, knew the meeting place by the reef, and named the fish Salar – the Leaper. So shall be called the big keeper, or male, fish who sprung toward the moon from the waves of one of the biggest tides of the year on that coast, the Easter tide.

Salar was one of many thousands returning from the ocean feeding banks. As the moon at night rose fuller, he had traveled on, pausing neither to feed nor to sleep. He had come at medium ocean cruising speed, traveling about one hundred miles from one sunrise to another, faster with the currents, slower aslant them. The current guided him; his body remembered. His mouth opened forty times every minute, and each time, as his mouth closed, his gill covers opened, and red gill rakers absorbed oxygen

58

from the water for his blood stream. In the blood stream were units of life, even as the fish was a unit in the living sea.

Salar was five years old. During the two years of river life he had grown to a weight of two ounces; three years of ocean feeding had added another twenty pounds to his weight. Growth had not been regular or uniform. In two periods of sea wandering he, with other salmon, had increased rapidly, while following herring shoals on their westward migration after spawning in the shallow waters of the north. Every day during those two periods Salar had gorged his own weight of herrings, catching them across the back as they turned from his upward rush, holding and crushing a fish in his jaws until it was dead, then swallowing it head first. Soon his shoulders were hog-curved.

Pursuing the salmon were porpoises. The porpoises hunted by swimming in formation under the salmon, which were under the herrings. They were invisible from above. The only warning of a porpoise's approach was by a swirl and sudden varying water pressure of the upward dash. A porpoise swam up under a salmon, gathered and launched itself at the fish, turned on its back and snapped at the salmon's belly. Porpoises fed by tearing away their bites; they seldom pursued a fish further. Being mammals, they had a sense of sport equal with the sense of feeding.

Salar had avoided death by bite of porpoise, shark, ray, and other predatory fish – nearly all fish prey on other fish – and now, five years and one month from hatching out of a round egg about three sixteenths of an inch in diameter in the headwaters of a mountain stream, he was more than a yard long, and his girth was half his length.

He was lying on the edge of a current where it dragged against an eddy or back trend of water, using one moving weight of water to buoy him against an opposing weight. He lolled there, at rest. He was nearly asleep.

III

During the time of one wave crest breaking white and re-forming again in phosphoric streaks, nearly a thousand salmon which were resting in the tail of the Island Race had broken formation and were zigzagging into the northerly sweep of the tide. Many schools had been hovering there in echelon, bound for their various rivers: very large springers, five- and six-year-old fish; smaller spring fish with between two and three years of sea feeding; mended kelts, – spawned fish that had 'cleaned themselves' after spawning, – the few survivors of the autumn run, biggest of the year, the authentic spawning run of salmon. The mended kelts would return along the way they had traveled as smolts.

A few of the schools were grilse, small fish which had been only a year in salt water, weighing from three to eight pounds, slender, silver-gray, unspotted except faintly on gill covers, with forked tail fins and gracile 'wrists' – the slender part of the body where it splayed into the tail fin. One of the grilse, of a school of eleven which had been skittering along the moonlit surface and sporting among the wave crests, was Gralaks, a young maiden salmon who had been born in one of the streams running down from the moor of the wild red deer, in the gravel redds above the pool called Fireplay.

When Salar came in from the Atlantic feeding banks, the rivers of that coast were low, for little rain had fallen since the New Year. He swam on without direction, followed by the school of young salmon which was making for the coast. The grilse were in familiar water, for here as smolts they had traveled the year before.

Salar, disturbed by a current of colder water into which he had swum, turned across to avoid it. Gralaks, entering the cold current a few lengths behind the big salmon, half-rolled and then thruddled up and leapt for joy. The other grilse did likewise. This was water of the Two Rivers, their mother stream, their home!

Salar cruised on slowly, alone. He rose to the surface and flopped out, falling back on his side, irritated by the sea lice clinging to his skin behind the ventral fins and on the descending taper of his back. The grilse falling made each a bubbled or seething hole, entering head first, with little splash: this was the joy leap. Salar made the smacking splash of an aimless fish.

He swam on, having crossed the layer of colder, less dense water, and came to warmer salt again. Seeing a pollack above him, he curved up and while on his side gripped it across the back. But he was not hungry; his flesh was stored full of power. He expelled the pollack from his mouth, caught it again head first, and then, after hesitation, closed his gill covers and the expulsion of water pushed it out. He swam on dismally, a lost salmon.

After four hours he had swum east nearly twenty miles; so he came into an area of strong coastal currents. They swept over jags of rocks faster than his slow cruising speed. This was the race over Dead Man's Reef. Had Salar chanced to stray here a few hours later or earlier he would have entered the current running north and gone with it along the rocky shore and past the Morte Stone and so to the Severn Sea, where he would have found the fresh-water guides to his parent river. Now a strong race was setting south; not liking white or broken water, Salar turned into the tide, and, swimming with it, he came to sandy shallows ribbed by the periodic sway and roll of waves. His nervous liquid cells knew the rhythm of these waves; it was the same rhythm of the Severn Sea, the pulse of shallow Atlantic rollers at the full of the moon. He leapt through a wave, a gleaming impulse of joy.

The sudden appearance of a large leaping fish startled a bird that was paddling aimlessly in the foamy back drag of creaming wave tops. It has-tened seawards, paddling a score of times and then ceasing through weari-ness. This bird had thick waterproof plumage and a long sharp beak: a guillemot. Its head, neck, and back were dark brown; its breast, which should have been white, was also dark brown, in clotted streaks of feather-lets. When it had been white-breasted the guillemot had enjoyed movement in air and water; now it was cold, weary unto death; the filaments of its feathers were stuck together with oil-fuel waste cast overboard by a ship. The guillemot had swum up from its chase of fish into a floating mass of crude petroleum, and thereafter it flew no more, its skin was painful, winds and tides drifted it away from its parent Island, it starved. Three years before, it had nearly caught the little smolt Salar as he swam with his brethren in the strange currents of the Race; now Salar, leaping near it, shocked some of its remaining life from it. He swam on under the guille-mot, seeing its two feet and air-glistening body mingled with the reflections of feet and body. Later the bird was thrown on the beach by the surge and dragged itself about until the shore rats found it dying and feasted on it; and soon it was water, air, sand, salt again.

Salar cruised on, jumping not so often as his excitement at finding shal-low water grew less. Stimulated by the vivid pulse of his blood, his parasites secured their holds between his scales and sucked that blood. He leapt and fell back on his side with a splash that set the gulls screaming in envious competition. A couple of hundred yards farther on he jumped and smacked down on the water again, on his other side.

The porpoises were following a large school of salmon making for the Two Rivers estuary. More than sixty fish were traveling fast before the black glistening-bottle-noses, which drove forward in two tiers, one layer or line diving below the other as it rose to the surface to vent. When hunting, the porpoises breathed thrice every sea mile. The lower tier swam under the salmon, gathering together again after a massed drive. Appearing suddenly from the invisibility below, the porpoises scattered the salmon in terror surfacewards, where they were pursued and chopped by the upper tier.

Behind the herd of porpoises, traveling fast, was Orca the grampus, the killer whale, blowing a jet of spray into the air as it rose to breathe every quarter of a mile.

As he was swimming under a ledge of rock above deeper water, Salar came face to face with Orca, who had just crushed a porpoise in its great teeth and swallowed the mid part of its body, leaving the head to float away on one side of its jaws, and the tail flukes on the other. Orca was eighteen feet long, and when it could get salmon to eat it ignored other creatures, except occasionally to chop them in fun.

Instantly Salar turned and shot away, but Orca was as quick, swishing forward under the salmon. Salar leapt thrice from the wide peg-toothed gape, each time nearly falling back into its jaws. He flickered and doubled, and scurried under an overhanging rock, and lay there with fast-beating heart, hidden by a fringe of bladder weed swaying gently in the tide. His head and body were in half darkness, and pressed against the rock worn concave by the sweep of sand and water at low tide. Orca tried to get him, but the head of the grampus was big and blunt; vainly it wallowed around the rock, shoving and blowing the sand about. It rose through the waves and gave a loud snorting grunt and swam out to sea, at a tangent to the direction taken by the porpoises. About a mile from the rocks it turned and swam back slowly, swinging down to the base of the ledge where the body and tail of Salar were still moulded in fear against the rock. It came to the surface, grunting angrily, and swam down once more, to swim up and jump clear of the water, showing its black fluked tail and mackerel-like shape in a wide splash. It swam away fast, throwing itself over lines of waves it crossed diagonally, in pursuit of the porpoises.

IV

An hour before midnight, in bright moonlight, a dozen crews of four men each, silently in rubber thigh boots, went down to their salmon boats moored on the sandbank at the edge of the deep water of the fairway. 'Let 'n come,' said one, truculently, with a glance down the estuary. All the fishermen felt an angry but subdued sense of injustice against water bailiffs employed by the Board of Conservators. They believed that the laws were imposed only for the benefit of rich sportsmen, while they themselves were poor men with families to feed and clothe from what they got by fishing. Most of the fishermen ignored the limits of the season for net fishing, and fished for salmon all the year through when the weather was favorable. During the close season they fished only at night, beginning two hours before low ebb, and continuing until the returning flow made the drag on the nets too heavy.

The tide ebbed brightly; the water looked white, and yet the dark shapes of boats going down were indiscernible. There was no wind. The night was in the moon's unreal power. Curlews and other wading birds were crying on sandbank and gravel ridge. In each boat two men pulled at the sweeps, a youth sat in the bows, the owner sat in the stern, where the net was piled.

An old man in the stern of one boat sat upright as light flicked on the starboard bow and was scattered in a loud splash. The oarsmen, dipping enough to keep way on the boat, looked over their left shoulders. Salar had leapt near the Pool Buoy, at the tail of The String, where the ebbing waters of the Two Rivers met and bickered.

On the shillets of the lower ridge known among fishermen as The Fat and the Lean, the keel shoe of the salmon boat grated; the man in the bows leapt out and held the gunwale. The boat swung round to the shore, noisy with the water streaming against its length. When the other three men had clambered out, he shortened the anchor rope in the ring and carried the anchor a little way up the slope of the ridge, putting it down carefully lest the clank of metal be heard over the water. The tide was too strong for shooting a draft, and they waited there quietly, talking in low voices and sometimes standing silent to listen for the sound of the water bailiffs' motorboat.

Soon the boat was heeling over, and they shoved it down into the lapsing water. Splash! 'My Gor, that was a master fish – thirty pound by the noise of 'n.'

'Shall us shoot, Feyther?'

'Bide a bit; 'tes rinning too strong, yet.'

They waited. The youth struck a match to light a cigarette.

'Put 'n out, I tell 'ee!'

'Aw, I ban't afraid of no bliddy bailies.'

'Nor be us, but us wants fish tonight, don't us? Tes no sense hadvertisin' us be yurr, be ut?'

Other boats were going down, gliding fast on the ebb and in silence but for the occasional squeak of sweeps in tholepins. A flight of shelduck went by overhead, wind sibilating in a wing where a quill had dropped. Far away down the estuary the piping and trilling of birds running and feeding by the wave-lap line were changing to cries of alarm as the first boats reached their stances on shore and sandbank.

In lessening tide the boat put out, leaving one man on the ridge. He took a turn of the rope round back and shoulder, trod a firm stand, and gripped the rope in his hands, watching the boat drifting down and across, shedding net from stern as it glided into luminous obscurity. It was a flake of darkest shadow in the moon dazzle on the water, and then was lost to sight. He braced himself and affirmed his footholds, to take the weight of water on rope and net which hung aslant in the tide between head rope buoyed with corks and heel rope weighted with lead. The boat turned into the tide, and he leaned against the curved drag of the net with its two-inch mesh stipulated by Conservancy by-law for the escape of smolts.

He heard the noise of the boat touching uptide, the others leaping out, the clank of anchor, and one of his mates hastening to help him. Together they took the strain on the rope and waited for the others, who were trudging down to meet them with the other rope. The arc cast by the two hundred yards of net was now an elongated and narrowing bulge which must be drawn in as quickly as possible before any fish found a way out by the space between ropes and the ends of the net.

They hauled slowly, steadily, hand under hand, leaning back against the scarcely yielding ropes, pulling against an area of water restrained by eight hundred thousand meshes. The two coconut-fibre ropes came in four yards a minute. Each rope ended at a wooden stretcher, to which were tied the head rope and the heel rope. At every concerted tug less water was restrained, and the net came in less slowly. Now the skipper became more anxious, and ordered two of the crew to haul at the heel rope to foreshorten the net under any fish which might be dashing about the enclosed water. The men at the heel rope hauled rapidly, bending down, their hands near the gravel to keep the bottom of the net as low as possible. The seine, or purse net, came in swiftly, seeming to hiss in the water. There was nothing in the net.

The fishermen showed no disappointment. They had been wet in sea labor since boyhood. The youth fetched the boat and they shook small crabs and seaweed from the net and repiled it in the stern of the boat. After a few minutes' rest they shot another draft, and hauled in again, bending low as before when the seine came fast and easy near the top of the water, which was asplash and glinting; they lifted the seine and ran back a few paces, while the youth dropped on hands and knees, and gripping a fish by the wrist, his thumb by the tail fin, lugged it out and struck vigorously the base of its head with a wooden tholepin. It ceased to slap the gravel, and lay still. He killed four other fish, three of them grilse. A good draft! One twenty-pounder, another fifteen, and the others between five and six pounds apiece.

The fish were flung in the well of the boat, and covered with sacks.

After a while of slack water, the tide began to flow, and with the flow came Salar and the school of grilse led by Gralaks, forerunners of larger schools to arrive from the feeding banks in later spring. Three of the grilse were gone, taken in the net.

Salar and the eight grilse swam a little ahead of the flow, to breathe and control the current. Suddenly alarmed by a fearful apparition, Salar shot up and across, breaking the water with a bulging splash and a glittering ream or traveling wavelet. Gralaks also leapt, and the watchers saw the arrowy glints of their reaming. They saw too a broader, slower flash, and thought this to be the roll of an immense fish. The boat was already afloat, the rowers waiting at the sweeps, the fourth man holding the wooden stretcher. Immediately the boat put out, the rowers bending the sweeps with full strength, across the tide, then with it, and back across; they shipped sweeps and ran ashore; the skipper threw out the anchor and hastened to help the fourth man. They heard and saw splashing, and imagined a great haul, bigger than the record of seventeen fish a few years before. As they hauled he exhorted the heel-rope men in a voice hoarsely earnest to pull faster, and together. Although only half the net was in, they could feel the jags on the walls as the fish struck them trying to escape.

Then a shout from the direction of the Pool told them of danger: the water bailiffs had landed on the ridge. The fishermen did not fear being fined if caught and convicted; they dreaded confiscation and destruction of their net, and their license for the season, soon to open, not being renewed.

Glancing over his left shoulder, the skipper saw several moving spots of light from electric torches, and realized the bailies were there in force. He knew they could not search without a warrant, and he could plead he was rough-fish catching; but if the bailies arrived while they were giving salmon a dap on the head, they would have all the proof needed. Gladly he heard the sound of raised voices up along, and hoarsely exhorted the others to get the seine in and away. He began to speak rapidly to himself: wife and children needing food and covering, one law for the rich, another for the poor, but 'if they bailies comed near, they'd find what they was n't looking for.' An extraordinary plunging and beating of the water inside the distorted horseshoe of corks made him pause in his mental tirade, and haul the stronger on his rope. He realized that something other than fish was in the seine; the tugging plunges against the net made him anxious lest it be broken.

The shouts from the upper end of the Ridge had ceased; the water bailiffs having come upon a boat with net piled for a draft, were moving down, hoping to find one in the act of taking salmon. "Errin' 'ogs!' cried the skipper, with a roar of disgust. 'Fetch the boat,' he ordered his son. Seven porpoises were clashing and threshing about in the seine. Gralaks was there, too, her sides and shoulders scored crisscross where she had driven against the net and broken her scales.

'Quick! Into the boat!' cried the skipper, shouting as a spot of approaching light wavered and dazzled his eyes an instant. Holding the head rope, he shoved off and scrambled aboard. 'Pull like something!' he cried, taking a turn with the head rope round a thwart, and hauling over the stern. The skipper did not swear – he was Chapel through and through, as he occasionally informed those who did. Several torchlights were flashing as the water bailiffs hastened over the gravel bank, wary of falling into pits left by the barges digging gravel.

'Make 'n spark!' cried the skipper, and the rowers grunted with their efforts. Then, seeing that the net was safe, the skipper bellowed indignantly, 'Why don't you chaps stop they witherin' 'errin' 'ogs – can you answer me that, tho'?'

The youth wanted to leave the net trailing in the water, to taunt the bailies into giving chase, and then clog the screw of their motorboat with the net. 'Tidden no sense,' grumbled his father, who was in shape not dissimilar from a *Meerschwein*. 'Besides, the tide be flowin'; if 't were ebbin', might be some use; 't would serve the bailies right to be drove out to sea and wrecked.'

The net was taken aboard, with one small porpoise, which was soon battered to death, and the boat made for the sandbank below the sea wall of the village.

There they were met by the skipper's wife, who whispered in a voice deep and hoarse that two bailies with policemen were waiting by the slip, up which they must walk to get home. 'They witherin' bailies, they deserve to get their boat rammed and zunk below 'em,' declared the skipper, in disgust.

The salmon were taken from under the sack. While the two hands and her son lit cigarettes at a discreet distance, the skipper's wife removed a wide black skirt much speckled with dried fish scales. Rapidly the skipper threaded a stout cord through gill and mouth of each salmon. The cord was then tied round the wife's waist, after which the skirt, by a feat of balancing made more difficult on the wet and infirm sand, was put on and fastened. Having anchored the boat, and carrying the oars, the crew went slowly toward the slip leading to the quay.

'What have you got in that bag?' one of the waiting water bailiffs demanded, pointing to the bulging sack on the skipper's shoulder.

'My own property.'

'Of what nature?'

''Og.'

'I don't want no sauce,' threatened the bailiff. 'I have a constable here. What's in that sack?'

''Og, I tell 'ee.'

'Turn it out.'

'You can't make me. Where's your search warrant?'

'I know what you've got. You're caught this time. Do you want me to go to a magistrate and get a warrant, when you'll lose your renewal of license?

I'll ask you once more, what have you got in that sack?'

''Og, I tells 'ee. For a bailie's breakfast, if you likes.'

'Turn it out.'

'If you promises to fry it for tomorrow's breakfast.'

'I promise nothing.'

'Why don't you try and search me?' screeched the old woman, amidst the laughter.

'For the last time I ask you, will you turn out that bag?' shouted the bailiff. 'Or shall I give you in charge?'

'Aw, don't 'ee vex yourself so,' said the skipper, in a gentle voice. 'Here's an Easter egg for 'ee,' and he dropped the heavy weight and tugged the sack from the blubbery mass.

'It's yours, Nosey Parker,' yelled the fishwife, as she staggered away, holding the arm of her husband and laughing stridently.

V

Salar knew now the meaning of a net, and he avoided those places in the estuary where strange enemy dropped slowly down the water, behind a more fearsome enemy, in shape between bird and seal, which moved with dip of wings or flippers along the surface. Whenever he saw a boat he sped away down the current, seeking a depth of pit or hole from which he watched while resting on the bottom.

A boat sailed slowly up The String, in it a fisherman holding tiller tucked between elbow and side. He held a line in his hand. In his other hand he held a rope, attached to a sail shaking in the wind abeam. On the submerged line was a lead weight, below it a length of catgut, and at the end of the gut was a hook half concealed by an artificial worm of red rubber. A nickel spinner just above the shank of the hook made a bright blur in the water, behind which the worm wriggled. The line slanted in the tide.

Salar did not see the boat until it was nearly over him, then he sped up against the current, turned, and went down to the bed of the Pool, with other salmon whose heads, fins, and flanks had been hurt in escape from nets.

While Salar was watching the lure, something was watching Salar. This was an enemy he had never seen in his life before – Petromyzon, the stone sucker. The Greeks were kind when they gave its family that name. Petromyzon was a relative of the hagfishes, creatures with a low organization of skeleton. Petromyzon was like an eel, or a worm, a huge torpid worm. Its body resembled the artificial rubber thing escaped from the fisherman's hook, magnified, discolored, sunk in living slovenliness, animated waste product of the spirit of life. Petromyzin had a scaleless body and a sucker mouth thorny with teeth for rasping off scales and flesh and drawing the blood of fishes. It had no jaws or ribs. It had no real bone in its body. It drew breathing life through seven branchial openings instead of gills. It had a single nostril at the top of its head. Now, stuck to a stone on which grew bladder weed hiding its head, Petromyzon was waiting to sneak up on Salar and clamp itself to the richness of his body.

Salar lay where the moving fronds of weed stroked the azure-white skin of his belly. Within his body, and under the forepart of his backbone, was a cavity or air bladder which automatically adjusted itself to the lift of the water: thus he was able to continue floating a few inches above the stone, for the pleasing sensation of being touched by the brown seaweed. Every moment the pockets and eddies of the tide were changing with the altering set of currents. Automatically the salmon shifted with them.

Petromyzon now loosened its ringed mouth on the stone, and slithered towards Salar. The thick soft lips of the sucker mouth began to work over the thornlike teeth. The expressionless eyes were fixed on the salmon's flank. Slowly it moved. Having no swimming bladder, it could only rise in water by muscular exertion; it quivered, seemed to shorten and thicken, and launched itself at Salar, rearing its head to strike at the scaled side, and instantly clamped itself there.

Salar's acceleration up the Pool, his turn and zigzagging dash down the tide, made other salmon leave their resting places and sink together to the bottom, whence they could observe the widest area of water above them. In fear Salar leapt out of the water, causing the boatman holding the line with the red rubber bait to sit upright and puff rapidly at his cold pipe. "'T was the largest Zeven-Ole I ivver zeed,' he told them later in the Royal George.

Salar could not shake off Petromyzon. The lamprey's mouth was stuck firmly to his left side below the medial line of nerves, forward of the ventral fins. Indifferent to the salmon's slipping and turning rushes, to his rolling staggers as he changed from one tide pressure to another, Petromyzon sucked the scales closer to his teeth, and began to rasp away and swallow skin and curd and flesh. He drew blood, and fed contentedly.

Salar rested on the bed of the Pool, exhausted, gulping water irregularly, for his fast-beating heart. In front of him the iron links of the Pool Buoy chain turned and re-turned slowly as the buoy above wallowed twisting in the combined weights of two tides. He could see the movements of the hind part of his enemy's body as Petromyzon allowed itself to be borne on the moving water, holding securely with its mouth. Starting forward with pain, Salar rolled and tried to scrape off the lamprey against a stone. Although the salmon weighed twenty pounds, his body had no weight in water; so Petromyzon continued to feed undisturbed. Suddenly frenzied by the feeling of lost freedom, Salar swam up to the surface and leapt with all his strength, deliberately to fall back on his side and knock away his enemy. Petromyzon, used since its earliest life to irregular motion when attached to its hosts, most of which were quitted only when they had died, endured the buffeting and sucked the harder.

After slack water, and the returning flow, Salar became accustomed to the lamprey. The pain had gone, and he had no more fear of it. Petromyzon was a hindrance, something to be gotten rid of by leaping and by scraping against stones. He was used to the extra drag, to the queerness of moving aslant when he meant to swim straight. In the tide's swilling murkiness he drifted, past lessening sandbanks and muddy glidders, a large quiet fish, as though unseeing among smaller coarse fish feeding eagerly. He moved slowly through the water, scarcely overtaking clusters of seaweed loose in the tide.

Higher up the estuary swam Salar, quiet among a drove of bass turning on their sides amidst seaweed, crabs, flatfish, and bubbles streaming from mudholes of cockles and ragworms. The tide poured into a deep pool with a rocky bottom and here the current divided, to flow up a creek which was the mouth of a small river.

A small boat was riding at anchor in the pool. As Salar approached the boat the fisherman was pulling in his line, with its two score of hooks. Flatfish, pollack, and bass were hooked. One of the bass was but a loose bag of skin and bones attached to a head.

This was the work of Myxine, the glutinous hag of the Two Rivers. The hag was a relation of Petromyzon, but one which lampreys avoided. Myxine's eyes were sunk beneath her skin, deep in the muscles of her head. They were without lenses. Myxine did not need sight, for much of a hag's life is spent within the bodies of fishes. While the bass had been struggling on a hook of the night line, Myxine had fastened to it and bored a way inside, eating steadily hour after hour until, gorged, she lay at rest in a bag of bones and water. The water poured out as the fisherman lifted it up, and the hag's head, with whiskerlike barbels, looked out of the bass's mouth.

The fisherman had never seen such a horrid sight before. With a religious exclamation he dropped it in the boat, and Myxine slithered out of the hollow corpse. He picked the hag up to knock it on the gunwale, but was horrified to find that it was turning itself into a length of slime in his hand.

'Ah, git out, you bissley bigger [beastly beggar] you,' muttered the fisherman, shaking the long hair grown to hide his stumps of ears – they had been frozen off during a blizzard aboard a whaler in his youth – as he flung the glutinous hag into the sea.

Myxine swam down to the bed of the pool, and rested there. The act of exuding slime from the thread cells along her body was additionally exhausting, and the hag lay still, unseen by Salar as he moved slowly in the wedge of tranquil water at the division of currents. Petromyzon waved indolently at his side. Salar had no desire to go up with the tide. His bounding sea vitality had shrunk within him through fear and the draining wound in his flank. He lay inert on a rock. Half his length away lay Myxine.

The hag saw the waving tail of Petromyzon, and the sight made her teeth work. She got under the lamprey's tail, and fastened her sucker there. Petromyzon lashed, but the hag stuck. In fear Salar started forward. By the time he had reached the sunken limekiln by the bend of the sea wall half a mile away, Myxine's head was inside Petromyzon's belly.

Salar waited in an eddy beside the rounded broken wall of the kiln, until the rising tide swept through the eddy and he went on, feeling strangely light.

By the Long Bridge of the port three miles distant he leapt, and a boy on the quay saw what looked like a red poppy on the silver flank. Less than three months later, all of Petromyzon was mud again.

II. Spring Spate

I

BY NOON SALAR HAD travelled under two railway bridges and one road bridge and come to a deep and wide pool above an elongated islet on which trees were growing. This was the Junction Pool. Its width and depth were carved by a small river flowing into the main river at right angles.

The varying movements and weights of flowing water maintained various movements and weights of fish. Slower, heavier salmon, which had been in the estuary for weeks, a coppery tinge on their scales of dull silver, lay in slower, deeper water. Salar was among them. With other large spring salmon he was lying over weed-waving stones on the edge of rapid water, just clear of the eddy tail, above the islet.

Gralaks and six grilse, forerunners of the main shoals of grilse which would enter the river at midsummer, swam near the surface. Sometimes one rose easily and half-lobbed itself out of the water and sank down to its place in the formation.

A school of small spring fish lay beside the heavier salmon, but in the quick water gliding past the islet. These fish weighed about nine pounds each. They had left the river two years before as smolts, weighing about two and a half ounces each. Now, assured and confident, they had come direct from the ocean, finding the water of their parent river immediately in the Island Race. In the estuary they had encountered neither seal nor net; they had run straight through on the tide. These salmon lay in swift water because its swiftness was their own.

Trutta the sea trout had pushed himself under some alder roots growing matted along the left bank, one of his homes, and there he lay, asleep, oblivious of all river life, even his own, yet automatically ready to move alive should the retina of his eye, or the nerve cells of his lateral line, be affected by alien movement.

Small brown trout, each having its hiding hole under bank or root or stone, were lying everywhere on the gravel except in the fastest runs. They were watching for food, displaced nymphs and stone-fly creepers, to move near them.

72

A shoal of resident dace, pink-finned, lay in characterless water near the old sea trout, idly waiting for drowned worms and insects to drift into the pit.

The Kelt, long-headed and lean, ravaged of spirit and consumed of body, its gills hung with maggots and its scales broken-edged, roved round the Junction Pool, unable to rest, gigantic disillusioned smolt. It lay awhile behind Salar, imitating his complacency; then wriggled upwards to Gralaks and her companion grilse, and sinuated quickly with the movement of young fish. Gralaks swam up slowly and leapt in a low curve. The Kelt leapt and fell back formlessly with a furrowed splash. From on high as they straggled over the hill on their way to known ploughlands, a flock of herring gulls saw the splash, and swung round, wheeling with petulant cries.

The splash was also seen by a boy as he was walking hurriedly across the meadow, carrying rod in one hand and tailer in the other. At the sight he began to run. When near the bank, he bent down, and approached more slowly, lest his footfalls be felt by the fish.

Kneeling, and giving repeated glances at the tail of the run, he drew a box of Devon minnows from a pocket and selected one. It was a two-inch length of phosphor bronze, a dull yellow. This he threaded on a trace of thin steel wire set with swivels. The rod was four feet long, made of steel, thinner than a rapier. It belonged to the boy's father, who had used it when fishing for black bass in Florida. He crept to the roots of an alder recently cut, found and tested foothold, stood upright cautiously, secured balance, gripped the rod in his right hand with thumb on beveled side of reel drum and index finger crooked round the special hold, and then, with a sweep and jerk of the little rod as he had often seen his father do, sent the minnow three-quarters way across the river. As it fell with a slight splash he slowed the reel, and, changing hands on the rod, began to wind in slowly, feeling the spinning drag of the lure under water. He quivered with excitement as a fish launched itself half out of the water behind the line, showing pointed dark gray head and white throat above its own wave.

The boy wound in the minnow, and tried to cast it in the same place, but it fell farther across the run, in front of Salar, who saw with his right eye a whir of light moving away in the water before him. It wobbled in the faster surface water, sometimes scattering behind it small bubbles. Salar had a

73

desire to take it. He swam up and was turning under it with open mouth when something flashed hugely beside him and seized it.

The Kelt's bony jaws clashed on metal with sharp pain. He opened his jaws to take in water and so to expel it; but it remained hard in his mouth. He could not close his jaws. He was not frightened, because in his past sea life he had occasionally taken food which hurt his mouth by its hardness and gave pain by its poison when crushed. He turned down to the bed of the pool to find a stone against which to rub it off.

To the Kelt's surprise and alarm he could not get to the bed of the pool. He could not swim freely as hitherto in his life. He shook his head violently; the thing in his mouth stabbed him, and tugged at him strongly. A shock of fear jagged through his body, stimulating him to violent action. Desperately he shook his head again, and leapt quickly from the water three times without knowing what he was doing until it happened. The aerial scene was a tilted blur of blue and green and white. In his open gills the air was harsh and choking. When in water again he turned with the flow and swam away with all his strength, causing the hovering grilse to scatter and instantly sink to the bottom. The terrified Kelt turned in the rough water which had been pressing his gills open, and lay behind a boulder, curling his tail against a stone that was not there.

Eighty yards away on the bank the boy held the rod with both hands, one thumb pressed tightly against the drum, and wondered what he should do. He put a steady strain on the steel until his wrists were aching, and he feared the line would snap. At last in fatigue he eased the strain on his trembling arms.

Behind the stone the Kelt lay in distressed bewilderment. He could not understand this enemy that prevented him from breathing and held him although it never pursued him. Indeed the Kelt did not yet define an enemy, although he was hiding in fear from the wire trace that extended taut in front of him, which vibrated its menace through his head and body.

He lay there, feeling weak and gulping jerkily until the trace slackened, and, feeling free, he moved sideways to rub his jaw against the edge of the stone. Since the trace did nothing to him, his strength returned and he swam hard against the stone, striking it with his head. The hooks drove deeper, and levered one against the other as he strove to wrench the thing from its hold in his mouth. The wounds, enlarged by the barbs, began to bleed. In pain and fury the Kelt dashed the trace on the stone, with such force that the minnow was impelled up the trace, and the barb pierced the main artery of his body, which lay under the tongue.

As he bled he weakened. He began to swim up into the pool again, away from the slight drag of the water on the trace behind him; but when the pull came from before him he swung round again and in desperation of life swam down the river to the sea, imagined refuge.

He could not breathe, swimming downstream less fast than the stream. He had to turn, and in a frenzy of fear he swam back into the Junction Pool with jaggered strength and leapt to shake off the wounding hardness in his mouth. Falling back, he felt the water too strong for him; it swept him away; he lost sense and power of direction, his body heavy with fatigue. The drift rested him, and he recovered, to swim feebly the way he was being drawn, sometimes trying to swim aside, but in vain. He was exhausted. Drawn near the bank, into slower water, he saw his enemy and the shock stimulated his wasted muscles. He struggled to reach the run, and in his effort to bore down into deeper water the river became strange and unfamiliar.

Exultingly the boy drew in the salmon to the bank, where it turned on its side, and lay still. Holding the rod in one hand, with the other he passed the loop of the tailer over the fish's tail. It was like a short-handled whip with a loop of twisted steel wire for thong, and, when lifted up with a jerk, the spring loop slid small, noosing the tail.

The Kelt struggled as it was being lifted; it flapped feebly on the grass; but three blows of the priest on its head killed it.

Its captor was trembling with pride and joy, and with these feelings was a slightness of regret that it was no longer alive and free in the river. Later, when he reached home, the stannic lustre of the Kelt was gone, its skin had shrunken, and its head looked too big for its body. To the boy's mortification, his father said it was a kelt. But, declared the boy, it was so bright that surely it was a clean-run fish, although there were no sea lice on it. Then his father showed him the fresh-water maggots on the gill rakers – a sure sign, he said; and, for confirmation, there was the spawning mark on the point of balance by the paired fins – where scales and skin had been worn away by the act of digging gravel, he said.

When cut, the flesh was seen to be pale and infirm, and the carcass was buried under an apple tree in the orchard.

II

Salar came to a bend in the river where, on the edge of white rapid water, a circular pool was in motion. Many fish were waiting in the pool, which was caused to revolve by a great bubble-churning rush of white water surging down the face of a sloping weir. The sill of the weir had been built with a cut or nick in its centre for the passage of fish. Here, therefore, the water was most violent in its descent, flinging itself in white surges against the edge of the deeper water below, making it to turn.

The farther edge of the water lapped a bank of shillets, which had been dug out of the pool and left there by spates after the building of the weir. The bank of loose flat fragments of rock shelved deeply. Sometimes the tail fin of a waiting fish showed a yard or less from the edge, to sink again casually. Nearer the pool's centre, dorsal fins lifted above the ruffled surface. A heron flying overhead saw a blotch of dark blue in the water, where fish were massed.

Other eyes too were watching, from behind a hurdle of sticks and weeds left by the receding spate against the trunk of an alder tree on the bank a score of yards below the pool.

One of the fish resting there shook its tail and swam down slowly, rolling on its side and turning up again in another direction, began to cruise round the pool, against the circular current. It was a fish which had been in the low reaches of the river since the New Year. It was about to make its fourth attempt to ascend the weir. At three points on the rim of the pool it rolled out of the water, showing dorsal and tail fins as it gathered its will within itself; then, heading resolutely into the secondary rush of bubbled water alongside the white, it moved resolutely along the rocky bottom, and resolutely swam up, accelerating with all its strength.

The winter salmon, flanks of tarnished silver and rust, leapt just beside, and clear of, the white thrust of water. It fell on the lower edge of the weir's apron, entering the thick cord of water descending from the gap in the sill above. The apron or face of the weir sloped at an angle of about twenty degrees. Slowly the salmon, swimming with all its power, ascended the cord, and, when halfway up, its strength grew less and it ceased to advance; it stayed during the time of a double wing-beat of the heron wheeling overhead; desperately it turned aside in the hope of finding easier water, and was swept down on its side, tossed from wave to wave of the white surge to which it abandoned itself, and, reaching the end of the water's thrust, with a slow sweep of the tail entered the circular pool and took place among the other fish which had failed to get over the weir.

On the farther side of the weir stood a pine tree. The heron alighted on the topmost branch, and perched there swaying, holding its head up as anxiously it watched for its only enemy – man. The grassy bank below the tree ended in a masoned wall under which the broken water surged over steps made to help fish over the obstruction of the weir. It had not occurred to the designer of the weir that a series of ledges, one below the other, would be avoided by salmon, since they had been built specially for them; the plan had seemed perfect. But running water usually does the opposite of what is expected of it by those not water-minded. The spate pouring over the sill down the steps made a white turbulence feared by every fish which ventured into it.

One of the men squatting behind the stick heap was binding with string the shank of a gaff to a six-foot length of ash plant cut lower down by the river. The gaff was forged of iron, large barbless hook. The shank was eight inches long, convenient size for concealing in the pocket.

The poachers were hiding because they had heard that one of the water bailiffs was in the neighborhood and might be about by the weir. They kept still, knowing that the heron's eye would detect the least movement.

Up in the dark green branches, tipped with the brown of new growth, the heron flapped to shift position, and then looked around anxiously, lest the flapping might have attracted attention from its enemies. Like most of the herons fishing the valleys of the Two Rivers and their feeder streams, the bird had often heard a loud crack followed by the whistle and rattle of shot when surprised by man. Quite half the bird's working hours were passed in waiting and watching lest one of its enemies appear suddenly to surprise it.

When one of the men waiting below had whipped the gaff to the ash handle, he took a small file from a torn pocket of his coat and began to stroke the point to needle sharpness.

The January-run fish tried again. It leapt from the deep water at the lower edge of the apron and splashed down on the slope, flapping sideways at the rate of nearly two hundred flaps a minute, appearing to plough its way upwards, a plume of water over its head. Making no progress, it altered direction and traveled aslant the glide, until it was within a foot of the edge of the grass, when it felt itself heavy with fatigue, and ceased to swim, lying there, a crescent fish, for a moment before turning its nose down and slipping back into the white churn several yards distant from where it had leapt.

Its long green toes gripping scaly boughs with excitement, the heron, giving a final hasty twist of its long neck as it glanced around, prepared to jump up and glide down to the top of the weir.

As the lanky gray bird paused, Trutta, the old sea trout, big-black-spotted and dark stain of bruise three inches deep on his shoulders, lobbed himself vertically out beside the central white thrust and was swept over on his back immediately.

The sight of the large white belly and red of open gills made the heron launch itself from the tree and glide steeply down over the river, to alight with counter beat of wings on the grass above the sill of the weir.

Its hunger overcoming anxiety, the heron stalked stiltedly down the grassy slope and stepped on the edge of the concrete at the base of the sill, by a crack where a dock root and a thistle root were about to unfurl their first leaves of the year. It assured itself of a good hold for its long green feet and peered over the water, holding beak down to strike should any sizable fish appear. Then it gave a jump and gape and squark and beat up violently, seeing two men rising out of the gravel bank near it. With long legs trailing, it flapped down the river, swerving as it saw the figure of a man looking over the road bridge.

This was the water bailiff, who wondered what had disturbed the heron, for he knew it had been startled by the quick way it was beating its wings when it had first come into view. The weir was hidden by a bend and trees from the bridge. He decided to go to the weir.

Crouching by the edge where the heron had been standing, the man with the gaff waited for a fish to show. His mate kept a lookout on the bank above.

The poacher was waiting, stiller than a heron but not so well clad, gaff in hand ready to snatch the first fish to come in reach, staring at the water when his mate turned casually towards him and shouted out, 'Bailiff!' while pretending to crouch from an imaginary wind in order to light a cigarette. Without turning his head or shifting his position, but with an instant move-

78

ment of the lower parts of his arms, he lanced the gaff into the white strakes of the surge. It was taken and turned up in the water before disappearing. Putting hands in the pockets of his torn jacket, the man stood there, looking at the water until, a couple of minutes later, he turned his head slowly to the voice of the bailiff saying, 'Ha, caught you this time, have I, Shiner?'

The poacher, known as 'Shiner' from the moonlit nights during which he worked, replied, 'Have 'ee got a fag in your pocket, midear?'

'Aiy,' said the bailiff. 'And have 'ee got a gaff in yours, by any chance, Shiner?'

'Aw, I ban't no water-whipping rod-and-line gentry; you should know that, midear. What be the like o' me wanting a gaff for? You'll be asking me for a gennulman's license next, or the loan of a maskell's guts and kid's-colored fishing fly. Search me if 'ee fancies it, midear.'

'You know I ban't allowed by law to search you,' retorted the water bailiff, disconcerted by the poacher's good humor. 'Got a gaff hidden under they bushes, have 'ee?'

'I ban't stopping you from searching, midear.'

'Well, then, will 'ee answer why you 'm waiting yurr?'

'Elvers be running, midear. They 'm poaching your fish too, I fancy. Why don't 'ee summon they, midear?'

He pointed to the water turning back under the bank, where the diseased and dying salmon had turned up slowly on its side, in a dark mass of midget eels round it like iron filings on a magnet. Its gills were clustered with wriggles. The fish swam away, slowly, doomed.

'There ban't no law against a poor man taking a dish of elvers for his tea, be there?' inquired the old man. Taking off his stained felt hat and kneeling down, he dipped it in the water. A dozen elvers swam around inside. He threw them back, and banged the hat on the grass to knock off the water. 'Well, midear, us must n't keep th' old crane from his dinner, must us? Else they Cruelty to Hanimals chaps will be after us, won't 'n?'

He pointed to the heron passing over high, flying slowly, legs straight out behind and neck tucked in. He walked away, laughing loudly.

III

The elvers were running. They darkened the green shallows of the river, and the eddies were thick tangles of them. They had come into the estuary on the flood tide, and in a gelatinous mass had moved into the still water of the tidehead. All fish in the river sped from them, for elvers were gill-twisting torture and death.

For nearly three years as thin glassy threads the young eels had been crossing the Atlantic, drifting in warm currents of the Gulf Stream from the Sargasso Sea. Here in deep water, far under floating beds of clotted marine wreckage, all the mature eels of the Northern Hemisphere, patient travellers from inland ponds and ditches, brooks and rivers, came together to shed themselves of life for immortal reasons.

Salar lay in fast water between Pine Tree Weir and the road bridge. He lay in front of a large stone, in the swift flume rising to pass over it. The flume streamed by his head and gills and shoulders without local eddy. No elver could reach his gill without violent wriggling, which he would feel. He was swift with the swiftness of the water. There was the least friction between fish and river, for his skin exuded a mucus or lubricant by which the water slipped. The sweep of strong water guarded his life. Other salmon were lying in like lodges in the stony surges. Salar lodged there until dusk, when he moved forward again. Gralaks moved beside him. They recognized and knew each other without greeting.

Many fish were at Pine Tree Weir before them, waiting beside the lessening weight of white water, in the swarming bubbles of the eddy. They lay close to one another. As soon as one fish waggled tail and dipped and rose to get a grip of the water, to test its own pulse of power, another fish took its place, ready for the take-off. Salar idled, alert, apprehensive, seventeenth in line. Sometimes two or three fish left the phalanx at the same time, and after nervous ranging set themselves to swim up through the heavy water.

At the edge of the turning pool, where Shiner the poacher had waited and watched during the day, stood Old Nog the heron. The bird was picking up elvers as fast as he could snick them. His throat and neck ached. A continuous loose rope of elvers wove itself on the very edge of the water, where frillets sliding down the concrete apron edge scarcely washed into the grass.

Old Nog had eaten his first thousand elvers too quickly, gulping with head downheld until his tongue refused to work. After a return to the tree-top heronry where three hernlets had craked and fought to thrust their beaks down his throat to take what he had, Old Nog flew back to the weir and picked and swallowed slowly, his excitement gone. All afternoon he flew back and forth. At dusk he rested, sleeping for three hours. By the light of the full moon rising he returned with his mate to the weir. They crammed their crops and necks and flew back to their filthy nest, where by midnight the three hernlets were crouching, huddled and dour with overmuch feeding. Old Nog then flew back to the weir, to feed himself. Most of the elvers were now gone, but he managed to satisfy his hunger. On the way home, however, an elver wriggled down his windpipe, causing him to choke and sputter and disgorge; the mass fell beside a badger below rubbing against its scratching thorn, causing it to start and grunt with alarm. After cautiously snuffing for some minutes, from various angles, the badger dared to taste; after which it ate all up and looked round for more. For the next few nights it returned specially to rub itself against the thorn, in the hope of finding such food there again. As for Old Nog, not an elver that year reached his long pot, as countrymen do call the guts.

During the time of the moon's high tides, more than two hundred salmon passed over the weir. Salar swam up on his second attempt; at first he had been unsure of himself, and dropped back almost as soon as he had got a grip on the central cord or spine of water. Swimming again with all his power, he moved slowly into the glissade of water above the white surge; staying a third of the way up, as though motionless, vibrating; then had gained over the water and swam stronger in jubilation, and suddenly found the sill moving away under him, release of weight from his sides, and calm deep water before him. He flung himself out for joy, and a young dog-otter, who was rolling on its back on grass at the pool's edge, where a bitch-otter had touched earlier in the night, instantly lifted its head, slipped to the edge, put its head under, and slid tail-last into the water.

Salar saw the otter swimming above him. The pool took the dull blows of his acceleration, and in three seconds, when the otter had swum nine yards against the current, Salar had gone twenty yards upstream into the mill pool, swerved from a sunken tree trunk lodged in the silt, zigzagged forward to the farther bank, startling other salmon resting there, and hidden himself under a ledge of rock. The otter, which was not hunting salmon, since in deep water it could never catch any unless a fish were injured, crawled out on the bank again to enjoy through its nose what it imagined visually.

An elver wriggled against Salar, and he swam on. The pool was long and deep and slow. He swam on easily, restfully, now slower than the otter had pretended to chase him. The wound in his side began to ache dully, and he rested near the surface, near water swilling over a branch of alder. At dawn he was three miles above Pine Tree Weir, lying under a ledge of rock hollow curving above him, and therefore protecting him from behind, with an immediate way of escape from danger into deep water. The salmon slept, only the white-gray tip of the kype – hooked end of lower jaw – showing as the mouth slightly opened. Fifteen times a minute water passed the gills, which opened imperceptively.

Salar slept. The water lightened with sunrise. He lay in shadow. His eyes were fixed, passively susceptible to all movement. The sun rose up. Leaves and stalks of loose weed and water moss passing were seen but unnoticed by the automatic stimulus of each eye's retina. The eyes worked together with the unconscious brain, while the nerves, centres of direct feeling, rested themselves. One eye noticed a trout hovering in the water above, but Salar did not see it.

The sun rose higher, and shone down on the river, and slowly the shadow of the ledge shrunk into its base. Light revealed Salar, a gray-green uncertain dimness behind a small pale spot appearing and disappearing regularly.

Down there Salar's right eye was filled with the sun's blazing fog. His left eye saw the wall of rock and the water above. The trout right forward of him swam up, inspected that which had attracted it, and swam down again; but Salar's eye perceived no movement. The shadow of the trout in movement did not fall on the salmon's right eye.

A few moments later there was a slight splash left forward of Salar. Something swung over, casting the thinnest shadow; but it was seen by the eye, which awakened the conscious brain. Salar was immediately alert.

The thing vanished. A few moments later, it appeared nearer to him.

With his left eye Salar watched the thing moving overhead. It swam in small jerks, across the current and just under the surface, opening and shutting, gleaming, glinting, something trying to get away. Salar, curious and alert, watched it until it was disappearing and then he swam up and around to take it ahead of its arc of movement. The surface water, however, was flowing faster than the river at midstream, and he misjudged the opening of his mouth, and the thing, which recalled sea feeding, escaped.

On the bank upriver fifteen yards away, a fisherman with fourteen-foot split-cane rod said to himself, excitedly, 'Rising short'; and, pulling loops of line between reel and lowest ring of the rod, he took a small pair of scissors from a pocket and snipped off the thing which had attracted Salar.

No wonder Salar had felt curious about it, for human thought had ranged the entire world to imagine that lure. It was called a fly; but no fly like it ever swam in air or flew through water. Its tag, which had glinted, was of silver from Nevada and silk of a moth from Formosa; its tail, from the feather of an Indian crow; its butt, black herl, of African ostrich; its body, yellow floss silk veiled with orange breast feathers of the South American toucan, and black Macclesfield silk ribbed with silver tinsel. This fly was given the additional attraction of wings for water flight, made of strips of feathers from many birds. Invented after a bout of seasickness by a Celt as he sailed the German Ocean between England and Norway, for nearly a hundred years this fly had borne his name, Jock Scott.

While the fisherman was tying a smaller pattern of the same fly to the end of the gut cast, dark-stained by nitrate of silver against underwater glint, Salar rose to midwater and hovered there. He opened his mouth and sucked in a nymph as it was swimming to the surface. The fisherman saw a swirl on the water, and threw his fly, with swish of double-handed rod, above and to the right of the swirl. Then, lowering the rod point until it was almost parallel to the water, he let the current take the fly slowly across the stream, lifting the rod tip and lowering it slightly and regularly to make it appear to be swimming.

Salar saw the fly and slowly swam up to look at it. He saw it clear in the bright water and sank away again, uninterested in the lifelessness of its bright colors. Again it reappeared, well within his skylight window. He ignored it, and it moved out of sight. Then it fell directly over him, jigging about in the water, and with it a thin dark thing which he regarded cautiously. This was the gut cast. Once more it passed over, and then again, but he saw only the dark thinness moving there. It was harmless. He ignored it. Two other salmon below Salar, one in a cleft of rock and the other beside a sodden oak log wedged under the bank, also saw the too-bright thing, and found no vital interest in it.

The fisherman pulled in the line through the rod rings. It was of plaited silk, tapered and enameled for ease of casting. The line fell over his boot. Standing still, he cut off the fly, and began a search for another in a metal box, wherein scores of mixed feathers were ranged on rows of metal clasps. First he moved one with his forefinger, then another, staring at this one and frowning at that one, recalling in its connection past occasions of comparative temperatures of air and river, of height and clearness of water, of sun and shade, while the angler's familiar feeling, of obscurity mingled with hope and frustration, came over him. While from the air he tried to conjure certainty for a choice of fly, Salar, who had taken several nymphs of the olive dun during the time the angler had been cogitating, leapt and fell back with a splash that made the old fellow take a small Black Doctor and tie the gut to the loop of the steel hook with a single Cairnton-jam knot.

Salar saw this lure and fixed one eye on it as it approached and then ignored it, a thing without life. As it was being withdrawn from the water a smolt which had seen it only then leapt open-mouthed at a sudden glint and fell back, having missed it.

On the bank the fisherman sat down and perplexedly reëxamined his rows and rows of flies. He had tried all recommended for the water, and several others as well; and, after one short rise, no fish had come to the fly. Mar Lodge and Silver Gray, Dunkeld and Black Fairy, Beauly Snow Fly, Fiery Brown, Silver Wilkinson, Thunder and Lightning, Butcher, Green Highlander, Blue Charm, Candlestick Maker, Bumbee, Little Inky Boy, all were no good. Then in one corner of the case he saw an old fly of which most of the mixed plumage was gone: a Black Dog which had belonged to his grandfather. Grubs of moths had fretted away hackle, wing, and topping. It was thin and bedraggled. Feeling that it did not matter much what fly was used, he sharpened the point with a slip of stone, tied it on, and carelessly flipped it into the water. He was no longer fishing; he was no longer intent, he was about to go home; the cast did not fall straight, but crooked; the line also was crooked. Without splash the fly move down a little less fast than the current, coming thus into Salar's skylight. It was like the nymphs he had been taking, only larger; and with a leisurely sweep he rose and turned across the current, and took it, holding it between tongue and vomer as he went down to his lie again, where he would crush and taste it. The sudden resistance of the line to his movement caused the point of the hook to prick the corner of his mouth. He shook his head to rid himself of it, and this action drove the point into the gristle, as far as the barb.

A moment later the fisherman, feeling a weight on the line, lifted the rod point and tightened the line, and had hardly thought to himself, 'Salmon,' when the blue-gray tail of a fish broke half out of the water and its descending weight bended the rod.

Salar knew of neither fisherman nor rod nor line. He swam down to the ledge of rock and tried to rub the painful thing in the corner of his mouth against it. But his head was pulled away from the rock. He saw the line, and was fearful of it. He bored down to his lodge at the base of the rock, to get away from the line, while the small brown trout swam behind his tail, curious to know what was happening.

Salar could not reach his lodge. He shook his head violently, and, failing to get free, turned downstream and swam away strongly, pursued by the line and a curious buzzing vibration just outside his jaw.

Below the pool the shallow water jabbled before surging in broken white crests over a succession of rocky ledges. Salar had gone about sixty yards from his lodge, swimming hard against the backward pull of the line, when the pull slackened, and he turned round head into current, and lay close to a stone, to hide from his enemy.

When the salmon had almost reached the jabble, the fisherman, fearing it would break away in the rough water, had started to run down the bank, pulling line from the reel as he did so. By thus releasing direct pull on the fish, he had turned it. Then, by letting the current drag line in a loop below it, he made Salar believe that the enemy was behind him. Feeling the small pull of the line from behind, Salar swam up into deeper water, to get away from it. The fisherman was now behind the salmon, in a position to make it tire itself by swimming upstream against the current.

Salar, returning to his lodge, saw it occupied by another fish, which his rush, and the humming line cutting the water, had disturbed from the lie by the sodden log. This was Gralaks the grilse. Again Salar tried to rub the thing against the rock, again the pull, sideways and upwards, was too strong for him. He swam downwards, but could make no progress towards the rock. This terrified him and he turned upwards and swam with all his strength, to shake it from his mouth. He leapt clear of the water and fell back on his side, still shaking his head.

On the top of the leap the fisherman had lowered his rod, lest the fly be torn away as the salmon struck the water.

Unable to get free by leaping, Salar sank down again and settled himself to swim away from the enemy. Drawing the line after him, and beset again by the buzzing vibration, he traveled a hundred yards to the throat of the pool, where water quickened over gravel. He lay in the riffle spreading away from a large stone, making himself heavy, his swim-bladder shrunken, trying to press himself into the gravel which was his first hiding place in life. The backward pull on his head nearly lifted him into the fast water, but he held himself down, for nearly five minutes, until his body ached and he weakened and he found himself being taken down sideways by the force of shallow water. He recalled the sunken tree and it became a refuge, and he swam down fast, and the pull ceased with the buzz against his jaw. Feeling relief, he swam less fast over his lodge, from which Gralaks sped away, alarmed by the line following Salar.

But before he could reach the tree the weight was pulling him back, and he turned and bored down to bottom, scattering a drove of little gray shadows which were startled trout. Again the pull was too much for him, and he felt the ache of his body spreading back to his tail. He tried to turn on his side to rub the corner of his mouth on something lying on the bed of the pool – an old cartwheel – again and again – but he could not reach it.

Fatigued and aching, Salar turned downstream once more, to swim away with the river, to escape the enemy which seemed so much bigger because he could not close his mouth. As he grew heavier, slower, uncertain, he desired above all to be in the deeps of the sea, to lie on ribbed sand and rest and rest and rest. He came to rough water, and let it take him down, too tired to swim. He bumped into a rock, and was carried by the current around it, on his side, while the gut cast, tautened by the dragging weight, twanged and jerked his head upstream, and he breathed again, gulping water quickly and irregularly. Still the pull was trying to take him forward, so with a renewal of fear he turned and reëntered fast water and went down and down, until he was in another deep pool at a bend of the river. Here he remembered a hole under the roots of a tree, and tried to hide there, but had not strength enough to reach the refuge of darkness.

Again he felt release, and swam forward slowly, seeking the deepest part of the pool, to lie on the bottom with his mouth open. Then he was on his side, dazed and weary, and the broken-quicksilvery surface of the pool was becoming whiter. He tried to swim away, but the water was too thick-heavy; and after a dozen sinuations it became solid. His head was out of water. A shock passed through him as he tried to breathe. He lay there, held by line taut over fisherman's shoulder. He felt himself being drawn along just under the surface, and only then did he see his enemy – flattened, tremulant-spreading image of the fisherman. A new power of fear broke in the darkness of his lost self. When it saw the tailer coming down to it, the surface of the water was lashed by the desperately scattered self. The weight of the body falling over backwards struck the taut line; the tail fin was split. The gut broke just above the hook, where it had been frayed on the rock. Salar saw himself sinking down into the pool, and he lay there, scattered about himself and unable to move away, his tail curved round a stone, feeling only a distorted head joined to the immovable river bed.

IV

All day Salar lay dully in the pool, under the roots of an alder, never moving. After the sun had set and other salmon were leaving their lies and lodges he swam forward slowly, painfully. The wind had veered to the north-west, bringing hard-edged clouds towering in blackness above the moor. Down in the estuary at midnight fishermen hauled on nets which held, draft after draft, only seaweed and crabs; they said nothing at all – they had been wet in empty sea labor most of their lives. Salmon from the sea jumped in the wide spate water of the fairway and passed up one or other of the Two Rivers. Some of them, fast travelers, moved beside Salar when next evening's sun was spreading rubicund on the hilltops.

Salar followed these keen new fish, his weariness eased, and by sunrise was lying with them in a pool called Denzil's, wide and deep, above another gristmill weir and the joining place of a third river. In this pool, which was deep because a ledge of rock crossed the river bed, the clay below having been scooped out by the centuries' spates, lay thirty salmon.

Many of these fish moved on at nightfall, and new fish came in, with

Trutta the sea trout, but Salar remained there. He was apprehensive, and deep water gave serenity. Many times he turned on his side and tried to rub off the iron lacerating the corner of his mouth. Soon most of the skin was rubbed off his jawbone. Body movement was no longer painful, but all his muscles ached.

Every day Salar, resting at the edge of deepening water, saw lines and lures, which he now recognized as enemies, moving, flickering, spinning at varying speeds over him. For a week the wind continued from the north-west, and nymphs delayed their hatching; and no salmon were taken from the pool, except one foul-hooked by a spinner which caught it in the gill, causing it to bleed to exhaustion in the water.

Salar had been waiting there nearly a fortnight when towards the end of a night, as the hollow ruin of the moon was rising through the trees, two fish sped past him, turned in shelving water, and sank beside him. All the fish shared an alertness of fear. A light darted in the water, moved about, and went out. Another light shone behind them. Salar swam into the deepest water, where he could see most – forward, above, and behind. Fish swung and thudded about in alarm. A strange smell came to him in the water, and he accelerated to the farther side of the pool.

Two men were wading above the pool, on the edge of the transverse reef. They carried armfuls of net, which they let down into deep water. A third man held the end of the rope under the bank. Sixty yards away two other men were taking a trammel across the river, in shallowing water below the pool. A sixth man stood on the bank, waiting silent and listening in the last darkness of night. A heap of old potato sacks lay near him, the temporary bed of a lean hairy dog with long thin legs, head, and tail. This was a lurcher, shivering curled as though to sleep, but flair-nosed, wide-eyed, cock-eared. It never barked or growled. It knew the smell of every water bailiff in the catchment area of the Two Rivers. The dog and its master shared a soundless language, of attitude, glance, and movement.

The six men belonged to a gang which worked pools of the Two Rivers only at night. The leader, who owned dog and nets, was a mild-mannered and bespectacled cabinetmaker by day. The lenses of his spectacles were of plain glass: he wore them to protect his eyes from wood dust, and also, by their absence at night, as a disguise. Four of the men had been fined by the magistrates of the local town for poaching. The fining had occurred before they had formed themselves into a gang, under the leadership of the cabinetmaker, since when none had been caught. Its members blackened their faces before leaving the old and unlicensed car in which they traveled on their planned raids. One man, however, knew why the car was used only at night; and that man was Shiner.

Shiner had made and used the trammel net until he had been surprised one night by the bailiffs, who had confiscated it. Shiner had been summoned, convicted, sentenced to imprisonment; and the Court made an order for the destruction of the trammel net which had been produced as evidence against him. The trammel, however, had been stolen from the courtroom, during the second prosecution by the Clerk to the Board of Conservators.

The trammel net was never missed, because the local police authorities thought the water bailiffs had carried it away, and the bailiffs thought the police had removed it. When he had served ten days in prison, Shiner, who had watched the net being taken, said nothing, although he knew who had it. He disliked the gang, because they sometimes worked with methods he considered dirty – they poisoned whole stretches of river by the use of chloride of lime, and blew the pits with gelignite, which destroyed all life in them. Shiner was awaiting an opportunity to get his own back.

The gang did not know, when they left their car behind a haystack in a field by the road a quarter of a mile away, that Shiner was watching in the next field. His tool cart – he was an odd-day gardener to various houses – was hidden behind another haystack. When the gang had left for the river, Shiner climbed through the hedge and, opening the bonnet of their car, unscrewed all the leads to the spark plugs, fixing them again in the wrong order; and then, to make sure the engine would not start, he emptied a small bag of sugar into the petrol tank. After this, struck by a sudden thought, he climbed through the hedge again and removed his tool cart to the other end of the field, concealing it in a dip in the ground.

Some minutes later he crossed the lane and listened. Then he wetted a forefinger to reassure himself that the breeze was moving from the pool in his direction. Afterwards he hid behind an oak tree on the bank above, and waited.

While he was standing there, the drift net was spread across the river. Its lead-weighted heel rope sank into deep water, its line of corks was bellied out by the surface current. Two men, one under each bank and holding an end of rope, began to work their way down the sides of the pool, wading sometimes to their armpits, and gripping branches which overhung the water.

As the drift net slowly moved upon them, the salmon became agitated, and moved at great speed up and down the pool. One shot through the wide netting of the trammel, turned immediately from the closer netting beyond, and was caught by the gills. The poachers heard the threshing of broken water, and began to work faster with the drift net. 'Go easy,' said the leader, standing on the bank above, a dim silhouette against the resolving twilight of dawn. Another fish began to splash.

In the centre of the pool lay Trutta, and near him were Salar and Gralaks. Trutta had known netting in Denzil's Pool two years before. Now, as the drift net came down, he swam aside to the alder whose roots in the water were like a thousand lobsters pressed together, and pushed under them. Because they recognised Trutta in the stimulation of fear which started old actions in memory, both Salar and Gralaks followed him now and thrust themselves under the mat of alder roots. They stayed there even when the noise and movement of legs were very near. As the disturbance went away another fish pushed in between Salar and Trutta, a terrified brown trout with a black and irregular underjaw, immense head, sharp teeth, and lean body. This was Garroo the cannibal trout. In a fury of fear at finding his retreat occupied, Garroo bit the tail of Gralaks, and received a slap on the side of his black horny head that caused him to lie limply, for several minutes, diagonally across the parallel bodies of Trutta and Salar.

While the four fish were hidden under the root clump, the drift net was approaching the trammel. 'Go easy,' said the leader. The area between the two nets was slashed with gleams as fish turned and re-turned. Up to their middle in water, the men who had dragged the drift net were now hauling in the twin ropes of heel and head, only a few yards away from the trammel. The net ends met on shelving gravel. Gradually the other end of the trammel was brought over, outside the drift net. Within the rocking corks more than a dozen salmon were struggling, torn of gill and tail, scales scraped off skin. The mass of fish was dragged to where the bank was broken by drinking cattle, and one by one they were hauled out on a gaff, and beaten on the nose by the cabinetmaker with a short club of yew wood weighted with an inlaid spiral of brass.

Nine fish were laid out on the grass, the largest twenty-eight pounds, the smallest seven pounds – one of the grilse of the school led by Gralaks. Quickly nets were stowed into sacks, and the gang, jubilant and now smoking fags, set off across the fields to the lane. It was half an hour to sunlight; the shine was already gone from the moon in the great azure glow spreading up the eastern sky. Clouds, hedges, haystacks to the west, were black. Their feet rustled frosty grasses. Bullocks which had been crowding and snuffling, black-massed, into the corner by the gate cantered away, ignored by the lurcher dog, which lifted one ear, and glanced at its master, as a cock in the farmyard half a mile away crowed to the morning star.

For nearly an hour they tried to get the car started. First one, then another, swung the handle, falling away and cursing in exhaustion.

The cabinetmaker took down the carburetor, and saw a dark sticky liquid, like crude petroleum, in the float chamber. Peering in the tank with the aid of an electric torch, he saw more of it lying at the bottom. He was bitter and blasphemous. It was run off; carburetor reassembled; handle swung again, many times, desperately. The eastern hill line was a haze of shining; soon the sun would rise and laborers be about. They began to quarrel. Some wanted to divide the fish, and make off homewards across the fields: others, supporting the leader, argued that they should best be hid in the stack, and fetched at night. At last the others agreed; but one said, would n't the car give away the hiding place? So the salmon, wrapped in sacks, were carried to the adjoining haystack, cut down one side, and concealed on the loose top of it. The nets were hidden in the hedge some distance away, and then, having washed the black from their faces in the ditch, the gang separated and went home across the fields.

A couple of hours later Shiner was wheeling his tool cart, apparently laden with horse dung, across the market square of the small town. 'Do you reckon it be time to till early tetties, midear?' he asked the police sergeant, who every year won prizes, for his potatoes, in the local Flower Show. 'Wait until the ground's in temper; 't is no use mucketing,' replied the sergeant, with amiable importance.

'You 'm right,' said Shiner, promptly. With a grin he added, 'You'd like what I've got in this cart, I dare say? Tes proper stuff for growing big tetties.'

The sergeant, who had had a kind thought for Shiner since he had been in prison for merely taking salmon, replied, 'You keep it for yourself, Shiner; you've worked hard enough for it, I reckon.'

'You 'm right, midear,' agreed Shiner, as he went on his way.

That night many of the leading citizens of the town, including several magistrates, dined on salmon which had been bought, surreptitiously, at their kitchen doors.

The old car was abandoned.

III. Winter Star-Stream

I

NEARLY A HUNDRED HOURS' continuous heavy rain had filled the underground lakes of the moor so that every spring was gushing. Sunken lanes – tracks worn deep by sleds of olden time – were noisy with cascades, their rugged surfaces washed away to reveal rock grooved and worn by iron and wood and horn.

As the flood withdrew from field and ditch and hollow, many fish were left in closed pits and shallows. There was a saying in the country of the Two Rivers that in a bygone age the agreements whereby boys were apprenticed to moorland farmers had a clause which stipulated the feeding of salmon to boys on not more than three days a week during a year. This saying was often repeated in books of the familiar kind which are derived from other books; but no such agreement had ever been found to prove the truth of the saying, which was intended to show how in other ages Atlantic salmon were as numerous in the rivers as their Pacific cousins are at the present time in the river of the Coast.

In the Great Deluge by which Salar returned to the stream of Red Deer Moor, nearly all the pigs, dogs, cats, and hens of the valley farms which remained alive turned away, after three days of feeding, from the flesh of salmon. Some say the sudden immense volume of water running into the Atlantic was so charged with the salts of artificial fertilizers washed in the soil from fields that most of the fish coming to the Island Race were unable to find the sea currents of their native rivers, and so all followed up the one overwhelming waterway to the Two Rivers.

Below Pine Tree Weir the bed of the turning eddy was covered by salmon, which were covered by a second and a third layer of fish. The water of the eddy was a dark purple. Every moment the circular racing surface showed a brown tail fin, a dark rolling back, a lead-gray or copper-brown neb. Fish six and seven together were trying to get up the weir. At the side of the concrete apron, where Shiner stood, small trout and sea trout leapt and slithered on the watery slope so frequently that he could, he told himself, have filled a bucket any moment by simply holding it there.

But Shiner was not there to get fish. Now that he had regular work he was quite happy watching them. Indeed, he felt the secondary feeling of all conquerors towards a subjected race: an attitude of benevolence and protection. Shiner had no gaff in his pocket. He was there because most of his life thought with the way of salmon. All day he had stood there, watching them. He ate no food; his hunger was to see the fish.

Shiner's arrival at the weir had disturbed Old Nog the heron, who had been killing every fish he could strike and lift from the edge of the slide.

So many peal – small sea trout – were leaping and falling within a few inches of the grassy edge that soon the old man's trousers were wet to the knees with the splashing. A few salmon, the tired ones which had come into the river in early spring, tried to get up the weir at the side, leaping among the smaller sea trout whose water it was. Shiner saw fish with long heads and out-thrust kypes, brown as summer algæ, the gristle of underjaws worn by rubbing and ringed with fungus. They sprang from the edge of the white surge which slanted across the pool's circle: some fell on their sides, heavily on the concrete covered by water less deep than their bodies, and lay stunned a moment before being washed down; others jumped too high, falling on the curl-over of white water and being flung back before recovering poise and swimming down with easy stroke of tail fin. Other stale fish had green on gill covers, their jaws looked smoke-grimy, their scales rusty. They were all shapes and sizes. The pool was more fish than water, fish flushed with the cold fever of spawning, all trying to gain the redds in the higher reaches of the river: danger for themselves, but safety for the fry hatching in the shrunken waters of spring.

Every minute several fish leapt askew and fell on the grass beside the concrete. Shiner eased them back into the water, wetting his hands lest his touch scald the sensitive skin. Nearer the roaring centre of the weir, stronger fish were jumping. Most of them hit the water and lost impetus before they could grip and bore a way up the slope. Shiner saw roseate hog-backed fish, with heads a canary-yellow: these were males of a late run, full of zest for spawning. They had no appetite for food; excitement had released much uric acid in their systems, which gave their skins these colors.

But while he watched, and as the sun broke through the clouds, Shiner saw a fish leap from the midst of the most broken turmoil – a curve of white and tarnished silver which fell and pierced the surge and moved up steadily, vibrating fast and surely, a fish that had learned a way through the varying pressures and water layers, beside the glassy spine raised from the gap in the sill above. It got nearly to the sill, where it seemed to hang still, moment after moment, then it was advancing, inch by inch, to where the spine was flattened just below the break in the hidden sill; and, as Shiner watched, it shot forward out of sight, to leap high from the calm deep water of the mill pool, and reveal, in the moment of rest at the top of the curve, a soldered mark on its side, as of a wound healed.

Such was the return of Salar – the Leaper.

II

As the heron flies, Steep Weir lay about six miles above Pine Tree Weir; but the journey was longer for fish. The river wound through the grazing meadows of its own past making – now running close to the feet of hills yellow and red and brown with the colors of leaves' failing life, now winding to the other hillside, to recoil upon itself, in wide pools of currents in confusion, rushing swollen and gleaming.

Steep Weir had been built in a past century, diagonally across the river, a barrier of slabs of rock.

The top layer of slabs overhung a vertical wall; water falling over fell clear of the wall's base. And it rebounded, because it fell direct on rock. There was no pool underneath, no deep water from which a fish could take off. It was the most harmful weir in the country of the Two Rivers, and, since it was usually unpassable, a favorite place of poachers when fish were running.

Where the sill of the weir stopped, a bank grown with alders continued to a half-rotten sluice. This consisted of a frame of three upright posts, bedded into masonry and morticed on cross-pieces. In the grooves of the upright posts the two doors or fenders had not been moved for more than thirty years. They were ruinous, and silted on the higher side.

Early one morning Shiner went to Steep Weir. He knew that some of the chaps from the town would be there, snatching fish. Since he had come to watch salmon for their own sakes, Shiner had appointed himself a sort of honorary elusive water bailiff. Herons and otters and snatchers he regarded as half enemies of his own life. Water bailiffs were enemies of the other half of himself, and when he saw one Shiner became elusive. He muttered to himself, feeling that they would not believe that he was by the riverside for the sake of the fish. Not for the sake of the Conservancy Board, which was made up of men there to represent and serve their own interests: nets-men for the increase of nets and extension of time to net, rod-and-line men to increase the number of fish in the rivers, by keeping the number of nets as low as possible and limiting the season of estuary fishing. Shiner knew all about the Board; and he muttered when he saw a bailie, for old time's sake and also because he was a solitary.

Shiner had a special grudge against the water bailiffs. Recalling the num-ber of fish he had snatched from below Steep Weir, he now thought of them jumping there hour after hour in vain, bruising and breaking themselves. 'Why had n't they bailies seen to it that the fender was rised? 'Twas n't proper!' Very well, he, Shiner, would do it himself.

Soon after sunrise on the Monday morning, he climbed over the fence by the road bridge below the gristmill and walked along the river bank. He was tall and thin, looking like a humanized alder trunk. His coat was shredded and gray like lichen, his arms and legs long and loose. He had a small face with pointed goatee beard and high pointed ears sticking up beside the upright brim of a very ancient and discolored billycock hat. His eyes appeared to see nothing; he never turned round or glanced about him; yet he saw all he wanted to see. He was a gray heron of a man, owning only his clothes, a few gardening tools, and himself. In summer he often slept out, beside ricks or in tallats or lofts of cattle sheds. He knew white owls which nested in the tallats, and they knew him. He liked wandering about alone, in the open air. During winter he lived in a room over a disused stable, for which he paid rent of ten shillings a year. He insisted on paying rent. The landlord, an innkeeper, allowed him to boil and fry in the rusty grate of the small disused harness room, hung with cobwebs. Shiner's only mate was a cat, an aged beast, which he called Kitten. It was the great-great-grandkitten of the original cat he had owned. He neither begged nor borrowed, nor would he claim an old-age pension. His secret fear was that in extreme old age he would be destitute and put in the Union, when he would not be able to see the river or the fields.

He walked along by the river, slowly, with an ash plant nearly as tall as himself in his right hand, continually glancing at the water moving almost bank-high on his left. Forward, and across the river, stood a plantation of thin trees almost hiding the mill house. He heard the roaring of the weir as he walked on. A raised bank of stone and earth, on which ash and other trees grew, was between him and the weir. Peering through a gap, he saw the figure of a man standing there, and recognized one of the gang which had stolen his trammel net in the police court. Then he saw the hat of another man moving behind some low-growing furze bushes. The river was over the bank beside the fender, running down the grass, and pouring over the edge of the sluice.

Moving on to another gap, Shiner stared at the weir. Fish were jumping into the white, to fall back again and be tossed and turned in the churn of water rebounding from the rock below. They were jumping all the time, and most of them were colored in shades of red and brown. 'They'm in full tartan, surenuff,' muttered Shiner – using a phrase he had heard years before from a visiting Scots fisherman.

In a bed of rushes fifty yards above the weir Shiner had found a rusty iron bar while poking about there a few months previously. This, he guessed, was the bar by which the fenders had been lifted years before. But if he went to get the bar now, and started to open the fenders, he might be pitched into the water while he was doing it, and no one any the wiser. They chaps was n't worth two penn'oth of cold gin; they would pitch him in if they thought no one would know. And taking red fish, too! Why, the eggs of a ten-p'un sow-fish weighed two p'un! 'T was no sense in it, taking full ripe fish.

Shiner had taken many hundreds of red fish at Steep Weir, and had often stated his opinion that October fish tasted better than clean springers; but that was when he had been younger and 'lived for devilment,' as he said. But a full ripe fish! 'T was n't no sense to it.

After wondering for some time what he could do, Shiner clambered over the gap in the bank and walked, looser-legged than ever, towards the men. The man standing back from the water saw him casually, and paid no heed to him. His two mates had been informed, however, of the approach, and when they saw who it was they bent down and withdrew each a long ash pole which had been hurriedly thrust into the growth of bramble and alder.

The poles had been cut from a near-by copse. To the slighter end a noose of twisted strands of brass wire had been tied. These were for tailing the fish waiting below the fender.

Shiner went to the edge of the sluice which joined the water roar at the base of the fall a few paces distant. Fish of all lengths and shapes and colors were jumping vertically under the spread of the weir. None could get up. One great fish fell back on a hidden pinnacle of rock and was washed away belly upwards. Shiner cracked his fingers, and muttered to himself.

'You won't do nought with that li'l old rabbit snare,' said Shiner. 'I was working here with a gaff when Adam was a proper pup. Besides, you 'm too late. There ban't enough water here to carry the fish over. Now if you could open the fenders a bit, to let some good water under, you 'd attract the sojers upalong the gulley.' 'Soldiers' was the poaching term for ripe autumn fish. 'Aiy, midears, that's what us did in th' old days. And if I don't misremember, there be a bar lying about yurr somewhereabouts.'

He began to mooch around, peering under furze clumps and kicking tufts of grass with his boot. He returned to the others, mumbling half to himself, 'You med get a vish by fixing a gaff on t'other end, and cutting the stick in half; maybe you 'd get a vish thaccy way, but you med be careful, midears, leaning over all that water. Tes a turrible master weight of water valling to-day. Aiy, it be, too true it be.' And, shaking his head, he ambled away, pretending to be looking for the bar. 'Th' old fool be wandering i' th' ead,' said one of the men, lighting a cigarette. Seeing this, Shiner came back, talking in a broader, old-fashioned way. 'I minds th' time when us took vower buttloads of vish from thissy place. But then us had th' bar vor open the trap, do 'ee zee?' And, shaking his head, he went away. 'Proper mazed fool,' said the young man, inhaling deeply of the fag.

Shiner was staring at the door of the fender, his billycock pushed over one ear, scratching his head. Jets of water were spirting through holes in the oaken planking, and gushing underneath, hissing white from the pressure of water above the fender.

As he watched, a small sea trout slithered up the white hiss of water, and, turning by the wood, slithered down again. 'You'll soon be upalong, midear,' said the old man. 'Shiner knoweth.'

He found the rusty bar in the nettles, and returned to the sluice. An oak plank stretched across behind the framework, and on this he stood, pushing the end of the bar into an iron notch. Each fender was the shape of a large square shovel, in the handle of which was a vertical row of notches. Levering against the crosspiece, he tried to raise the fender. It was wedged in the lower grooves of the posts, held tight by the weight of silt against its other side. By crashing the bar against the plate Shiner at last shifted the wood, and immediately the gush below changed to mud color.

He shifted the end of the bar to a lower hole, and raised it another notch. Thus slowly one fender was lifted; then he began to raise the other. While he was doing this one of the men came to him and asked him how much more he was going to 'rise' it. 'Hey?' said Shiner, pausing to put a hand to ear, and then bending down to lever again. The man shouted at him, soundlessly in the roar of water now passing under. 'Hey?' said Shiner, pausing a moment. The man came on the plank and bawled in his ear, 'If you open it to the top, you bliddy old vool, all the vish will rin though, won't 'm?'

'Aiy, you 'm right, midear,' replied Shiner. 'Bootiful water, bootiful rinning water!'

'I said to you, you old vool, I said, "You 'm letting all the vish dro, ban't you?"'

'No, I ain't got no gaff,' replied Shiner, lifting the fender another notch. 'If I had, you should have it, midear.'

The man seized the end of the bar. 'Stop, wull 'ee?'

The second fender was almost as high as the first.

'Aiy, you 'm right,' said Shiner. 'Only don't you go telling they old bailies that I was a hacsessry after the fack of this yurr raisement o' the fender,' as he inserted the end of the bar into the last hole.

The second man now stepped on the plank and gripped the bar. 'What 's the flamin' bliddy idea?' he shouted. 'Here, you give the bar to me!' – and he raised an arm with clenched fist, while pulling with the other.

'Yurr, take it,' said Shiner, suddenly thrusting the bar at the other.

The man who had shouted had been braced for resistance; he lost his balance. He clutched at the other man, who in turn grabbed the third man.

The trio leaned back, swaying and clutching. The weight of the bar pulled the first man askew, and all three fell into the water. Instantly they were swept down the sluice. One got hold on an alder bough in the eddy by the curve of the sluice; another held him; but the third man was carried down into the main rush of the river. He could swim, and so kept his head up. He was washed helplessly down-river until he found himself in a backwater. Shiner, who had been following downstream, helped him out.

When the three were together again he said, 'You 'm a proper double couple o' Adam's pups! Goin' givin' an old 'un like me a proper scare! And where be the bar you was so anxious to get hold to? Like as not in the flamin' sae by now. And I can't reggerlate no fenders just as I was preparin' to do when you boys thought you knowed best. I tell 'ee, midear, they be wedged tight by now, and nothin' will shift 'em. Hullo, hullo! Did 'ee zee that li'l booty? My Gor, 't was a bootiful sight!'

A salmon had leapt out of the white curl-over below the open fenders, had pierced the green glissade descending, and had swum through, a dark shadow vanishing. Above in the pool it leapt again – Salar.

III

Shiner walked up the valley, beside the river. He did not hurry. He stared and quizzed and wondered. The cottage garden where he worked was under four miles from Steep Weir, and there was little to do at the fall of the year; and Shiner was not the sort to make work. He was a free man. It took him all the forenoon and two hours after midday to arrive at Sawmills Weir. There a gamekeeper saw him. The gamekeeper was also a local preacher.

'Up to your old games, I see,' was his greeting to Shiner.

'Aw, you must have second sight, midear,' retorted Shiner, looking at the water. 'How be the fezzans this year? Got this yurr grouse disease from Scotland yet?'

'You 'm a smart one, Shiner, you be. Got a gaff in your pocket, by any chance?'

'You got any 'baccy in yours, midear?' countered Shiner.

'I ban't a smoker, you knows that.'

'Nor be I.'

'Then why do 'ee ask?'

'Aw, just another idle business question, midear. Hullo, did 'ee see that girt old black poll? Proper old berry-gatherer, I reckon.'

Garroo the cannibal trout, who had hidden with Salar and the others under the roots when the gang had worked the trammel in Denzil's Pool, had just jumped and fallen back. He was lean and thin; his head was the shape of a lobster's claw. He looked like his own effigy in a glass case; for his spots were large and very distinct, the red very red and the black very black, while he glistened as though newly painted in hues of blue and brown, and over all a high gleam of varnish. Garroo was too old for spawning, but that did not prevent him from doing what he had done for many years: joining in the general excitement of migration upstream, and gorging on salmon eggs – whence Shiner's description of berry-gatherer. The keeper, who knew almost nothing of fish, thought the old man was merely stupid and garrulous. His lordship did not fish, and his lordship's agent always let the fishing to tenants. Shiner knew this; he had no ill feeling against the keeper.

'Maybe a master girt wind after frost will blow away the leaves for 'ee soon,' he remarked, changing the subject to suit the keeper. 'I seed many young fezzan chicks as I was in the swamp tilling tetties for my chap this spring. Th' ould birds eat my cabbage plants, but us don't grudge them a bite or two, sir. Live and let live, my chap saith: all complaints at the Judgment Seat. He be proper mazed about salmon, – writing a book about 'm, he did tell me, – so I bin and opened the fender down to Steep. You'll see no more snatchin' there, like I used to before my guts dried up.'

The keeper looked at Shiner with a new interest. Shiner, knowing this, began to speak about the fish which were trying to get up the Sawmills Weir. He pointed out how salmon made many attempts to feel the weights of the water; that they were not jumping every time they showed. They were feeling their way, time after time. Different parts of the weir suited different-sized fish. Directly below them salmon were showing, half leaping; but none would try and get up there, said Shiner. That was the small sea-trout place, where the school peal got 'up auver.'

The weir was built in a series of steps or ledges descending; the water fell from ledge to ledge, descending in white violence. A salmon appeared to push itself out of the lower white and to swim up in foaming water: actually it was slithering on mossy rocks which gave it a good grip. But the water there was too broken for its length, and it fell back, to lie in a trough in the rocky bed below, beside three other salmon which were touching, and over whom the bubbled water raced. The middle fish was Salar, who had arrived at Sawmills at the same time as Shiner.

Immediately on arrival Salar had moved into the leaping-off place, and sunk to rest. He let the water seethe over his head and tickle the underpart of his body pleasantly. Salar did not like breathing bubbled water any more than any other salmon; but he lay there easily because, although his body was enswirled and stroked by bubbles, his mouth was thrust into a crevice where water welled in the dark green moss as from a spring.

After enjoying the highly oxygenated water for a while, Salar moved back with the churning strakes and sank down to the bottom. There he balanced himself under the fog of bubbles. Above him the bubbles hissed; under him the rock rumbled. He lifted himself off the rock, felt the rhythm of power along his muscles passing into the water. He gaped faster at the water, while the flexions of his body rippled faster. He fixed his sight above the fog of bubbles and sprang, but checked at the last moment. Shiner saw him, a fish of new-cut lead and new-cut copper sliding up moving snow.

Salar had checked on a sudden doubt. The doubt was due to the change of his nature, which had been going on slowly all during the summer, delayed by return to the sea and renewal of feeding, and now was hastening upon him with the season of colored leaves and sap sinking in trees and plants. His nature was drawing into itself; he lived more an inward than an outward life. He had no interest in moving things, food, while he was swimming up the river; but when he rested his old nature returned upon him, and he was irritated and stirred by smaller fish and leaves and twigs and other movement. He took many pieces of black water moss in his mouth, holding a bit sometimes for a minute or two before expelling it. Then all interest in moving things, which might have been food, was gone; he would sink into himself, his power withdrawn to give color to his body, — skin and fins, — to lengthen his head and give strength to the hook of his lower jaw. His skin was thickening, a pattern as of green and brown and yellow marble scrolled thereon.

A confusion of personality had checked Salar's jump; but after another rest he gathered himself and swam up, and leapt, to be shocked by the warmth of air, and to fall beside the stone and swim up against the blank gush of water. He knew the way, and swam more strongly, reaching the straightness of the wall at the back of the weir, two feet from the top. The water gushed off his back, and then he was lying beside the wall, parallel to it, in a narrow trough no wider than himself, and well under the curve of water.

He slithered along, and then found he was lying behind the tail of another salmon. The tail was dark brown. This was one of the grilse which had followed Gralaks into the river.

In front of the small fish lay two other salmon, one a yellow-headed cock fish with a porpoise bite out of its tail fin; the other was Gralaks, who had been washed down the falls by the flood, and was now making her way up again.

Soon afterwards another salmon wriggled up and rested its chin behind Salar's tail. An almost continuous line of salmon, hidden by the curve of falling water, was now lying across Sawmills Weir.

When Gralaks, the leading fish, was ready to go over the lip of the weir, she slewed her tail round so that the falling water beat on it. She lay between two mossy slabs of rock. She curled her tail for a jump; she sprang, her flanks gripping the hard descending mixture of air and water with scale and caudal fin; she bored into it with nose and eye and gill and all the determined strength of life being urged forward. She slapped the water with the sideway sweeps of her body, and then she was gone, her passing over the last weir revealed only by a momentary bulge in the smooth bend of water.

IV

High over the valley the last swallow was hurled in the wind which streamed the leaves from the oaks and kept the tall spruce firs of the hillsides swaying in slow weariness of gray clouds of sky. By the river the bullock paths were pitted and sploshed yellow, under alders dispread black and bare. Over the viaduct a miniature train moved in silhouette, creeping across the sky, antiquated goods trucks on webbed wheels swept about by scattered steam.

From the top of the hill, reddish brown with larch and dark green with spruce plantations, came little reports flattened away by the wind, the first pheasant shoot of the year. Old Nog the heron was trying in vain to outfly the winds over the hill. Higher and higher they took him, turning and slanting and flapping without forward movement, scared by the reports of guns which he thought were all aimed at him. When a thousand feet high he gave up and swung round, and swept across the valley; but a report louder than the others, coming direct to him in a pocket of wind, made him tumble and turn and fly into the wind once more, determined to fish in future only in the wide safety of the estuary. Old Nog had been scared a hundred times before; he always forgot it.

Within the river many salmon and sea trout were moving. The fenders at Steep Weir were gone; posts, doors, framework, weighing more than a ton, had been jostled to the sea, no more to the river in spate than a few twigs and leaves. Already barnacles were laying their eggs on the wood, beside the jelly sacs of river snails' eggs killed by the salt.

Every tide brought in more salmon, which reached Sawmills with their lice still alive, four days from the sea. The gravel of the river bed was stirred and shifted by a myriad changing weights of water pouring around and eddying from fish on the move. And by mid-November, when the river level was steady with fast water running clear as glass, the gravel was being cut up by the tails of female fish – from above the Carrion Pit to the runners on the slopes of the moor, streamlets scarcely wider than the step of a boy.

Gralaks lay above the Fireplay Pool. The eggs which had been growing within her all the summer were now one fifth of the weight of her body. She was full ripe, ready to drop those eggs. Three male fish, knowing this, were near her, waiting to shed their milt on the eggs. One of them was Salar.

Behind the three cock fish lay Garroo the cannibal trout. Behind Garroo lay two smaller trout who had tasted salmon eggs before. And lying close beside Gralaks was Grai, a salmon parr weighing two ounces, who had fallen in love with Gralaks with all the volume of his milt, which weighed one tenth of an ounce. Gralaks was aware of Grai; indeed she was pleased by his nearness. Grai knew the other fish were there because of Gralaks, but his feeling for her, especially when she lay and hid him, was stronger than his fear. Grai was determined that no other cock fish should lie beside Gralaks.

No other cock fish had yet noticed Grai.

At nightfall Gralaks moved slowly forward on the level shallows above the throat of the pool. At once Salar and his two rivals moved behind her. She turned on her right side and sinuated in an arrested swimming motion, lifting by suction a few stones, which fell back with the stream. Watched by Salar and the other cock fish, Gralaks settled into the slight furrow and thrust herself into it, to widen it.

During a pause in the digging, Grai darted forward from beside Salar's left pectoral fin and took up his rightful place beside the mighty mistress of all sensation. The swift movement loosened a mistiness into the water behind the parr's tail.

The effect of this milt passing by the gills of the cock fish was one of action and turmoil. One turned and slipped over Salar, and with open mouth made as if to bite the salmon on the other side of Salar, who drove at him, also with open mouth. The three-sided chase rocked the water of the Fireplay.

All during the night, at intervals, Gralaks was digging the redd for spawning – sweeping the gravel sideways and scooping a pit in which she lay.

For nearly a week the water ran colder, slower, clearer. On the first evening of December, the wind went round to the west, the water became warmer, and fish became active. Gralaks was now ready to lay her eggs. Nearly five thousand were in the cavity beside her shrunken stomach. Spawning began towards the end of the night. During the darkness Salar had been roving round the pools, swimming from Fireplay down the run into Wheel, questing under the ledge of rock and hollows under the bank of alders. But always he had returned in haste, to move behind the trough where Gralaks lay, beside one or another of his waiting rivals. Both pools were astir with restless fish.

At last the tail of Gralaks began to work more quickly, and immediately one of the cock fish moved up beside her and shouldered her from the pit she had dug. Grai the parr pressed himself beside a large flat yellow stone which had been exposed by the digging. So tiny was Grai that the cock fish did not even know he was there. Thrust off the redd, Gralaks swam forward her own length, and lay still, while Salar moved in beside the cock fish. Immediately this fish turned with a sweep of its tail and came at Salar with open mouth. Salar swung round to avoid the lunge and also to grip his rival across the wrist. The swirl lifted Grai and scattered gravel. Grai recovered and darted to the trough again, to be behind the tail of Gralaks.

Heedless of the turmoil behind her, but newly excited, Gralaks had turned on her right side, to bend head and body backwards until her belly was curved palely like a water-sunk reflection of the young moon. She jerked and shook on her side, as though trying to touch the back of her neck with her tail. Eggs dribbled quickly from her, sinking with the current amidst gravel and silt and rolling into the trough.

The sight of the eggs and the taste of the water made Grai quiver; and as Gralaks moved backwards he moved forward, feeling as though he were being drawn from underneath by a lamprey of sweeter and sweeter sensation. His milt flowed from him in a mist, millions of invisible organisms wriggling in the water. Some of them found eggs, into the skins of which they bored, desperate for security. Those which were successful in finding the liquid within were lost in the creation of new life; the rest drifted away, to perish in water palely lighted by the star galaxy of night, whose mirrored fate was as their own.

Salar tried to move on to the redd, but his larger rival seized him by the tail and held him despite his violent lashings. Salar's head was downstream; the water was opening his gills; he could not breathe. The big fish swam upstream, to drown him. The water was beaten and the two bodies rolled over. The other fish which was attending Gralaks was a grilse from her own school, which she had led from the Island Race; and this fish, whose back was a marbled pattern of green and pink, followed the struggle and in his excitement bit the larger salmon across the tail. This made it lose its hold of Salar, and dash downstream, to swing up again below the redd and lie there. Salar returned more slowly and lay behind it, and to one side. The grilse also returned, and the three fish lay there, at rest for the moment. Grai lay beside Gralaks, by her right pectoral fin, which was wider than his own width.

A fortnight before Christmas the weather became cold again. The river was running low. Many of its feeders on the moor were fringed with ice. Fungus grew rapidly in cold water. Soon Salar's jaw was cream-colored. The edges and centre of his tail fin were corroded, too, and his skin, which had thickened and caused the scales to shrink since his return from the sea, was also patched with fungus where it had been bruised on weir and by fighting.

The shrunken water was riffled by the stones of the redd. Salar had to go past the stones and drift down to settle in the trough by the side of Gralaks. While he was coming back tail-first, the smaller grilse slithered over the heaped gravel and bit Salar across the wrist. Salar slashed the grilse away, and the movement scattered some of the eggs, which Garroo caught on the end of his kype. Shiner, watching from the tree, hard a distinct snapping noise as each egg was sucked into the trout's mouth.

Another time, Shiner saw Salar chase Garroo round the pool, down the run into the Wheel Pool, and up again to the Fireplay, where the salmon caught the trout across the back and shook it, his head out of water. "T was just like a terrier shaking an ould red rat,' said Shiner.

As the days went on, Salar became most weary. He and the large cock fish seldom fought now. Many small trout lay close to the redd, undisturbed. The male grilse went away. Garroo dropped downstream, to the deeper waters of the Wheel Pool.

Gralaks was empty of eggs, and weary. When the last one was gone from her, hidden under the stones of the redd, she drifted down the river, and came to the remembered shelter of the alder roots above Humpy Bridge.

She lay there, day after day, night after night, waiting for the rain and the spate which would take her down to the sea. Near her lay a sea trout, also exhausted. They lay side by side, thin, discolored, empty of all feeling, patiently awaiting the rain.

V

The colder the water, the greater its density. In the frosty nights of the year's end fish sunk close to the rock and gravel of the pools, hardly moving. Those late-running salmon which had paired, and had not yet spawned, lay side by side in the fast water, which hid them although their back fins were above a broken and uneven surface. The fever smouldered in them, as they waited for the frost to go.

Ice began to dull the sight of the river where it was least alive – at the edges of pools and by the bays in the bank trodden by cattle. The frost had brought down the last leaves of waterside trees, and these had caught, one behind another, against outstanding stones of the shallows. The water flow pressed them together in the shape of fir cones, scores and even hundreds of leaves wadded together, and beginning to decompose on their undersides. This gave a little warmth, which was sought by snails and shrimps. Frost put its blind gray seal around the cones of leaves; frost bound together the roots of rushes; frost sealed the trickling places of the river, and thickened the icicles under the falls. Water found new trickling places; these too were sealed. Rocks and snags lipped by water were given brittle gray collars, which became wider until they broke off and floated into eddies and were welded into the local ice, strengthening it.

The slow solidification of eddies and still stretches by the shallows made the runs faster. New eddies were formed in reaction, new ice affirmed their stillness.

Up in the Fireplay Pool, Salar lay below the redd, as though guarding it. Clots of semi-opaque, jelly-like water passed him – a slush of ice. Rapidly within his body the germs of salmon pest were multiplying; and as they conquered the living tissue, weakened by the long strain of waiting without food, – nine months now, – so the vegetable fungus strengthened its hold on that tissue. Other forms of life were claiming that which Salar had assembled and used for a racial purpose of which he knew nothing. Salar was nearly emptied of self. He lay behind the redd, awaiting the rhythm of desire and all pleasure, seeing the stars flashing bright as he had seen them in the lustihood of Atlantic nights.

The ice began to thaw with the coming of the southwest wind. Its melting released oxygen into the water, and Salar was stimulated to leap from the pool, falling back in a formless splash. Shiner saw the leap; he saw the lean rusty-brown body, the prolonged misshapen head covered with creamy fungus, green slime on the gill covers, and the blackened jaw with its great white hook twisted and tipped with yellow. Edges of all the fins were yellow, too, while a rosette was fixed to the side, spreading out from the scar of the lamprey wound.

'Poor old chap,' said Shiner. 'What you needs now is a nice li'l fresh, to take you down to the sea, to clean yourself.'

The southwest was blowing, but it brought no rain. By the beginning of February the river was at low summer level again. The phantom of spent passion for which Salar had remained by the redd was gone from him; he lay now in the deeper Wheel Pool, under the shelf of rock beside Trutta. At night the two kelts moved up to the edge of the run where it broke over the shallow. Warmer water had delayed the growth of fungus, but the pest bacillus had spread through his body, heart, liver, kidneys. Strips of his skin, which fungus had covered, had broken away, and he had no strength for regrowth.

In the still deeps of the pool a dim white length lay, the rival of Salar. Two more dead cock fish lay on their backs in the Fireplay. They had died while waiting by the redds in the shallows above, and the stream had brought them down. Every pool in the Two Rivers held dead or dying male fish. The wind was now from the northeast, a barren wind of drouth, a dry cutting wind which made lambs on the moor huddle into their ewes, and drove all birds into the lower valleys and the estuary.

When Shiner next saw Salar, the kelt was lying at the edge of the Fireplay, in still water, over a silt of mud and buried sticks. Salar did not move as Shiner knelt down and stared at him. He did not see the man above him. Even when Shiner put a hand out and curved it under the kelt's body, as though to support it, there was no movement. Only when he lifted it did Salar come back from his farawayness of self, and feel a shock, and move off slowly into deep water.

'You must n't bide by the bank, midear,' said Shiner. 'That ould crane ban't like Shiner, you know. He'll give 'ee a dap that won't do no one no good.' Old Nog, passing in the sky, uttered a screech. 'You bestways must wait where you be now, until the rain cometh, midear.' The pale mask in the water moved forward. 'That's right, midear. Shiner knoweth.' And, talking to himself, the old man ambled away along the bank, peering into the water, seeing almost everything that happened.

Night after night was starless, and clouds passed over the valley from the west, driven by a high salt wind which ruffled the pools and scattered the packs of leaves on stones of the shallows. Plants of hornwort and celery began to spread on the gravel their first leaves of the year, and the crow's-foot was lengthening green near them. The dipper sang its soliloquy of stones-and-water; the kingfisher lanced its cry under the leafless alders. On the top of a spruce higher than the railway viaduct a missel thrush sang to the flaming purple sunset.

With the last of the winter's night, snow began to fall on the moor, moulding itself thinly on the windward side of writhen beeches and thorns, falling thin and pale and becoming beads of water, but always falling, until the black places where turf had been cut were white, and clumps of moor grass were cowled in white, with flakes falling thicker until all save water was white. In the morning it was a new world upon which the sun looked briefly before clouds hid it again in snow with which the wind whitely streamlined all things standing from the earth – pillars of the viaduct, trunks of trees, felled timber, ploughshare left in an unfinished furrow, abandoned motor cars, and sheep huddled under the hedges. Through the snow the otters romped, making a slide down the cattle break in the bank by the yew trees, whose portent dark loomed through the night's glimmer.

When the moon rose in a clear sky the otters remained by their slide of trodden snow, sliding together and singly, violently and easily, into the water, whistling and talking and wrostling and splashing until sharp heads pointed up the pool, to the noise of a jumping fish. Salar had leapt, the second time in the New Year. A wild hope of a spate and the sea had stirred in him. Together the otters slipped into the water.

Trutta lay beside Salar. Wherever Salar had gone during the past month, Trutta had followed, following the phosphoric gleam of the kelt's head and flank and tail. When Salar saw the swimming shapes of otters above him, he went wildly away downstream; but Trutta, sure of the deep water, turned with open mouth and swam up hard and bumped the larger otter. Then Trutta, his mouth still open, swam down and swam up again to bump the other otter. He did this again and again, following them round the pool. Shiner was hidden behind the oak tree, and saw what happened. The big pug bumped the otters again and again, until they were growling with rage and one of them ran out on the bank, standing up on its hind legs and 'chittering.' Then it either saw or smelled Shiner, for that night he heard them no more.

But when Shiner returned the next day he saw, lying on the gravel edge above the Fireplay, lapped by rising colored water of the thaw, a great head with twisted kype joined to a backbone from which the flesh had been stripped, and a large tail fin frayed convex at the edges. The otters had returned, and driven Trutta into thin water, where he was helpless; and when they had killed and left him, a fox, who while passing over the viaduct had heard the noises of splashing and growling, had crept down to the river with his vixen.

And a hundred yards below the Fireplay Shiner found a kelt with fungus on its head and tail and flank, lying on its side in water not deep enough to cover it. Salar had got so far with the last of his strength, and had died in the darkness.

The spate rose rapidly, and washed all away, to the sea which gives absolution alike to the living and the dead.

In the redd of the moorland stream the eggs were hatching, little fish breaking from confining skins to seek life, each one alone, save for the friend of all, the Spirit of the waters. And the star-stream of heaven flowed westward, to far beyond the ocean where salmon moving from deep waters to the shallows of the islands leapt – eager for immortality.

September – November 1935

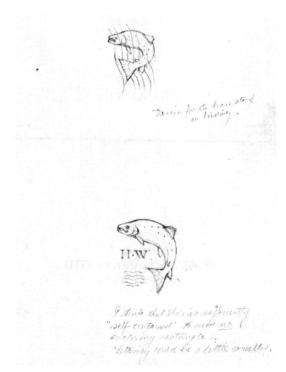

C. F. Tunnicliffe's pencil sketches for a salmon colophon,
with his notes, made on the reverse of the proof
title page of Salar, the Leaper

A CROWN OF LIFE

I

FOR FIVE CENTURIES FROGSTREET farmhouse was thatched, the kitchen floor was cold and damp and uneven with slate slabs, and there was nothing to do on winter nights except to sit round the open hearth, on which all the cooking was done, and which smoked – nothing to do except go to bed, if you were one of the children, and listen to Father's voice mumbling through the floor, the whining of the new puppy shut up in the barn, cows belving for lost calves, the owls hooting in the trees, and the rain dripping from the thatch.

For five centuries the walls and the downstairs floors were damp and the rooms were dark. The yeomen Kiffts worked hard from before sunrise to after sunset during three of the four seasons; they possessed the lives of their sons, who were forced to work often beyond middle age, without pay, for their fathers; they shouted at and kicked their ferocious barking cattle-dogs as a matter of course; they thought nothing of beating, with their brass-buckled belts, their unmarried daughters if they stayed out late without permission; they went regularly to church on Sundays; and they died of rheumatism usually before the age of seventy. A small stream ran under part of the kitchen floor, giving the place its name of Frogstreet.

When Clibbit Kifft inherited the property, it already had a mortgage on it, raised by his father because wheat no longer paid, owing to the importation of foreign corn; and Clibbit was forced to raise the second mortgage to pay death duties. Then he married the young woman he had been walking out with ever since his mother had had her second stroke and died. Clibbit Kifft had hated his father, believing that the old man's wickedness had killed his mother. Clibbit had loved his mother dearly.

Clibbit's wife was a large woman, retaining through life the fresh red cheeks and brown wondering eyes which made her prettiness when Clibbit had been courting her. She had been sorry for Clibbit, knowing how, when a boy, his father had thrashed and starved him. His long swinging arms were said to be so loose because of the number of times his father had caught hold of him by the arm and swung him round before hurling him on to the kitchen floor. As a young girl, daughter of Vellacott farm, she had pitied the poor young man with the shy and awkward manner. After his mother's death, when they were walking out together, he had never seemed to want to take her in his arms, but always to be clasped and held like a child. He was often querulous and moody for no reason that she could see, liable to leave her suddenly and not come near her again for days.

They walked out during the fall and winter, and when the warmer days came they went among the furze brakes on the combe side and she was tender to him, and during that spring he was almost happy, often making her laugh with the way he imitated and mocked his father's ways; but when one night she told him they must be wed, Clibbit got into a real rage and shouted just like his father, before breaking into tears with the thought of what his father would do to him now that he would have to find a cottage and work for wages – saying that Father would n't have no strange woman about the place.

Father told him to go and never show his face again; but the parson helped Clibbit, giving him two days' work in the Rectory garden, – that made three shillings a week coming in, – and lent him seven shillings to buy a pig. The parson also gave him an old bed and a table with three legs which had been lying for years in the disused Rectory stables. Clibbit rented a cottage for fifteen pence a week, and the banns had been read in church, – none too soon, said the neighbors, – when Clibbit's father died without making a will. Clibbit had been an only child, otherwise the farm would have been sold and lost to the family a generation before it actually passed into the hands of strangers.

When Clibbit's fourth child was coming, Clibbit was past thirty, and growing just like his father in every way, said the neighbors; with one exception: the old man had been a limmer, drunk or sober, while Clibbit was sweet as a nut when drunk.

Clibbit's wife, and his small children, lived in perpetual fear of him. She never knew what he would do next, or how he might appear. He might be home on time for his supper, the last meal of the day and eaten about six o'clock, or he might come an hour or two late, and find his plateful put back in the oven. He might eat it in silence; but he was just as likely to mutter that he did n't want no supper, then take it out of the oven, give it a glance, and declare that it was 'zamzawed' (dried up), or not cooked enough, and tip it on the floor for the dog. Whatever he did, his wife would say little, but look at him and then at the silent children with apprehension. This look, and the unnatural stillness of the children, set him off in a proper rage; and as the time for her fourth confinement came nearer, so his moodiness and fits of violence increased.

One Sunday's dinnertime he seized the tablecloth and pulled it off the table and sent all the things clattering on the floor. He kicked the loaf of bread through the window, where it was sniffed out by the sow and promptly eaten with grateful grunts. After that he neither ate nor spoke for three days, except to reply, once, to his wife's faltered, 'Won't 'ee have your dinner, won't 'ee, surenuff? Tes no use denying your stummick further,' that he could n't 'afford to ait no more meals, what with all the mortgage money vor be paid next quarter day.' On the fourth day of his fast he came home 'mazed drunk,' said the neighbors, who behind window curtains watched him lurching down the street, followed by his Exmoor pony; and they listened at their thresholds for noises following the opening and banging-to of the farmhouse door. Clibbit had had only a half quartern of whiskey, and after eating his supper and saying it tasted 'proper' he slouched about the kitchen, smilingly patting his children's heads, shaking his wife's hand with beaming solemnity before taking off his boots and leggings, and going 'up over' – to sleep exhaustedly in his clothes.

So the years went by. One August his eldest son – who had just left school, being fourteen years of age – was sent to the inn for two bottles of beer. Returning with these, the boy jumped down into the field which they were reaping, and the two bottles, one held in each hand, clashed together and were broken. Unfastening the leather belt with the big brass buckle which had been his father's and grandfather's 'girdle,' Clibbit roared out a curse and ran after the boy, pursuing him across half the field, whirling belt in one hand and holding up his breeches with the other. He stopped only because his breeches were slipping down. The boy ran on, and when he disappeared over the sky line, nearly a mile away, he was still running. The

113

village thought this was a good tale, and it was laughed over many times during the next few months – the beer bottles 'knacking together' and young Kifft 'rinning like a stag' over the sky line. The boy never came back, finding a home and work with his uncle at Vellacott Farm.

II

Clibbit Kifft's appearance was remarkable. Village boys called him Sparrow behind his back, but never to his side-whiskered face. They would sometimes dare to jeer when he had gone round the corner, riding his short moor pony. The intense wild blueness of his eyes under shaggy brows was instantly noticeable because of the long nose with its crimson tip. He was tall and very thin, a bony animation of long arms and legs in ragged clothes. His ancient cloth cap was so torn by brambles, as he knelt to till his gins and snares for rabbits, that only the lining and half the peak and shreds of cloth were left. Likewise jacket and breeches; and his gaiters were almost scratched away by his work.

Passing through the village on the way to one of his fields, riding the shaggy pony bareback so that his great nailed boots on the long legs almost knocked on the road, his sharp-featured head glancing about him from side to side, he appeared to some onlookers to be gazing about him in search of further devilment. The rims of his blue eyes were always inflamed and his voice was perpetually hoarse. The Adam's apple in his scrawny neck was almost as big as his nose. 'Clibbit's throat would cut easy,' the hen dealer would remark at cottage doors after one of Clibbit's domestic rages.

The thatch of Frogstreet farmhouse was so old and rotten that docks, nettles, and grass grew out of the clumps of green moss on it. Oat sprays grew every summer, too, near the base of the chimney stack. The green waving awns of June always pleased Clibbit. 'Tes ol'-fashion like,' he used to say to the Rector in his scrapy voice. 'Tes wonnerful old, thaccy wuts up auver. 'T was me girt-girt-granfer, I reckon, laid thaccy wut reed up auver, 'cording to the records in the Bible box.' Thatch was usually laid with wheat 'reed,' or unbruised wheaten stalks; oat or barley reed did not last so long as that of wheat. 'Aiy, tes a wonnerful long time ago, when you come to think of it, y'r riv'rence. 'T was a master lot of smut that year, and the wheat crop was ruined, so they laid wut reed upalong. November, seventeen-seventy, George the Third's reign, I reckon, zur. A long time ago. Aiy. Wull, us'v all got to go sometime, beggin' y'r riv'rence's pardon.'

Everyone in the village liked the parson.

Rain went right through the remains of seven thatchings – the thatch was relaid four or five times every century, and the oat berry which sprouted and started a colony beside the chimney stack of Frogstreet farmhouse must have lain dormant in the roof for more than a hundred and sixty years.

Starlings, sparrows, and swifts made their homes under the eaves of Frog-street, and every year a pair of martins built a mud nest over the front door, which opened on the road. In summer the stone of the threshold was con-tinually being splashed by the clotted wreckage of flies, as the parent birds cleaned out their nest. Just like Clibbit Kifft, said the neighbors, 'to be heed-less of they dirty birds biding there'; but let it be remembered, now that all the life of that farmhouse is passed away, that Clibbit once said to the par-son that the martins were God A'mighty's hens, which he liked to hear twit-tering there in the morning before he got out of bed.

When at last he was alone; when his three sons had run away, one after another, at school-leaving age; when his wife, whose cheeks were still fresh and eyes candid as a child's despite her experience, had left Frogstreet final-ly, taking away the four smaller children; when the cows and horses and sheep and the last pig were gone; when the various inspectors of the Royal Society for the Prevention of Cruelty to Children, and the Royal Society for the Prevention of Cruelty to Animals, had paid their last visits; when for years no one in the village except the parson said a good word for the farmer, the martins were still there. It is unlikely that they were the original pair: so many long flights to Africa and back would have worn out those tiny hearts. Let it be thought that, although the old birds were long since dead, the impulse and desire to fly home to the English spring and the place of their birth was immortal. It lived on in the younger birds, and, when they too were fallen, in their nestlings.

The soft waking twitter-talk of house martins in their nests before day-break is one of the sweetest and happiest sounds in the world; and, although Clibbit's head was often poked out of the window just by their nest, the martins of Frogstreet farm never had the least fear of him.

III

'Aiy, Clibbit let bide they dirty birds,' a village voice declaims, but what about the long black pig Clibbit shot? 'A raving bliddy madman was Clibbit,' declares the voice; 'a proper heller, that should have been stringed up long ago.'

Yes, Clibbit shot a pig, a long black pig it was, that had been reared on a bottle by his eldest daughter. A sow died of fever, and the surviving seven of the farrow of little black pigs were placed in a basket before the kitchen fire. One of the elderly female cats that lived about the place attempted to adopt them, with an obvious lack of success which amused Clibbit greatly. Six of the piglets were fobbed off on Ship, the gray bitch who drove the cows to and from milking; her litter of mongrel pups had recently been drowned. She took to them as gladly as they took to her, and the old cat derived pleasure from helping Ship wash them. The other piglet was bottle-fed on cow's milk and afterwards grew to the habit of coming into the kitchen to see the elder daughter, who had fed it, and also to rout for and crunch in its jaws charcoal in the hearth. Clibbit drove it out with kicks and blows, and the pig learned to be absent whenever it heard his voice or foot-falls, but when, after listening and staring and snuffing, it thought he was not about, it would walk in and begin its eager search for charcoal. It so happened that one evening Mrs. Kifft 'put back' Clibbit's supper on the hearth, and the animal had just finished a baked rabbit stuffed with sage and onions, a dozen potatoes, and a score or so of carrots, when Clibbit walked in. He swore and jerked his head about with rage, while the frightened animal bolted behind his wife's skirts. 'The withering limmer!' roared Clibbit. 'The flaming bliddy hog won't ait no more zuppers nowhere, noomye! Why didden 'ee stap the bissley bigger aiting vor my zupper, you?'

'I didden hear nor see nought!' cried the wife.

'You vexatious li'l loobey, you!' screeched Clibbit, 'd' ye mean vor say you didden hear no flaming bones crackin'?'

'I did hear something, surenuff, midear, now you do mention it, but I thought it was only th' ole pig chimmering 'bout in they embers, I did.' She looked at him, her eyes wide with fright, and the look as usual set him danc-ing and swinging his arms with rage, while he ground his teeth and hit his head with his fists. Then, seizing the gun from the nails driven into the lime-washed beam across the kitchen ceiling, he whirled it round his head, took aim first at his wife, then at the baby happily gnawing a carrot in the decrepit perambulator in the corner, and finally pulled the trigger when the barrel happened to be pointing at the head of the pig. When the policeman, hastily summoned from sleep and wearing his helmet, with his tunic imperfectly buttoned over his nightshirt, knocked at Frogstreet door, entered, and asked sternly what 't was all 'bout, Clibbit replied that he knew of no law against killing a pig after sunset, and asked if he could sell him a nice li'l bit o' fresh meat.

Shortly after the incident of the pig shooting, Clibbit was summoned for cruelty to a cat, 'in that he did cause it grievous bodily harm by compelling it to inhabit an improper place, to wit, a copper furnace of boiling water used in the process known as the washing of soiled domestic linen.' Clibbet said he was sorry, and he looked it, and the chairman of magistrates, a prominent stag hunter, said he jolly well deserved to be pitched into boiling water himself just to see how he liked it. Fined two pounds or a month's imprisonment.

While Clibbit, his small head jerking about like that of a dismayed turkey, was trying to say that he did n't have the money, a voice at the back of the court said, 'I should like to pay the fine on behalf of my friend, if he would permit me.' It was the village parson.

A woman cried out that such brutes should not be given the option of a fine, but should be flogged, and then be shut away in solitary confinement.

'Order!' cried a voice, while the clerk prepared to read the next charge. Clibbet went out of the court, wondering what he should say to his reverence; but the parson was gone. He saw the woman who had cried out; she was waiting for him among a group of friends with blank faces; and she said, 'We're going to watch you, let me tell you, and you won't get off so easily next time with your revolting cruelty. We know all about you, so you need n't think we don't!' He did not know what to say, but stood there blinking awhile, smelling of moth ball, and jerking his head about, unable to look at any face; then, touching his 1884 bowler hat, – for he wore his best clothes, which also had been his father's best clothes, – he muttered, 'Yes, ma'm,' and shambled away to where his pony was tied up. He would have liked a drop of whiskey, but did n't like to go into any of the pubs lest he be recognized.

So he went home, and ploughed the three-acre field called Butts Park until it was dark, having had no food that day. The kitchen was dark, the family in bed. He lit a candle and took down the gun from the beam. He sat down in a chair, the gun across his knees, and tried to cry, but he could n't. The poignant mood passed, and he put the gun back, thinking that he would sell the calf next market day and pay back the parson.

Clibbit did not sell the calf, nor did he pay back the two pounds fine. He avoided the parson, or rather he avoided the awkward feelings of gratitude and obligation, almost resentment, within himself by keeping out of the Rector's way. He was in debt already, for he could not work the farm single-handed, and the fields were poor, the crops taken out of them not having been 'put back' in the form of artificial and stable manure. Farmers at that time were exempt from paying rates and taxes on their land and farm buildings; but, in spite of this, many small farmers were being sold up, noticeably those who spent many hours every day in the inns.

IV

At last Mrs. Kifft made up her mind for good and all, she told the neighbors; her brother at Vellacott had lost his poor wife, and was agreeable to have her live there with the children. All the neighbors watched the departure. Clibbit, after a couple of calls at the inn, helped load the boxes and perambulator on the long-tailed cart.

'What, be goin' vor leave your old feyther?' he squeaked to the baby, also called Clibbit, as Mrs. Kifft turned to give a last sorrowing look at the room, and the broad bed, with its wire mattress like a chain harrow, where her children had been born. Clibbit bent down and wriggled a scarred forefinger at the blue-eyed baby. He saw the tears in his wife's eyes, and spoke loudly to the baby. The baby smiled at Clibbit. 'Proper, proper!' said Clibbit. 'Be goin' vor leave your daddy, hey? Aw, I ban't chiding 'ee, midear!' he said in a serious voice, gazing at the infant, whose eyes were suddenly round. ''Tes proper, tes right, vor you to go away. I ban't no gude. You go away, li'l Clibbit, and don't trouble nought about I. Go along, missus, your carriage be waiting, midear.' Blinking the tears from her eyes, the woman went downstairs with the baby, and out of the house, and Clibbit was left alone with his pony, his dog, a pig, and two cows.

That night he spent in the inn, smiling and nodding his head and praising his wife in a voice that after four glasses of whiskey became soft under its perpetual roughness. The neighbors remained silent. Clibbit told them what a beautiful animal was Ship, the gray long-haired sheep dog that followed him everywhere. 'A master dog, aiy!' Ship's head was patted; her tail trembled with gratitude on the stone floor. They said nothing to that, thinking that in the morning the dog's ribs were likely to be broken by one of the farmer's boots. Ship had long ceased to howl when kicked or beaten by her master. Her eyes flinched white, she crouched from the blow, her eyes closed, and a sort of subdued whimper came from her throat. She never growled nor snarled at Clibbit. Nor did she growl at anything; she seemed to have none of the ordinary canine prejudices or rivalries. Ship was old then. She was a gray shadow slipping in and out of the farmyard doors with Clibbit, or lying in the lane outside, waiting to fetch the cows for milking and returning behind them afterwards. Strangers visiting the village in summer, and pausing to pat the old dog, were likely to wonder why there were so many bumps on her ribs; explanation of the broken ribs was always readily forthcoming from the neighbors.

That evening Clibbit was drunk, but not so happy that he could not find his way down the lane to Frogstreet. He sang in the kitchen, and danced a sort of jig on the slate floor; the first time he had danced and sung since his courting days. In the morning he awoke and got up before daybreak, lit the fire, boiled himself a cup of tea, and ate some bread, cheese, and onions. He milked and fed the two cows himself, watered and fed the pony, gave the pig its barley meal. Afterwards he and Ship followed behind the cows to the rough pasture in the marshy field called Lovering's Mash; all day he ploughed with a borrowed pair of horses, and towards dusk of the wintry day he and Ship brought the cows back to be milked and stalled for the night.

After more bread and cheese, he went up to the inn, drank some whiskey, and then smiles broke out of his angular, tufted face and to the neighbors he began to praise wife, li'l ol' pony, dog, and parson. When he had gone home, the neighbors said he was a hypocrite.

Clibbit's lonely farming became the joke of the village. He was seen pouring away pails of sour milk into the stream which ran under Frogstreet and through the garden. He tried to get a woman to look after the dairy, but no one would offer. A letter written by an anonymous neighbor brought the Sanitary Inspector to Frogstreet; one of the cows was found to be tubercular, and ordered to be destroyed. Clibbit sold the other cow to a butcher. He sold his sow to the same butcher a month later. His fields were overgrown with docks, thistles, and sheep's sorrel. A plough stood in one field halfway down a furrow, its rusty share being bound by stroil grass whose roots it had been cutting when the neighbor had come up and taken away the pair of horses. This neighbor, a hard-working Chapel worshiper, intended to buy Frogstreet farm when it came into the market, as inevitably it must. He was the writer of the anonymous letter to the Sanitary Inspector, and saw to it that everyone knew the property was worth very little; meanwhile he waited to buy it. Clibbit still worked at his traps, always accompanied by old Ship, getting a few shillings a week for rabbits. The neighbors said he did n't eat enough to keep the flesh on a rat.

The pony, already blind from cataract in one eye, and more than twenty years old, developed fever in the feet, and hoping to cure it, for he was fond of it, Clibbit turned it out into Lovering's Mash. It was seen limping about, and inspector came out from town, and Clibbit was summoned to the Court of Summary Jurisdiction.

The stag-hunting chairman of the bench of magistrates, after hearing the evidence of the prosecution, and listening without apparent interest to Clibbit's stammered statement, remarked that he had seen the defendant before him on another occasion. The clerk recalled that occasion. H'm, yes. For the callous neglect of the horse, which with the dog was man's best friend, – for a most un-British line of conduct, he would remark, – defendant would be sent to prison for seven days without the option of a fine, and the pony to be destroyed by Order of the Court. A woman cried, 'Bravo, English justice!' in a shrill voice; she was immediately turned out of court. The clerk read the next charge, against a terrified and obese individual who had been summoned for riding a bicycle at night without sufficient illumination within the meaning of the Act, – to wit, a lamp, – who said he had forgotten to light the wick in his haste lest he be late for choir practice. He led the basses, he explained, nervously twisting his hat. Laughter. Clibbit, following a constable through a door, thought the laughter was against him. He had not eaten for three days.

That night Ship broke out of the barn, wherein she had been locked, by biting and scratching a way under the rotten doors, and in the morning she was found sitting, whining almost inaudibly, outside the prison gates. The sergeant of police on duty, recognizing her, said he would report the stray for destruction, but a young constable, to whom as a small boy Clibbit had once given an apple, said he would look after it until the old chap came out.

When Clibbit came out, his hair cut and his nose not so red, Ship ran round and round him in circles, uttering hysterical noises and trembling violently. Clibbit patted Ship absentmindedly, as though he did not realize why he or the dog was there, and then set out to walk home.

Next day he was seen about his incult fields, followed by Ship, and mooning about, sometimes stooping to pull a weed – a man with nothing to do.

It was a mild winter, and the frosts had not yet withered the watercress beside the stream running through the small orchard of Frogstreet.

Three weeks before Christmas, Clibbit picked a bunch of watercress and took it to Vellacott farm. 'For the baby,' he said. His brother-in-law told him to take himself off. 'The less us sees of 'ee, the better us'll be plaised,' he said. Clibbit went away immediately. His body was found the next day lying in Lovering's Mash, gun beside him, and Ship wet and whimpering. Watercress was found in his pocket. The coroner's court found a verdict of *felo-de-se*, after much discussion among the jury whether it should be 'suicide while of unsound mind' for the sake of the family.

The neighbors were now sorry for Clibbit, recalling that he had been a 'wonnerful generous chap' sometimes, especially when drunk.

V

A fortnight before Christmas the ringers began their practice, and the pealing changes of the Treble Hunt fell clanging out of the square Norman tower. It was freezing; smoke rose straight from the chimneys. The first to come down the stone steps of the tower and out of the western door, carrying a lantern, were the 'colts,' or youths still learning to ring; they saw something flitting gray between the elms which bordered the churchyard and the unconsecrated ground beyond. The colts gave a glance into the darkness; then they hurried down the path, laughing when they were outside the churchyard. But they did not linger there.

Others saw the shadow; the constable, followed and reassured by several men, went among the tombstones, cautiously, flashing an electric torch on a heap of earth, still showing shovel marks, without flower or cross: grave of the suicide.

Frogstreet was dark and still, save for the everlasting murmur of flowing water; people hurried past it; and at midnight, when stars glittering were the only light in the valley, the grayness flitted across the yard and stopped, lifting up its head, and a long mournful cry rose into the night.

Towards dawn the cry rose again, as though from the base of the elms; and when daylight came the mound of earth was white with rime, and the long withered grasses were white also, except in one place beside the mound where they were pressed down, and green.

The church choir, grouped forms and shadows and a bright new petrol-vapor lamp, went round the village, singing carols. Snow was falling when they walked laughing by the door and blank windows of Frogstreet, on the walls of which their shadows slanted and swerved. The girls laughed shrilly; Christmas was coming and life seemed full and good. Above the wall of the churchyard, raised high by the nameless dead of olden time, two red points glowed steadily. A girl ceased laughing, and put hand to mouth to stop a cry. In the light of the upheld lamp the red points shifted and changed to a soft lambency, and they saw the face of Ship looking down at them. 'Oh, poor thing!' said the girl. She was kitchen maid at the Rectory. The cook told the Rector.

The Rector was an old man with a white beard, a soft and clear voice, and eyes that had been very sad when he was young, but now were serene and sure. He had no enemies; he was the friend of all.

Late that night he went to the ground left unconsecrated by ecclesiastical law westwards of the elms and stood by the mound, listening to the sounds of the stream and feeling himself one with the trees and the grass and the life of the earth. This was his prayer; and while he prayed, so still within himself, he felt something warm gently touch his hand, and there, in silence, stood Ship beside him.

The dog followed him to the Rectory, and, touching the man's hand with its nose, returned to its vigil.

Every morning the Rector arose with the sun and went into the church-yard and found Ship waiting for him, and his gift of a biscuit carried in his pocket. Then he entered the church and knelt before the altar, and was still within himself for the cure of souls.

On Christmas Eve the yews in the churchyard were black and motionless as dead Time. The ringers going up the path to the western door saw between the elms a glint and shuffle of light – the rays of their lantern in the icicles hanging from the coat of the dog.

And on Christmas morning the people went into the church while the sun was yet unrisen behind their fields, and knelt in their pews and were still within themselves while the Rector's words and the spoken responses were outside the pure aloneness of each one.

With subdued quietness a few began to move down the aisle towards the chancel to kneel by the altar rail behind which the priest waited to minister to them. He moved towards them with the silver paten of bread fragments.

'Take and eat this in remembrance . . .' he was saying, when those remaining in the pews began to notice a small chiming and clinking in the air about them, and, as they looked up in wonderment, the movement of other heads drew sight to the figure of the old gray sheep dog walking up the aisle. With consternation they watched it moving slowly towards the light beginning to shine in the stained glass of the tall eastern windows above the altar. They watched it pause before the chancel step, as it stood, slightly swaying as though summoning its last strength to raise one foot, and a second foot, and again one more foot, and then the last foot, and limp to the row of kneel-ing people beyond which the Rector moved, murmuring the words spoken in olden time by the Friendless One who saw all life with clarity.

The verger hurried on tiptoe across the chancel, but at the look in the Rector's eyes, and the slow movement of his head, he hesitated, then returned down the aisle again.

The dog's paw was raised to the rail as it sat there, with dim eyes, waiting; and at every labored breath the icicles on its coat made their small striking noises.

When the last kneeling figure had returned to the pews, with the carved symbols of Crucifixion mutilated in Cromwell's time for religion's sake, the Rector bent down beside the dog. They saw him take something from his pocket, and hold it out to the dog; then they saw his expression change to one of concern as he knelt down to stroke the shaggy head which had slowly leaned sideways as sight unfocused from the dying eyes. They heard the voice saying, slowly and clearly, 'Be thou faithful unto death; and I will give thee a crown of life,' and to their eyes came tears, with a strange gladness in their hearts. The sun shone through the eastern windows, where Christ the Sower was radiant.

January 1936

THE RENEWAL OF SELF

T HE PANES OF GLASS in the windows of my writing room are old and discolored. Some are curved, flawed with bubbles and twists in the glass which distort the trees outside. The view from the window is enclosed, for the cottage stands in a combe, or valley, descending from fields on the southern slope of Exmoor. It has, like most of the North Devon combes, sides that are steep, and what I usually see through the gray panes of my upstairs writing room is a fringe of thatch and a blur of trees, most of them leafless, some grown with ivy, others tall and like bedraggled green feathers – these are the spruces that I have seen so many times swaying slowly to and fro in the southwest gales which sweep up the valley and puff the smoke of the open hearth into the room. Day after day the same view of the same trees, with sometimes the hoarse craking of a disturbed pheasant, smoke drifting from the chimneys of cottages at the end of the lane, the sight of the farmer's wife walking along the narrow strip of grass between the lower edge of the wood and the little stream or runner which divides the farm and the swamp at the bottom of my garden.

A dull and melancholy existence, you may say. Does n't anything ever happen out your way? Sometimes I see two pink sows trotting down the field, uttering cries of complaint and grumbling; and shortly they return the same way, following the farmer's wife and sniffing the bucket she carries. Occasionally something really exciting happens, as it did this morning. Such a barking and shouting and bellowing at the corner of the field near the lane, and there was Varmer waving his stick at three cows which had somehow got into the enclosure round the haystack. Then a couple of hundred yards up the lane, which goes through the wood, there is a quarry, where they dislodge the rock with gelignite. I don't know which is the louder – Varmer and his dog driving cows away from his stack or five tons of stone tumbling down the face of the quarry.

But Varmer is a good farmer, and his cows seldom stray, so it is not often that his voice gives me the excuse to push aside the three-legged writing table and go to the window. Sometimes the foxhounds go past; but the covert on the hill behind my cottage is dense with plantations of larch and spruce, thick with bracken, and many foxes live there, and are too cunning to leave the dense undergrowth. So after a while the clip-clop of stray passing hoofs in the lane is less interesting than the writing on the table; and writing is about the dullest job on earth after the first ten years – except perhaps mining, which takes a man completely out of the sunlight.

The writer knows every grain and crack and mark on the surface of the table which bears the little world he creates by 'chipping every word out of his breastbone,' to use the words of V. M. Yeates, who wrote that magnificent story of flying in the Great War, called *Winged Victory*. Day after day and night after night the writer hears the same lesser sounds about the house: the *crack, crack, crack* of the floor when the hot water is turned on and the iron pipe underneath expands and pushes up the boards; the rustling gallop of one solitary rat down the thick cob wall just after half-past eight every night; the voices of very small children crying 'appull' or 'bikky' or other words which polite grown-ups pretend not to notice; the chirping of sparrows at the thatch; the dry flitter of a red-admiral butterfly, awakened from winter sleep behind the bookcase, at the window; the varying notes of the car engines of newspaper man, baker, butcher, and fishmonger; the distant cawing of rooks; the merry shouts of children home from school, the *tottle-tonk* of the African bullock bell which calls the members of the household to meals at the long oak table in the room immediately below – the table which takes five strong men to lift, and which is only just big enough for all to sit down at.

And the writer sees the same walls and rows of books day after day, and the flawed gray windowpanes with the dull and distorted trees fifty yards away on the combe side. He sees these things as insubstantial surfaces. They are not of the real world, which for him is in his mind. He writes, he sees and lives, in ancient sunlight, which arises before and around him with an integrity he trusts and uses. The writer *must* trust that other self, that scarcely known visionary ghost which lives independently, and often with torment, within his being, if his work is to have its authentic life.

But that being needs nourishment; it needs the sun in the sky if its own inner sun is to shine truly. With what relief does the body and its outer mind leave the confined space of house sounds and gray windowpanes, and go forth under the wide sky, and become a natural man again! The sunlight lays the little visionary ghost; bird song becomes real, part of the springtime, of the earth; the larches, as one climbs higher up the rough track through the plantations on the hillside, are gemmed with living green; the buzzard soaring between white cloud edge and blue glowing sky shows smoky-brown markings as it turns in its orbit; the nostrils draw deeply of the scent of tree trunk and earth and sun. The dull, complaining creature that sat in the room under the thatch below is changing with every step; every moment the sunlight is removing the creases of winter, as it warmed and reglowed the color spots and bars on the wings of the red-admiral butterfly which escaped with him.

On the top of the hill the natural man is fully in accord with the sun and all the life around him. He is I. I am alive and joyous in the English countryside, seeing valley after valley lying away into the mists of the south and the noonday sun. And I had thought, only this morning, the twenty-first of March, that the first day of spring meant nothing to me, that a primrose at the river's brim was not even a primrose to me nowadays – it was just something that the children were discouraged to pick, with a vague irritation when a little hand was held out with a bunch of flowers and a shy, hesitating smile, by the timidly opened door of the writing room. Why, these primroses growing beside the runnel of spring water still have the soft, pure, sulphur color of youth; and the leaves, not yet fully unfolded – was there ever such a pristine green? And the ringing cry of the great titmouse, – that perky bird over there on the ash tree, with the white cheeks and black cap, – its cry is like a little hand bell for spring. How has he got so clean and new-looking? He is so spruce and his colors so new that he might just have flown out of a box. That's a stupid simile, – 'just flown out of a box,' – bringing the idea of shops and houses to this Devon hill; but that's how I thought of it. Fifteen years ago my younger self would have sought for a precise and harmonious simile, all in accord with the natural scene. All taint of civilization would then have been obliterated with scorn.

'Just flown out of a box' – now that phrase actually has a significance, but very different from the one which occurred to me when first I saw the titmouse. A short while ago I was staying in a house where one of the boys kept a small aviary of caged birds. I happened to come down to breakfast first one morning, and, looking at the letters by my plate, noticed a small cardboard box on the table beside me. It was about eight inches long, six inches wide and about an inch and a half to two inches deep. While I was opening a letter I heard a slight fluttering quite near me, and stopped to listen, but, hearing nothing more, went on reading my letter. The noise came again, with a faint scraping sound, and then a tapping, followed by a very feeble but unmistakable cry. I picked up the little box, and noticed that there was a row of holes, scarcely bigger than pinpoints, in two of the sides.

When the boy came down he picked up the box eagerly, and his eyes shone. Do you know what was in that box, which had come over a hundred miles in the post? A wild English linnet, price one shilling. Does that mean anything to you? I don't mean the shilling, because that, after all, is the price of a good square meal to many of us; but the linnet in the box?

The bird had been trapped by a thing called a clapnet, after being decoyed by another linnet, tied by a foot with string to a stick pushed into the ground of some bit of wasteland outside a town somewhere. The trapper had pulled a string when it had flown down, in answer to the distress cries of the decoy linnet, and the net had sprung over and held it down until it was picked up and thrust into a cage with other birds taken in like manner. It is quite usual to see such birds, if one comes suddenly upon a clapnet in operation, with blooded beaks thrust frenziedly through the bars of the cages, while the trapper lies there, waiting for other birds to fly down. They take skylarks that way, and goldfinches, and other singing birds. It is against the law; but the law is easily evaded. There is a demand for wild singing birds, and the trapper is a man like anyone else, who needs a shilling for a good square meal.

Should the trapper be put in a cage called a prison? Is it not better to bring up little children to know how wildly happy singing birds are when free, and how they beat themselves almost to death when first captured, and what it must feel like to be shut in a cardboard box, to be shaken and battered in prolonged terror of darkness, gaping with thirst and sickness, for a day and a night and a morning?

Well, the small boy with whose parents I was staying was very fond of his birds, they told me, and the linnet was put into the large cage with a score of other birds, so that it might grow tame and add to the pride of its owner. I don't know if the bird got used to its new life, or whether its feathers, so disheveled and broken, and its eyes, so distraught and distended, grew more like those of a wild and happy linnet's. It would be good to think that the boy released it into its native sunshine, so that it could wander the world of trees and hedges and heath land, and seek a mate with feathers almost as auburn as its own, and choose a furze bush somewhere, for its nest, hollowed smooth inside by the mother bird turning round and round as she pressed her breast against the lining of grasslets and horsehairs.

Have you heard a linnet singing in early spring? The bird has one note that is like a glowing stroke of color released into the wind. When I came to the heather of the high moor this afternoon I heard that lovely note coming from a solitary thorn tree. The thorn was shaggy with gray lichens, and bent over to the northeast, away from the gales which blow from the sea. The bent-over shape of trees is common on exposed ground of the west, near the Atlantic. I say 'bent-over shape' because that gives a picture of them; but actually they are not bent. What happens is that the branches of the tree towards the southwest are slowly killed by the periodical blasts of moist salt air, but while they are dying, or trying to live, they give shelter to the branches on the northeast side of the tree.

Sometimes you will see a stark and stripped branch growing upright, the ruin of the main trunk, or what would have been the main trunk if the thorn had grown in a combe under the wind. For perhaps a century that trunk had fought the salt and the wind. Every spring it had put forth ruddy new shoots and green leaves; and every spring the gales had burned those leaves, shriveling them brown at the edges. A tree breathes by its leaves, and grows by them, taking part of its life from the air, as we do. Later in the summer the thorn tried again, with a second growth of leaves; and again they were shriveled. So it tried for a hundred or more springs; until at last it was beaten, and the trunk died, and rotted, and fell, and only the northeast portion of the tree remained huddled away from the harrying elements.

The stray thorns on the moor are all sown by birds, dropping the hip or seed as they fly over. I love those writhen trees; they symbolize man's struggle for spiritual growth, for a fuller life. They are tormented, but they go on striving. Is this why, long ago, the wild men of the hills used to worship solitary thorn trees? Certainly the wild linnets worship in them, sitting side by side on the twisted branches in early spring, talking in soft twitter among themselves; and sometimes a cockbird uttering that ravishing stroke of color, of purest joy, as though in one note all its life were being released into the sky, because it is spring again.

June 1936

MY BEST HOUR OF FISHING

EVENING IS THE BEST time to cast for trout in the small stream which runs down the valley, a few yards away from my cottage door. For, as the low sun lengthens the shadows of the oaks in the deer park, the spinners appear over the trout stream.

A spinner is a water fly rising and falling regularly in flight as it prepares to lay its eggs on the water. It is a beautiful, delicate, ethereal creature, subsisting only on air and sunlight during its brief winged life since hatching from the river bed in the morning. These ephemeral flies live, usually, only a few hours; and at evening you see them rising and falling over the water, dropping their eggs until, exhausted, they sink down and, with wings spread flat, drift away with the current, and so out of life – their cycle or racial purpose completed.

I was standing still by the bend of the river, a rod in my hand, and watching the fast run of water slowing up into deeper water below. I was about to make my first cast into the run. The river running through the deer park is only a few miles from its source on Exmoor, and in summer the water is usually low, and generally clear, except when cattle in the morning and afternoon heats have been cooling themselves under the shade of alders. Toward evening any slight cloudiness has settled, however, and the river runs clear, so that in the glides one can see every stone and speck of gravel, every tiny red-spotted samlet of that spring's hatching. During January and the early part of February the water had been high, and salmon coming in from the Atlantic had been able to run much farther up the river than usual at the beginning of the year. As the river became smaller in April, they sought the deepest water they could find. And as the river shrank during May and June they were forced to spend most of the daylight under the muddy roots of the waterside alders, waiting for twilight and cooler water and safety from the glare of day.

There was a solitary salmon lodged under a clump of roots a few yards below where I was standing at the bend. The water was about two feet deep only – and that salmon was trapped.

I had been watching that fish for more than two months. Its life was one of solitary confinement. When it had first appeared, it had been a bluish silver, and very lively; now it was a pinkish brown, and obviously dejected. I could usually see its tail sticking out of the roots about eleven o'clock in the morning, before the shadow of a branch hid it. And if I went to the bridge again about noon I was likely to see the salmon sidle out of the roots, turn slowly into the shallow current, idle there like a great trout for a few moments, its back fin out of the water, and then gather way while it prepared for a leap – a great *splash*, and it had fallen back, and the narrow river rocked and rippled with the impact. After remaining in midstream for a minute or so, the fish would drift back toward its hiding place, in obvious dejection, and push itself under the roots again.

Now on this particular evening I was standing beside the run, a small seven-foot rod of split cane in my hand. I was about to drop lightly an imitation of a red spinner, tied to a cast of single horsehair, into the run. To a trout this lure of steel and silk and twisted gamecock hackle gave the effect of a live fly; and by this trick I hoped to get my breakfast. But for nearly twenty minutes I had been standing motionless at the bend of the river, hardly daring to move. For when I was about to make my first cast, standing still in water about ten inches deep, the salmon had swum slowly up the run, and paused within a few inches of my feet.

Very slowly I turned my head to watch it. After a while it turned on its side, and sinuated on the gravel, as though trying to scrape away the itch in its gills – from minute fresh-water maggots which were beginning to cluster there. It actually pushed itself against my left boot. Then it idled awhile, before beginning a series of gentle rolling movements, porpoise-like. Then it swam up the run, pushing waves from bank to bank; and, making a slashing turn in water shallower than its own depth, it hurtled down the run again, making a throbbing or thruddling noise as it passed. Entering deeper water again, it leapt, and smacked down on its side. Then up it came once more, lifting half of itself out of the water, and idled in the run, maintaining its place with the slightest of slow sinuating movements, scarcely perceptible. I saw a bit of crowfoot weed drifting down. As it passed the fish, it was seized, held in its mouth, then blown out suddenly.

Then the salmon turned round violently to seize it again. It was playing with the weed. I stood there more than an hour, the finest fishing hour of my life, watching that lonely salmon playing by itself — a fish a yard long, imprisoned in a few square yards of space, threatened by asphyxiation in warm water, by gaff of poacher, by beak of heron, by eels which would eat it alive, by disease, by otters, by many other dangers. I watched until dusk, when it moved down into deeper water below.

If it survives, if rain comes to widen and deepen the river, that salmon will wait there, or in a like place, until October, when with others it will spawn, – which means it will spend itself for the future of its race, – and then, in all probability, being a male fish, it will die. Meanwhile it lies there stagnantly throughout the long hot summer days, waiting until the going down of the sun, and twilight, and darkness – full of glowing life, and stars, and cold running water which is its very life.

November 1936

EAST WIND

I

THE EAST WIND WAS blowing dry sand from the sand hills over the wet shore, toward the dirty brown wavelets almost a mile away to the west. I came down from the fields, past the great white hotel, awaiting its hundred and fifty Easter guests, and by the steep path to the beach. A small boy was with me, holding my hand. An old cap of mine was on his head, the peak pulled over an ear. Under the cap his hair stuck out like part of an old haystack that cattle have eaten.

When last I walked along this shallow coast, the boy had not been born; and now he was seven years of age, and wanting to do all the things that his father had done. It seemed strange that he should be beside me, because this tract of sand hills, this Arabian desert in miniature made beautiful by the Atlantic, had always been to me a place of the solitary spirit, of aloneness. There is a distinction between loneliness and aloneness. A man might be lonely in the vast white hotel on the cliffs; indeed, walking through it just now, I seemed to be voyaging the Atlantic in the *Berengaria* two years ago – one of the most desolate experiences of life so far. It was the large windows, with their views of only the sea and the sky, and the huge empty drawing-room which gave a momentary illusion of being on a liner in mid-ocean. Almost I expected the floors to become harder to my footsteps, and the line of the sea to sink with that inevitable slow rising and falling which fills the nauseated landsman, desperately trying to acquire sea legs, with a desire to hide away and die.

This does not imply a dislike of hotels, and inns, and taverns; there's a warm human spirit beginning to appear in most of them to-day, as there used to be before the invention of the railway. Nearly everyone went by train; the inns, old coaching houses, declined. Now that the roads take so many people on wheels again, the hostels – to use a good old English word – have become alive once more. This particular hostel – or hotel, as it calls itself – was somewhat terrifying by its white vastness and its newness; and besides, we had had only one half pint of beer and a small bottle of lemonade to justify our leaving a six-year-old open-bodied sports car alongside luxurious-looking automobiles which surely belonged to champion golfers, film stars, leaders of dance bands, and others of the supertaxed. We saw some of them sitting at the great windows of the dining room as we slunk past. They looked so small as they gazed, as though half lost, at the blankness of sea and sky instead of the traffic of streets and buildings and the noises of towns they had left. We had some bread and cheese and fruit in a rucksack, and did not envy them behind all that glass, with their central heating and polished floors. We were going with the wind and the sand; we were adventurers, about to journey across the Arabian Desert, not knowing how far we should travel, or in what plight return.

The little seven-year-old by my side, with elflike face and haystack hair, was excited when the yellow skeins of sand began to drive against our shoes. 'Supposin' we get buried by a huge enormous storm, what will we do until they find our bones?' he asked, his eyes alight with the memory of some story in the children's section of the newspaper he pounced upon and read so eagerly every Saturday morning.

'Well, if this wind keeps up, the sand hills will cover us completely; they may never find even our bones.'

'Then you and me will be proper skeletons, won't us?' Adding to himself in a musing undertone, 'I'd bestways eat my apples and chocolate biscuits first.' And then to me, 'But the sand hills won't really move, will they?'

'They are moving all the time,' I told him. 'Look over there at that dune. The sand is simply pouring away from it.'

'It's like a waterfall, is n't it? Oh, some sand got in my mouth. It's a good thing we did n't bring Robert after all, is n't it, because he would not only get sand in his mouth, but in his ears and eyes, would n't he?'

Robert is his three-year-old brother, who had climbed into the car that morning and gripped the wheel, roaring with rage at not being allowed to come. Robert is a very determined young person. He has long yellow curls over his shoulders, and blue eyes set close together, and will probably be a champion boxer or all-in wrestler; he punched and slapped us soundly and screamed at us as we detached him from the car. And the last I saw of him as I went round the corner in the car was a little child lying huddled up in the lane outside the garage, sobbing with his face in his arms, and shaking his curls as the gentle voice of his mother invited him indoors to have an apple – or rather six apples, for Robert is never content with one of anything, and instantly demands six. 'Would you like a chocolate bicky?' I said to him, finding him already at the wheel of the car, and trying to start the engine. 'No – six,' he promptly replied, and when I gave him one he threw it on the ground. 'I'll have six,' he decided, as the farmer's dog crunched up the biscuit. So he had six – which means one in each hand.

II

Yes, it was a good thing the three-year-old was not with us, for, as we walked on, the sand began to stream faster over the shore from the ragged sand hills. The white warren on the cliffs behind us, whenever we looked over our shoulder, was always a little bit smaller. We were alone on the shore of the world.

It was a rasping east wind, and it was returning the sand, which a thousand centuries of waves had ground from rock and pebble and shale, to the ocean again. Originally this coast was part of the old river bed. When the river moved away to the south, trees sprang up from acorns and other seeds brought down by winter floods on shoal and mud bank. It is said that a forest stood here in ancient times, where moose and red deer roamed, preyed upon by wild dogs, and wolves, and dreadful sabre-toothed tigers. Less than three miles away, just across the river estuary to which we were walking, the carbonized roots of some of these trees can still be seen at low tide, embedded in sand, and men digging there have found the bones of these animals.

The east wind was a destructive wind; it was trying to tear down the sand hills which the west wind, from the sea, had piled up. The southwest is a genial, boisterous wind, which adds to the sand hills until they are smoothed by the pouring force and the weight of its swift sea airs. The hillocks and slopes are bound by marram grass, with creeping roots and long rounded hollow stems which sway and shake and ripple in the wind, and draw aimless arcs and circles with their sharp points drooping on the sand. All winds are the enemies of the marram grass. When the southwest gale drives the long rollers in from the west, then the roots of the marram grasses are exposed, to hang ragged down a sandy face or cliff which the day before was a long smooth slope where the naked feet of pilgrims had sunk to the ankle at every step in hot sand. For usually it is in summer that these sand hills are visited, when all sense of time and place is lost, and a man becomes a spirit of sea and air and sky, feeling the everlastingness of life while larks sing shrilly overhead and the bones and skulls of rabbits lying in the desert are of the incandescent whiteness of eternity.

We walked on, and came to the stump of a tree lying in the sand and playing to itself a strange tinkling music, which was puzzling until we went round the other side of it and found hundreds of barnacles clinging there, their dried and shrunken pipes and fragile gray shells faintly clashing in the wind. While the boy listened to this elfin music there came another sound in the wind, like a flung stone whimpering across the ice of a frozen lake; and we saw a small gray and white bird with sharp wings flying round us in a wide circle. It was a ringed plover. As we walked on we saw its mate running before us among the stones and loose sand above the tide line, then standing in grave silence to watch us, before running on again to draw us away from her eggs laid somewhere in a slight hollow amid the stones. The boy wanted to find them, so that he could write in his diary that he had found the third nest of his life; but the eggs were the color of the sand and the stones, and we might look all day and all the next day and never find them.

The timbers of a wooden ship were embedded in the sands before us, and, seeing them, the boy forgot about the ringed plover and went forward to see his first wreck, which he studied gravely, before suggesting that we should come back here in the summer with spades and buckets and dig for the gold which, he declared, might be buried beneath it. For, he said, it might have been a pirate ship, might n't it? Anyhow, he thought, he would like to bathe by it in the summer and so we must come back even if it was n't a pirate ship after all. And we must bring Robert to see it, must n't we, and also all the other children.

III

The hotel was now a small elongated white honeycomb. Perhaps most of the diners had moved into the other room, and were watching the sea and sky through other windows, and wondering, a little wistfully, if they too ought not to go down to the sands by the sea and defy the wind. The thought reminded us that we had not yet eaten.

So we moved toward the shelter of the sand hills, to find a place out of the wind. We stopped to watch how it had strewn dry sand behind the stones and sticks lying on the shore, gradually filling up the idle or windless spaces before and behind the obstacles, thus giving each the effect of a streamline. We found a sandy cliff where the sun was warm and the wind did not eddy, and scratched ourselves holes to sit in; and then, opening our rucksack, we drank milk and ate our food. We were still some way from the estuary, where we hoped to see salmon boats, but the boy said he was not tired, so after our meal we walked on again. While walking toward the sea to find a firm foothold, we saw a beetle hurrying down wind as fast as it could go, to find shelter.

'But,' cried the boy, staring at it, 'if it goes on this way it will get to the sea and then it will have to turn round and run all the way back against the wind. 'T is one mile there, and one mile back; that will be two miles.' He gave this information and stared at me with round eyes.

'Let's turn it back,' I suggested. But at the touch of a finger up went its tail, and the wind caught that little black sail and skidded it a couple of yards before it found its feet again, to hurry on to escape its enemy, the wind.

'Well, perhaps the sea trout will find it and eat it, and that's something,' said the boy. So we walked on, the beetle forgotten, and came to another wooden wreck, half sunk away in sand. We passed a little red tower standing at the edge of the sand hills, called by sailors the Blinker, because at night the oil lamp in its lantern winks towards the dangerous sand bars at the mouth of the estuary, to give pilots a bearing.

It was obvious that the Blinker had been needed on that coast, for after another half mile we came across a third wreck bedded in the sand, with seaweed hanging on its timbers from which the iron nails had long since rusted.

The sand was now uneven, and giving way to patches of shingle, telling that the tides ran strongly here. Soon we saw the northern shore of the estuary in front of us, and two small boats with men waiting at the edge of the sea. We hurried forward, because these were salmon boats and the tide had turned and they would not be able to fish much longer. Each boat had a crew of four, and while one man held the rope on shore, the boat was rowed in a semi-circle by two men, while the fourth man threw the net over the stern. The boat returned to the shore when the two hundred yards of net had been dropped, and then began the slow haul-in against the tide. The wind was very cold now that we had stopped walking, and we helped to haul. And then, as the tide-distorted arc of the net grew smaller, we stood apart and watched.

IV

There was a swirl as the seine or purse came near the shore, and at once the four men seemed to change their natures, and indeed their nationality, becoming almost Spanish in the quick and eager way they spoke. It was said that many of the fishermen of the village across the water had Spanish blood in them, from ancestors who had been wrecked on this coast after the defeat of the Spanish Armada. The skipper told them to take it easy so that the heel rope, weighted with lead, should come in slowly along the bottom and give no chance for the fish to escape. The purse of the net was lifted up on to the shore, and in it two salmon slapping about. One man put his boot under a fish and kicked it away from the edge of the sea, where it slapped the sand, and, heaving itself upright on its pectoral fins, tried to writhe away down to the water. Meanwhile one of the crew of the other boat fifty yards away – the net of which was being hastily repiled – had thrown a wooden billet through the air, and with this the fish were thumped on the base of the skull and killed.

Salmon usually come into fresh water in schools, each school following a leader; and so as soon as the net of the other boat had been shaken out and repiled they shot another draft. One of the men gave a shout, having seen a fish leap near the shore. The sweeps were bent as the boat cleft the water. When the net was hauled in, there was one fish in it, about eighteen pounds in weight. It was a female fish, like the other two. Female salmon usually come into the rivers together in spring; they are more slender and graceful in shape than the males, with smaller heads, and their underjaws have not the kype or hook which males have. When taken in the net they seemed to struggle with only part of their power, as though they were still dreamy with the depths of ocean – pale green travelers from the rocky glooms of under-sea twilight, having come hundreds, perhaps thousands, of miles across the Atlantic. The boy whispered to me that perhaps the fishermen would give us a salmon if we told them that they might be the little smolts, no longer than a man's hand, which we had fed two years before in the river at home, before they had gone down to the sea; for there is a pool above the bridge in the deer park where every year hundreds of trout and samlets await the daily showers of artificial food.

'But the fishermen must sell them to buy food and clothes for their children,' I told him. 'Now for that big fish there, eighteen pounds weight, they will get thirty-six shillings.'

'Thirty-six shillings!' he repeated. 'Why, that's an awful lot of money, is n't it? They must be rich, must n't they?'

It was explained that perhaps it was the first fish the boat had taken that week, and also that there was a license of five pounds to be paid every season, which lasted only from April to the end of August. Most of the fishermen have a hard time to live.

'Well,' the little boy whispered in my ear, 'I have some pennies at home, and perhaps we could find out if they don't catch any more fish and we could give them my pennies, could n't we?'

The wind was blowing colder, the sun was behind clouds, the fishermen went home on the tide, and we went all the way back along the sands, the boy's feet getting heavier and heavier, apples and biscuits and figs eaten, and all the milk drunken, until the only thing to do was to get on Father's back and dream of coming here again in the summer, when the wind was gone and the sand was shining, and dig for that treasure underneath the wreck with all the other children. Return we shall, to find our treasure in the silver of the waves and the golden glance of the sun.

May 1937

RICHARD JEFFERIES

I

THERE WAS ONCE A poor man who in moments of inspiration believed himself to be a prophetic thinker and writer of the world. The world did not think so. He died half a century ago, worn out at the age of thirty-eight. During the later part of his life he was ill as well as poor; and two years before his death he lived in perpetual agony. Some doctors thought his illness was imaginary; that he was a hypochondriac; that the wasting away of his body and the perpetual pains he suffered were due to hysteria. Actually he suffered from tuberculosis of the lungs and intestines, and the intestines were ulcerated as well. Also he had fistula, which is a most torturing thing. All during his life he was working; and the theme of his work was the creation of, the burning hope for, a better, truer, more sunlit world of men.

Richard Jefferies was the son of a Wiltshire farmer. He was a genius, a visionary whose thought and feeling were wide as the human world, prophet of an age not yet come into being – the age of sun, of harmony. He was derided in his father's house, upbraided for idleness and stupidity; considered 'loony' by the neighbors. Since a man can be truly friends with his peers only, Jefferies was friendless to his life's end.

During his boyhood and youth he lived at Coate Farm, in the parish of Chisledon, near Swindon. The farm lay under the chalk downs. Behind the farmhouse were trees, and then a broad sheet of water, with reeds and rushes and wild fowl, and two islets near the shore. Pike lived in there, with roach and rudd and perch, and other fish. From his boyhood memories of this place the best boys' book in England was written – *Bevis: The Story of a Boy*.

After his death, there was some controversy about whether or no he died a Christian. His life's work was indignantly attacked in the *Girls' Own Paper*.

142

This was stupid; and it was wicked. Stupidity is the same thing as wickedness, or the devil, to this modern age of half-sun. It was wicked because it denied and persecuted the truth of heaven. During his lifetime Jefferies had to fight against much ununderstanding; and it wore him to an early death.

The affinity of Jefferies with Jesus of Nazareth is patent in nearly all his work. If Francis of Assisi is a little brother of the birds, Jefferies of Wiltshire is a little brother of Jesus, of the sun, of clarity, of all things fine and natural and designed and efficient. Jefferies saw with paradise-clearness.

The century that slew him passed away, and still he remained insufficiently esteemed. The following is typical. Thirty-three years after his death, when I was a reporter in Fleet Street, I was talking to an old literary gentleman about Jefferies. It was in Carmelite Huse, then the home of Lord Northcliffe's newspapers. It was a wearing life, for men of sensibility. The old chap was a special writer for an evening paper; he was a scholar whose writings were famous to a small circle only, and to first-edition collectors. He was always violently bitter about the British public. 'Don't try and write for a living; keep pigs,' was his immediate reply to the young aspirant who approached him timidly in the little room, always lit by artificial light, where he worked. He waved hand and arm in a sweep of derision of the whole building. Then he began rolling Latin verse off his tongue. His tie was always askew around his tall 1890 collar. Red-faced, big-headed, he looked like a monk with his long white bobbed hair almost touching the shoulders of his cloak.

I felt it a privilege to hear this famous writer talk like that. I had bought some of his books, but had dipped into them only, and never finished them. The famous prose did not stand out of the pages. One day, meeting him again in the corridor, I dared to ask if he liked the works of Richard Jefferies. 'Jefferies? A mere cataloguer of sights and sounds,' he replied, and had nothing more to say, and I knew then what I had suspected, that he had not that *something* that marks out a writer of genius from the writer who is scholarly, pretentious, literary, whose work is a gilt of borrowed gold, imitation of poetic vision. (This was probably youthful intolerance; for he was a passionate writer.) When I saw him coming along a passage, I used to turn away and hide. He had called my Jefferies a 'mere cataloguer.'

During the sixteen years that have passed since the advice to keep pigs (advice which I am ready to take now) I have collected various opinions of

Jefferies by other writers, with the intention of quoting them in an essay on his work, to show why those derogatory or disprizing remarks were merely an indication of a lack in the writers themselves: such lack going hand-in-hand with their non-success as writers with the general public. But it is not worth doing.

The works of D. H. Lawrence, another writer who has much in common with Jefferies, contain many portraits of his detractors or non-appreciators, all of them arising from Lawrence's own tortured sensibility. Such writing is a mistake. It is not truly creative. The writer should shine on his characters with the serenity of the sun.

II

Jefferies was born two, perhaps three, generations before his time. In May 1925, nearly forty years after his death, I made a journey to his birthplace, and stared at the farmhouse where he had been born, at the gable window from which he had looked when writing his first pages. I walked round the broad or lake, and thought how much smaller it was than in *Bevis*. It had been made into a public bathing place, with huts and rails and diving boards; but the fish were still there. There was talk of turning the farmhouse into a Jefferies museum, for a memorial. Soon nothing, I thought, would be left of the place as he knew it, except in those pages of his which glowed and shone with ancient sunlight.

While I was musing thus, standing in the roadway before the farm, an old woman came out of a small cot of tarred wood, obviously the work of a laboring man, and scrutinized me. The little black house stood under a hawthorn, then in pink blossom. 'Come to see the house where Loony Dick was born, have ye?' she inquired. We talked for some time. She was remarkable for her vivacity and straight way of looking at things. Years before the war she had adopted a foundling or waif from the Union or workhouse; raised him as her own child, found him a job when grown up; and then the war came, and killed him. What she could not make up her mind about at the moment, she told me, was whether or not to adopt another 'chiel.' There were plenty of 'm about, she declared, since the soldiers had gone. Was she too old, did I think? I said surely not, that she had many years to live. Don't ye be too sure, she said, and defied me to guess her age. 'Sixty?' I said. 'Git out,' she replied; 'I knew Loony Dick as a boy, did n't I tell 'ee just now? "Moony Dick," some called him. A lazy loppet, he was, too. A proper atheist. Lots of folks asks me if I have read those books. Why should I read them? I know it all as well as he. He can't tell me anything new. I've had to work all my life. Why should I read in books what most folks knows already?'

(After his death, a relative wrote of Jefferies as a boy, 'Dick was of a masterful temperament, and though less strong than several of us in a bodily sense, his force of will was such that we had to succumb to whatever plans he chose to dictate, never choosing to be second even in the most trivial thing.')

All the strain and desperation in much of Jefferies's writings, and his sickness and premature death, can be traced to the human surroundings of his childhood, youth, and early manhood. Those who called him, to his face, Loony Dick or Lazy Loppet, who laughed at his aspirations and derided his early efforts to be a writer, were to him so narrow and warped and ruined that he could say nothing to them. The poor boy with the instincts of an aristocrat shut himself away from them; he lived in books, and wandered on the downs, spreading himself in the air and grass and sky until he was recharged with vitality and hope, and made eager once again for a fuller, a happier life for all the warped and ruined human minds he saw about him in both the slums of Swindon and his own hamlet.

After he left school, the young Jefferies, a mixture of indolence and sharp imperiousness, got a job on a local paper, the *North Wilts Herald*. At night he wrote novels and romances in the seclusion of the gable room, which had a pear tree trained against the outer wall. *Cæsar Borgia, or The King of Crime*; *Verses on the Exile of the Prince Imperial*; *Fortune, or The Art of Success* (he sent this to Disraeli, who returned it with a tactfully insincere letter); *Only a Girl* – how he worked, burning candle after candle into midnight and dawn.

Work on a country newspaper is good training for a young writer. There is not the hurried pressure and thwarting of nervous energy as in supplying small and often silly news stories for Fleet Street newspapers; there is no perpetual callousing and humiliation of feelings, no distortion of truth in the manufacture of 'news.' A country newspaper is usually tactful, kindly, and its detail truthful. The meticulous gathering of names and facts of the little things of country life – the more names the better for the circulation of the paper – may be dull at times; but it is not degrading. And the young Jefferies was fortunate in having a sympathetic editor who believed that his young reporter had a distinct talent for writing.

This editor's belief was justified when, at the age of twenty-four, Jefferies wrote a long letter to *The Times* in London; and *The Times* printed it in full, several thousand words, about the Wiltshire Laborer. It was read and discussed in Swindon; the writer became a local figure. His chance! He found himself, suddenly, to be an authority on agriculture.

Imagine the tall, loose-limbed young man striding home from Swindon, paler than usual, the large blue eyes in the softly brown-bearded face almost lifeless in the reaction of excitement, entering his father's house with an added lassitude of his drooping mouth and narrow shoulders, to stand about, silently, almost dully, and say casually, 'My letter's in.' 'What letter, Dick?' asks his mother, ironing on the kitchen table. 'In the paper.' 'The *Standard*? It's early this week, is n't it?' 'No, not that. I mean *The Times*.' His mother glances at it, and puts it down, while her son waits like a hawk for what she will not say. She says she is too busy just now, but will read it later; and he goes up into his room beside the cheese loft, and flops down in his chair, and feels more desperately than ever the awful deadness and dullness of house life and 'civilized' people. They will never understand. After supper he has violent indigestion, and cannot write a word of the new novel.

But he has begun. One day they will know what their son *is*.

III

In those days, before compulsory schooling taught almost everyone to read, there were in England newspapers and periodicals which were written almost entirely by knowledgeable, or professional, writers. Among them were *Fraser's Magazine*, the *New Quarterly*, the *Standard*, the *Graphic*, the *Pall Mall Gazette*, the *Fortnightly*, the *Gentleman's Magazine*, *Longman's Magazine*, the *National Review*, the *English Illustrated Magazine*, and others. The editors of these papers and magazines, attracted by the letter in *The Times*, began to ask for and to print Jefferies's essays. A London evening newspaper, the *Pall Mall Gazette*, published a series of his articles, anonymously, under the title of *The Gamekeeper at Home, or Sketches of Natural History and Rural Life*; and then another series, *Wild Life in a Southern County*. When these were reprinted in book form, Jefferies was acclaimed as a writer in the class of White of Selborne, and a public of discriminating sportsmen and country people began to look out for everything he wrote.

He was married now, to the daughter of a neighboring farmer, and had a son. After the wedding the young couple had lived at Coate Farm, but soon found that life there was not possible; the ideas of the old people smothered the inspiration of the young author. So they took rooms in Swindon. Then, to be nearer editors, they moved to the suburbs of London, first to Sydenham and then to Surbiton. He worked every day; and the work of this period was always on a high level – informative and of the authentic countryside. Sometimes it was inclined to be static; for he had to write every day to support wife and family. It was then that other lesser writers began to use the label 'cataloguer.'

Most young writers who have had a sudden success ease up for a while, and thereby lose their form. Not so Jefferies. He wrote as before, novels and essays. In a recent critical appreciation of Jefferies, by a living writer who is also a Wiltshire man, I was shocked to read the opinion that all the Jefferies novels could be 'thrown into the wastepaper basket.' But there are some beautiful things in the novels, even in the very early ones, when Jefferies was writing of scenes or incidents he had observed. Most of the early novels have scenes and characters based on what he had read in boyhood and youth: novels based on the fictional idiom of the day, and therefore blind or conventional writing. But among the novels are the exquisite *Greene Ferne Farm*, and *The Dewy Morn*, and *Amaryllis at the Fair*, one of the most lovely calm and balanced novels of country life and people in our literature. There is a naturalness, a bloom on *Amaryllis* which is not to be found in any of the novels of Hardy or the books of Hudson; and Hardy in the authenticity and detail of his country scenes is in the very rare first class with Shakespeare.

What is meant by the term 'very rare first class'? Let me try and explain this as a thing occurring in certain men and women; and why it happens. This is what one man thinks, remember; it may be true only in part, or it may be wholly wrong. Nevertheless, it may indicate why the lives of so many men of genius are tragic. This is my belief:

The base or foundation of a first-class talent is eyesight. The man who sees more, who perceives quicker than his fellows, is of a larger intelligence only by reason of that superior sight. Some people, educated unnaturally, seldom see for themselves; they don't know why things happen in the way they do: that every effect has a cause. An observant person is never stupid. Wisdom is the essence of observation.

The first-class writer always has first-class eyes. Often he is solitary from his companions in youth because they do not see so quickly or so widely as he does; and therefore do not think so quickly, or so plainly; and tend to ridicule what to them is not usual or ordinary.

It is as wretched for a slow-seeing person to be with a quick-seeing person, after the fact of difference has been established, as it is for the quick one to be with the slow one. Jefferies knew no one like himself, so he kept by himself. The derision and smallness of his fellows sealed him away from them; he was forced into solitude, where his enlarged and numerous faculties watched the actions of other life – clouds, grass, birds, fish, and natural men. He began to perceive why things happened; and reacted violently from conventional religion because it did not perceive how things happened. He judged religion by its ordinary exponents: the unintelligent mediocrity, men with minds spoiled in early life. In his lonely meditations on the downs he thought about the people in the houses and fields below, and wondered how their lives could be made happier. In such solitude it was inevitable that he should strain to perceive or discover the meaning of life: to strain after that meaning, to try to force his thought through space to a definite meaning.

Later, the sight-records of what he had seen in those early days were used for reproduction on paper.

In the world of men speech came before writing: sound of words before sight of words. The first-rate writer always has a fine ear. He may be deaf in later life; but when young he must have *heard* acutely, as well as have *seen*, unconsciously to prepare the quality and substance of his writing. He writes by ear, balancing his sentences, sometimes automatically but usually deliberately, for their *inner* music, which is the essence of life. It is an alchemic process, a spirit arising from a blend of transmuted sight-records and ear-records.

If you consider a moment, sight is responsible for almost all of the human world as it is to-day. So is sight the foundation of nearly all literature. (Mr.

Robert Graves, himself a fine, austere poet, once declared that Keats had an unusually developed sense of taste – 'And lucent syrops, tinct with cinnamon.')

Some of the villagers in Ham, where I lived during the first decade after the World War, possessed copies of an old romantic novel with most of its scenes laid on the coast and country of North Devon. Someone lent me a copy, and I read first the descriptions of those places in the district I knew. They were accurate, and yet somehow they were insufficient, unsatisfying. It was not the style, which was no better and no worse than that of a hundred other novels of its period. The descriptions were somehow so bare, so colorless, although the fields were green, the sea was blue, the sands yellow, and so on. The book was pallid, unsunned. In my youthful intolerance I scorned the book; until I learned that the author had been blind from birth.

All writing of the first class comes from exceptional sight and hearing; and insight arises from stored physical impressions of sight and sound. Those who observe quickly and vividly hold us with their detail, which is fresh and vivid; and they hold our attention because, being quick and vivid, their stories or pages have a flow which carries the reader. Now the rare first-class writer has, in addition to keen sight and hearing (it may be because of them), feelings or emotions which are equally keen. He has the keenness of a wild animal. He is natural. He is an authentic animation of the sun.

And because he is wild, natural, it is probable that he will be repressed and thwarted and made miserable in helpless childhood. This may cause him to be an ineffectual rebel, a liar, a bit of a thief, deceitful – if he has parents or mentors who, themselves victims of a repressive and unnatural upbringing, are without true or natural understanding and sympathy. Part of his natural integrity will thus be maimed; and that part will grow inwards, and perhaps mortify, and be the source of desperately sad and resurrectional poetry and dream and vision later in life. This is what happened to Shelley, to Byron, to Francis Thompson, to Shakespeare (who outgrew his Hamlet), to Jefferies, to D. H. Lawrence, among many others in our literature.

It can be said of all of them, facilely, superficially, that they have a dual or multiple personality; but the truth, or cause, is as written above. Jefferies has two distinct styles. One of them is straightforward and concrete: the style of a natural man. The other is a candescent, and often incandescent, flow of words driven from him, as he wrote, by his dæmon (in Shelleyan language): the dæmon being his repressed or mortified self. It is this part of a man that strives to reach God: the death, or mortification, in him striving to overcome his life.

Because of these two distinct styles, both of them authentic, Jefferies has two kinds of reading public. The one appreciates his straightforward descriptions of country scenes and characters, such as are to be found in *The Amateur Poacher*, *Wild Life in a Southern County*, and *Hodge and His Masters*; and this kind of reader does not like *The Story of My Heart* and the later essays wherein he wrote about himself and his own feelings. And there is the second kind of reader, who is pathologically akin to Jefferies, who prefers his introspective, sensuous writings to his matter-of-fact chapters.

It is always dangerous for a writer to write about himself and his own feelings; but when there is an intensity and power behind them he produces a flow, a blend of sensuous records with emotion; and this is called poetry.

If circumstances or fate permits the metaphysical poet to outgrow the effects of his early mortifications, and through natural love, accompanied by hard physical work (the natural life), to reassert himself to himself, he will become one of the rare first class, like Shakespeare, who, by virtue of his own experiences, real and imagined, understood all human actions and characters with clarity and the sweetness of truth. The rare first-class writer is then a universal representative of humanity, having attained wisdom by trial and error, by discarding parts of his earlier self through struggle and self-searching, and, above all, by self-criticism. So he achieves natural harmony: and thenceforth will have no regard for his writings, – as a butterfly has no regard for the caterpillar, – but wish only to live happily; and, if he writes at all, will write only for money. Jefferies had just become a writer of the rare first class when the struggle broke him.

IV

Such men are born leaders of men; but early circumstance drives them within themselves, and out of that inner mortification, from their own slain image, they strive to re-create the world. A visionary poet is a frustrated man of action. The natural poet, a very rare thing, is joyous and therefore the friend of all, the born leader, the truly civilized man. The visionary poet, the philosopher striving that future men shall not suffer in childhood as he suffered, the little brother of Jesus (the man of sorrows and acquainted with grief), writes, out of his enlarged and maimed senses, that children of the future shall be happy: that the sun shall shine on all men equally.

Richard Jefferies, the Wiltshire farmer's son, perceived this; and formulated much of it into words half a century before the World War, by whose glare and shock men began to perceive, beyond the faults of their past lives and education and upbringing and conventions and limitations, the idea of a new world, a natural world, a world wherein men would be happy because of the new wideness of thought arising, phœnix-like, from the mortifying battlefields. Of this world there have been many prophets, whose thought arises into life from faraway centuries and civilizations; and the greatest of them is Jesus of Nazareth. This was the realization of Richard Jefferies during the last days of his life: the attar of his wisdom.

Thus for the mind of Jefferies.

And of the dying man himself, what can be said? He wrote, in his last year, 'Three giants are against me – disease, despair, and poverty.'

> My wearied and exhausted system constantly craves rest. My brain is always asking for rest. I never sleep. I have not slept now for five years properly, always waking, with broken bits of sleep, and restlessness, and in the morning I get up more weary than I went to bed. Rest, that is what I need. You thought naturally that it was work I needed; but I have been at work, and next time I will tell you all of it. It is not work, it is *rest* for the brain and the nervous system. I have always had a suspicion that it was the ceaseless work that caused me to go wrong at first.
>
> It has taken me a long time to write this letter; it will take you but a few minutes to read it. Had you not sent me to the sea in the spring I do not think that I should have been alive to write it.

An artist friend has described his physical end in words that can hardly be read, by those who love Jefferies's work, without tears.

> It was in the early summer, two or three months before his death, that I saw Jefferies for the last time alive. He had then been living at Goring for some short time, and this was my first visit to him there. I was pleased to find that his house was far pleasanter than the dreary and bleak

cottage which he had rented at Crowborough. It had a view of the sea, a warm southern exposure, and a good and interesting garden: in one corner a quaint little arbour, with a pole and vane, and near this centre a genuine old-fashioned draw-well. Poor fellow! Painfully, with short breathing, and supported on one side by Mrs. Jefferies and on the other by myself, he walked round this enclosure, noticing and drawing our attention to all kinds of queer little natural objects and facts. Between the well and the arbour was a heap of rough, loose stones, overgrown by various creeping flowers. This was the home of a common snake, discovered there by Harold, and poor Jefferies stood, supported by us, a yard or so away and peered into every little cranny and underneath every leaf with eyes well used to such a search until some tiny gleam, some minute cold glint of light, betrayed the snake. Weakness and pain seemed forgotten for the moment – alas! only for the moment.

Uneasily he sat in the little arbour telling me how his disease seemed still to puzzle the doctors; how he felt well able in mind to work, plenty of mental energy, but so weak, *so fearfully weak*, that he could no longer write with his own hand; that his wife was patient and good to help him. He had nobody to come and talk with him of the world of literature and art. Why could n't I come and settle by? There was plenty to paint. Though Goring itself was one of the ugliest places in the world, there was Arundel, and its noble park, and river, and castle close by. I must go and see it the very next day, and see whether I could not work there, and come back every day and cheer him. I was the best doctor, after all.

Poor fellow! I did not then know or believe that he was so utterly without sympathetic society except his devoted wife. It was so. I am one of the dullest companions in the world; but I had sympathy with his work, and knowledge, too, of his subjects. Well, nothing would do but that I must go to Arundel the next day, and Mrs. Jefferies must show me the town. 'He would do well enough for one day. A good neighbour would come in, and with little Phyllis and the maid he would be safe.'

Therefore we went to Arundel (a short journey by train), and on coming back found him standing against the door-post to welcome us.

I have seldom been more touched than by my experience of that evening, finding, amongst other things, that he had partly planned and insisted on this Arundel trip to get us away so that he might, unrebuked, spend some of his latest hard earnings in a pint of 'Perrier Jouët' for my supper.

Do you know Goring churchyard? It is one of those dreary, over-crowded, dark spots where the once-gravelled paths are green with slimy moss, and it was a horror to poor Jefferies. More than once he repeated the hope that he might not be laid there, and he chose the place where his widow at last left him – amongst the brighter grass and flowers of Broadwater.

He died at Goring at half-past two on Sunday morning, August 14, 1887. His soul was released from a body wasted to a skeleton by six long weary years of illness. For nearly two years he had been too weak to write, and all his delightful work, during that period, was written by his wife from his dictation. Who can picture the torture of those long years to him, denied as he was the strength to walk so much as one hundred yards in the world he loved so well? What hero like this, fighting with Death face to face for so long, fearing and knowing, alas! too well, that no struggles could avail, and, worse than all, that his dear ones would be left friendless and penniless. Thus died a man whose name will be first, perhaps for ever, in his own special work.

June 1937

RAVENS IN DEVON

I SUPPOSE MOST PEOPLE remember, from their childhood days, the story of Elijah in the wilderness being fed by ravens. From the hazes of childhood I recall a picture of an old man with a beard, holding up one arm, and two black birds flying down to him. In early youth, whenever the picture came into my mind, I thought vaguely of the birds bringing berries, or wild grapes. It was possible that the hermit had tamed two young birds, and that stray visitors saw him take the food from the ravens, and perhaps put it between his lips for the birds to retake. A charming picture of the old philosopher and visionary in his retreat – one of his lighter moments. But as for birds feeding him seriously, it was absurd. Why should two birds of the Crow family bring food to a human being?

But to-day I am not sure that the feeding of Elijah was a mere fable, embodied into the history of a desert nomadic tribe. My son, looking over my shoulder as I write, informs me that the birds brought bread and meat to Elijah twice a day, at morning and evening. How about that? Berries might have been dropped accidentally by the birds, and the starving Elijah comforted by the thought that Providence was with him; and afterwards the story got about, and became part of the tribal folklore. But bread and meat, regularly twice a day! What does one think about that?

One spring, a year or two ago, a pair of ravens built a nest in the fork of an oak tree. In April, when the young ravens were out of the nest, a fledgling was picked up on the ground below. It appeared to be deserted by its parents, and so the finder put it, not without trepidation for the big beak which the bird opened in fear, into a basket and took it home. The raven very soon became tame and followed its mistress, croaking for food, and flying to perch on her head or shoulder. It grew into a large heavy bird, which bullied everything about the farm.

The raven would hide in the branches of a tree, and when it saw a cat returning with a rabbit it would fly down when the cat had passed, and let out a low-pitched *krok-krok*. Immediately the cat would drop the rabbit and flee. The first time the raven encountered it, the tomcat growled and spat and showed fight; but one dab of the raven's beak, gravely administered as though it were merely a rebuke for bad manners, sent the cat flying. Thereafter, when it heard the low, warning *krok-krok*, the cat would drop its rabbit and slink away.

But after a while, when it saw that the raven meant nothing personal, as it were, the cat merely dropped its rabbit and sat by while the raven killed it with blows of its beak and then picked out its favorite delicacy – the eyes. Afterwards, the cat could have the rabbit. Eventually the cat not only brought every rabbit it caught to the raven, but learned to obey the *krok-krok* call to proceed to the warrens to stalk and catch a rabbit for its corvine master! At any rate, that is what appeared to happen.

There was a spaniel dog in the farmyard, chained to a barrel lying on its side – the dog's kennel. The wretched dog often used to bark, begging to be released from its prison. It barked furiously whenever it saw the raven approaching, for it was afraid of the bird. And no wonder! The raven used to steal its bones while the dog was asleep, and place them just outside the arc of movement made by the chained animal. Then it would tap the dog on the pate and hop back, making noises just like the dog growling. It used to bow and open its wings, and squint along its five-inch black beak, set with black bristles, obviously daring the dog to come near and attack it. The dog did that but once – when the raven dug a little hole between its nostrils. The bird became such a bully that its master threatened to shoot it, for it was, he said, spoiling his dog, which became afraid to leave its barrel and begin its dinner when the raven was near.

With human beings the raven was wary and inoffensive, although it trusted its mistress, who had first fed it. Something happened, however, in its second season, which almost caused the farmer to carry out his threat. And that was the disappearance of his ducklings. The first brood were picked up and swallowed, despite the agitated clucking of the hen foster-mother. The second brood were shut up in a stable with the hen. But the raven discovered a drain beside the door, and after peering within and cocking its head first on one side, then the other, as though listening intently, stepped back and *thought*. A bird *thinking*, exclaims the scientific reader. Well, let us continue the three-dimensional description. The raven stepped back and stared at the drain hole. After staring for some moments, it went forward with its feathers fluffed out, as though it were a hen, and, crouching by the hole, clucked like the hen when she was calling her fosterlings. Down the hole a duckling waddled, and was picked up and swallowed. *Cluck-cluck-cluck*, and another duckling appeared and disappeared.

After that, the raven was caught and put into a wire-netting cage built on grass near the house. It spent much of its time quizzing other birds in the sky. One morning, early, its mistress saw a wild pair of ravens by the cage. And during the winter she observed it passing bits of food through the netting to one or another of the wild ravens. It was a time of hard weather, and the ground was frozen. When the spring came, she watched the caged bird again passing beakfuls of its plentiful larder to the wild birds. They flew off with full craws, westwards, in the direction of the headland where they had a nest. They returned for food, again and again.

When their young were flown – towards the end of April – the old pair began to dig a tunnel under the bottom of the wire netting. The tame raven's mistress feared they might be going to kill her pet, for this had been the fate of a tame raven in a a neighboring valley. Her husband persuaded her to wait and see what happened. He would n't be sorry, anyway.

The tame raven did no work in the scheme for its liberation. It merely watched. Was it afraid? Was it dreading the moment when the two wilder, stronger birds would fall upon it and knock its head off? At last the tunnel was finished. The wild ravens croaked, and the tame raven crept forth – free. After talking together, the trio flew off towards the sea.

The tame raven remained away for some time, and its cage was left on the grass.

One morning the farmer's wife saw it back again in the cage. It croaked a welcome to her.

And that is all I know about the bird. But I no longer think to myself about the story of Elijah being fed with meat and bread by a pair of ravens as being a fable. I see no reason why it should not be literally true.

March 1938

THE CHILDREN OF SHALLOWFORD

I

IN THE FALL OF the year we spent much time by the river, for that was the time of the salmon and sea-trout 'running' up to spawn. Leaves swirled away with the brown waters of the river, roaring under the triple falls of the bridge. Walking with the children by the irregular ribands of moorland reed, feathers, sticks, tins, and bottles from the higher villages and hamlets, which lay over the banks in the meadows, I told the bigger boys what to do if one of the small children were to fall in. The only chance, I said, was to run downstream, in the hope of the drowning child's being taken into an eddy where the water either stayed slack or returned upon the main stream. It would be useless to try to get the child by leaping into the raging spate. 'Coo, yes,' said Windles, eying the white leaping waters below the falls. 'Don't be scared if a child falls in. Use your head. There may be a chance for one of you to grab it out, at an eddy. Let's come downstream to Stag's Head weir and see if any salmon are jumping. It's time the greenbacks, or early clean-run fish, come into the river. Look, that's what is meant by an eddy. See how the water's pushed backwards by the main flow? You could get a grip on a kid washed into the deeper water here. It would be your only hope.'

As we climbed over the wooden fence by the road bridge, John said that no salmon would be running. Asked why, he explained that he had seen two 'ould cranes' standing beside the river higher up the valley, at the edge of the smooth water. If the fish had been below the falls, he said, the 'ould cranes' would have been at Stag's Head falls.

I was delighted with this perception and reasoning, and said, 'There, that's a fine bit of natural reasoning. How came you to think of that, John?' John colored slightly and said, 'Well, you see, Dad, that's what you told Windles and me last year, and I minded it.'

The river level was dropping fast, the water 'fining down.' The rain had not lasted long enough to break the springs after the unusual winter drought.

It took about half an hour to reach the falls. We went along the path through the wood, up and down a rocky place, more adventurous than by the meadow on the opposite bank. At the weir, we stood and gazed at the thundering water. After staring at the white cascades, it seemed as though the river above the fall were moving backwards with the landscape. No fish appeared, and we thought we would go and look at the spillway of the mill-stream which fed the water wheel of the sawmills. It was Sunday, and no men would be working there.

The water was now fallen enough for me to walk across the sill of the weir.

Taking off shoes and socks and rolling up trousers, I felt my way, foot sliding before foot, across the slippery slabs of stones mortared there. Halfway across, judging it to be safe, I returned for John. The water was only about six inches deep, but it pushed hard against my legs, and made my bones ache. Dumping John on the other side, I returned for Margaret. She whimpered a bit, and clung tensely to me. Meanwhile, Windles had disappeared. Returning with painful feet, I joined the two on the other bank. We went along a path through brambles, and over a narrow plank parallel to the iron doors or fenders under which the millstream boiled and swilled. Then we were safe on grass.

We crossed the millstream again by a narrow bridge made of two planks laid together, and so to an island where heaps of sawdust were dumped among pines and rhododendrons. As the mill wheel was not working, the water escaped over a spillway. We sat above it and watched thin white water surging down the sloping stone face of the spillway.

We had not been there a minute when a sea trout appeared out of the white turmoil below and swam violently up the spillway. The water was shallow, and looked like white fleeces lying on the slope. The upper part of the fish's body was in the air. Halfway up it was exhausted, and lay on its side a moment before being washed down again. As we watched, another smaller fish swam up and rested in a tiny eddy just below the lip of the spillway, where a rusty fragment of scythe blade was wedged. Slowly it edged itself up to the water-fleece before giving a leap and threshing up in what looked like a series of leaps.

The little spotted mother-of-pearl fish got to within three feet of the top and then clung with its paired fins to the stem of a dock which was growing in the crevice between two stones. The water, almost as thin as a snail's shell, barely washed over it. It rested there nearly quarter of an hour, its tail curved round the base of the dock. Just above it was a miniature turbulent pool about as big as my two hands, made by the dislodgement of one of the stones. With a sudden spring and rapid flicker the fish was in this pool and lying there with its brown tail out of the water.

'Isn't it a darling little fish?' said Margaret. 'Coo, sporty,' said John.

It was past teatime, but the sun was shining, and we wanted to see what the fish would do. 'Look, Margy and John, this fish has come about twenty miles in from the sea, after traveling scores of miles around the coast to find the mouth of the river where it had been born.' 'I hope they ould cranes won't get it,' said John. Hardly had he spoken when there was a harsh cry of *Krar-k!* in the sky, and, looking up, we saw a heron flying over. 'It swore at us, John.' 'Bissley ould bird,' said John. 'I don't like 'n,' said Margaret.

The next day, returning from school, John went alone to the spillway, and there he saw two large square tails, side by side in the turmoil below the spillway. As he was leaving he saw a heron circling above the treetops, so he went back and tapped the tails with a stick. 'Cor, they salmonses didn't half spark,' said John.

II

Next Sunday the conditions for seeing salmon were better. It rained all the Saturday night, a proper sou'wester, the wind blowing smoke into the sitting room. A puff or two of smoke didn't matter; it was aromatic wood smoke, not filthy coal smuts. It was a good feeling, when the rain was lashing down the windowpanes, and the wind thundering in the chimney, to sit before our fire and play games. Windles, now ten years old, played draughts with me, and, with two off my side of the board, he usually beat me. Then he played with John, with three off his side, and it was anyone's game. Afterwards Robert, who was not yet three, played with John, but before John could win Robert usually got tired of draughts, and started playing wheels with them all over the board, and rolling them on the floor. While he was doing this, Baby Richard would be trying to climb up my trousers to see if there was anything eatable on the table.

When we set out in the morning the sun was shining through the clouds. 'Why does Mummy never come for walks with us?' asked Margy. We stopped. 'Let's ask her,' I said. Now I came to think of it, Lœtitia hadn't come for a walk with us for years. She was always working, from before seven in the morning until after ten at night. We asked her now, but she said she had the Sunday dinner to cook, and the little ones to look after. 'Don't worry about me; enjoy yourselves,' she said. So the three children and I set out together. The boys had on their Wellington boots, and mackintoshes, and carried sticks. We should need the sticks, for we usually went along the slippery, rocky path at the bottom of the wood, which went up and down, sometimes very steep and narrow, then down again beside the river.

To get to the wood, we had to cross a small meadow. Our feet squelched in the grass. By the gate where we went in, two moorhens were squatting in the hedge. They flew away at once, back to the river. 'I expect they're a bit cold,' remarked Windles, 'and sitting up there to keep as dry as possible.' John thought for a moment before replying, 'But they be water birds, like ducks, ban't 'm, and they shouldn't mind a bit of wet, I should think.' 'Perhaps they are up there to keep out of the way of otters,' and I told them how once I had found a rabbit crouching in the grass, badly hurt by an otter, which had mauled it and then apparently let it go again. Otters usually live on fish, which they hunt under water and eat on the banks; but when the river is in spate they find it hard to catch fish, and hunt the runners, ditches, and rabbit warrens.

The path through the wood was almost hidden by leaves which had been blown down in the gale. Branches of fir trees lay there too, torn off by the wind, and also fir cones. We picked our way across the path, taking care to tread firmly on the patches of rock which showed along the path. At length we came to where the path rose steeply, and a slip on the gray shaly rock would mean a fall directly into the swollen river below. Rubber Wellington boots are liable to slip on rock, and so I climbed below and stood at the edge of the river, in case one of the children should slip and fall. The river was brown-colored and running as fast as a trotting horse; but it was fining down; most of the washed-out soil from the field drains and ditches had been left in the eddies, or gone out from the distant estuary. The falls were about a quarter of a mile below, and we could already hear the great noise of the tumbling waters.

As we came nearer the weir, the dull growling echoing back from the trees became a roar. A mist of spray hung about the trees beside the falls. The water bended over the weir-sill smoothly before gashing itself white and plunging on the rocks below. Half a tree, uprooted and washed down so far by the greater spate of the night before, was lodged on the rocks. We stood on the bank below the weir, in the misty roar, and suddenly we started back, for from just below our feet a big gray bird flew up, and flapped desperately away over the weir. 'Darned ould crane!' cried Windles and John together, and burst out laughing, for they too had been startled. For an instant it looked as though the heron's wings might strike the branches of the uprooted tree, but it just cleared them. It was nearly five feet across the wings, with a long thin neck and sharp yellow beak, and legs atrail like stilts. It had been standing on a ledge of rock below, waiting to spear any trout that should come within striking distance. There were many trout, both silver sea trout and brown river trout, trying to jump over the weir, and the heron was amusing itself lancing them. The larger female fish it picked open, for the rows of berry-like eggs within.

We had not been waiting more than a minute when we saw a fish about a yard long leap out of the white water and fall halfway up the face of the weir. As it struck the water again it swam vigorously, and we could see it hanging there, as though trembling violently. It clung there for about ten seconds, holding by its paired fins, and then it gave up, and was washed backwards, turning upside down in the boiling white water, and away in the surge of white waves. The water was too strong for so big a fish.

Almost immediately afterwards another salmon leapt about two yards from where we were standing. It fell on a hidden branch of the tree, and clung there. We could see the water pounding its body. Then with a half spring and desperate wriggle it was two feet higher up, swimming with all its strength, gradually moving upwards. But the fall of water was too heavy, and it too was swept backwards. We saw the spots on its red flank and yellow head as it turned over. It was a cock fish, a 'soldier,' for at spawning time some of the cocks turn almost as red as a brick, and their heads go as yellow as a canary. It was the wedding dress of the new-run fish. He had come into the river direct from the sea.

161

The hen salmon varied in color from dark bronze to olive-brown. Some of the fish had yellow fungus patches on fin and scale; these were the fish which had come into the river months before the spawning season, and had languished in the shallow waters of summer without feeding.

We saw several salmon trying to jump the weir, but none got up. There was a fish pass at the side of the weir, but the wooden door was closed. We tried to lift up the fender with rotten sticks, but it was stuck too tight. So I stood in the water to my waist and heaved it up with my fingers underneath the half-rotten bottom. Then we went back to below the weir, and watched the mud being swept away. Afterwards, when it had cleared, we saw a reddish back fin and tail tip sticking out of the water, in the calm between stream and eddy now formed. I touched it with my stick, and it did not move. Perhaps it was a fish that had hurt itself on the rocks, and was feeling numb along its body. So I climbed down and, putting my arm in the water, pushed it away into safety – for the heron would return when we were gone, and would stab it with its beak. The salmon slowly swam away.

Too soon it was time to think about returning for dinner. What a nuisance meals were! We said we would wait until we saw a fish get over the weir. We were lucky, for soon afterwards a sea trout, about twelve inches long, succeeded where the heavier fish had failed. The small silver fish, with dark spots and clove-shaped marks on its flanks, leapt with superb confidence out of the boiling white water, fell on a mossy rock, and, after resting a few seconds, started to swim straight up into the solid fall of water. We watched it moving inch by inch upwards, seeming to vibrate within the water, and to be drawn upwards slowly on an invisible string; and at the very lip of the water it gave a sort of spring, and was over the bend of the sill and in the pool above. There it gave a leap and fell back with a splash, as though of joy for its success. It seemed a good ending to our visit, and we went home to dinner, only fifty minutes late.

III

A few weeks later, in the middle of January, I went away to London. While I was there, something happened that I learned of only when I read *About My Life*. When I questioned Lœtitia and John about it, I pieced the facts together, into the following account. I have also got permission from the author of *About My Life* to print his book, or such selections of it as are deemed fit to be published (and one chapter at least is starkly realistic, with ancient Anglo-Saxon words that are not usually printed). In those pages the reader will note the laconic calm of John's classic style, in comparison with my subjective or romantic idiom. Here is the fuller story of John's walk beside the river with Robbie and Rosie.

At this time Robbie and Rosie were two and a quarter years old, and John was seven. John was a kind child, and always ready to help or amuse the younger children. Robbie and Rosie loved being together, and playing together, but they also loved the same toys. Often, therefore, when they were left alone in the nursery, there came from that room screams and swearwords, and, looking through the upper glass panels of the door, the beholder would observe two diminutive individuals pulling one another's fair hair, while hitting, tugging, kicking, and even biting. But when John played with them, Rosie and Robbie loved one another. Rosie had only to go away for a week to stay with her grannie for Robbie to be most unhappy; and when she returned, cries of delight would accompany the armfuls of his toys held out for Rosie to accept. There was a difference between them that I observed more than once. If Robbie had a bag of sweets, he would offer them all round; if Rosie had a bag, she would hold on to it if grown-ups were about. Alone with the children, however, she would become more open – less of the screwed-up-tight sort of feeling – and would naturally share with the others. Her grandmother adored her, and upset the balance of the child's personality; but among children Rosie was unprecocious, natural.

Holding in each of his small hands a still smaller hand, John set out. It was a Sunday afternoon, and for a treat he thought he would take them to Stag's Head weir. 'I'll take 'ee to see Daddy's samons; you'll see them jump-ing about, you will.' 'Yaas, us wull, won't us? See Daddy's samons,' said Robbie to Rosie and Rosie to Robbie.

It was too difficult to go by the woodland path, so John led the two small-er children along the road to the bridge, and then over a keeper's stile into a meadow. They walked through the grass. The river was still high after the rains. The water ran fast, much faster than they could walk. White waves broke over hidden rocks. 'There be lots of samons in there, only you can't see 'm,' said John. 'Yaas, there be lots, ban't 'm, Robbie?' 'Yaas, Rausie, there be lots and *lots*.' The river swirled deeper under the trees on the opposite bank. It was salmon-running water, sparkling with oxygen. The first flush of dirty road and ditch water had ceased to stain the sea of Bideford Bay for several days.

The trio had to unclasp hands in order to get through a black iron-railing fence, but, once through, they joined up again and went on beside the deepening water of the mill pool. When almost across the second meadow John stopped, just as he remembered his father had once stopped, and said: 'Can you hear the weir roaring? 'Tes the thunder of the falls!' They listened. Robbie said, 'Yaas, Robbie can hear, Johnnie.' And Rosie said, 'I can hear too, can't I, Robbie?' She stared at the sky. 'No, that's rookses cawing up there, Rosie; that ban't the thunder of the falls,' said John in his gentle voice. 'Yaas, it be, ban't it?' cried Rosie. 'Come along, Johnnie will show 'ee the weir,' and the three trailed on through the grass.

On the right bank of the river, at the apex made by bank and weir, the water wimpled deeply away under the iron fenders or doors, on its way to feed the mossy water wheel. The iron fenders could be worked up or down, to pass a larger or smaller flow to the wheel. When let down, the doors stopped all flow of water. The millstream – or leat, as it is called in Devon – was about a hundred yards long, about eight feet wide, and six feet deep. The weight of water falling continually on the troughs of the wheel bore it round, and turned a shaft on which pulleys revolved to turn belts to work the saws which cut tree trunks into posts and rails and planks, to repair the gates and cottages and fences and farmsteads of his Lordship's estate.

'Tes Cold Pudding who owns all this yurr wood you see,' said John, in a hushed voice. 'He's a dear little man, if you don't vex him by saying he rides a sheep instead of a hunter. Us'll go quietly now, Rosie and Robbie, and us may see Cold Pudding.'

The great circular saws, which whirl round and cut swiftly into trunks with rasping, screeching noises, are silent on Sunday. No timber wagons, with horses mudded to the knees, stand there; no men heave at the straight and massive trunks with crowbars, or make piles of new-sawn wood. The sawmills are silent, save for the thresh and ply of water cascading down the spillway of the overflow.

Stepping cautiously to the waterside, John peered into the deep, dark mill-stream. Was that a salmon down there? Robbie and Rosie peered too. No, it was only a bit of an 'ould tree,' declared John. Robbie and Rosie both declared it was only a bit of an 'ould tree.'

A thick plank crossed the millstream, lying almost level with the water. It was on this plank that wheelbarrow-loads of sawdust were taken, and dumped on the waste ground beside the river. Beyond were the loveliest heaps of sawdust. Oh, they must get across, and play with them! 'Be careful,' said John, as all three crossed slowly on the plank. It was scarcely more than a foot wide. The water rippled as they trod on it.

A happy child has no sense of time, and hardly an idea of place. It lives as the air moves. Among the sawdust, John and Robbie and Rosie played, crying to one another to see what each other was doing, discovering, pretending. They ran up and down and fell over, they grabbed handfuls and flung them into the air, they chanted 'King of the Castle' and Robbie said he would t-t-t-tell Jannie suthin': he would have a sawmill when he was a man, so's he could always play all day with the sawdust.

One heap was white, from ash trees, sawn for making parts of carts; another was pink, from the thousand-year-old yews. After a while, Robbie said, 'I-I-I-I'll tell 'ee suthin'! Let's pretend us be feeding daddy's samons! and ran with two fistfuls to the water's edge. He stood on the plank and cast handfuls into the water, where it floated. It made patterns as of lace, the idle current slowly gathering it to the plank at their feet, then slowly sucking it under. Robbie went back for some more. He was enchanted by the way it lay on the water, and stood there alone while John and Rosie played in the pink heap. 'Come yurr, Rausie, midear, 'tes sporty,' he cried, and thought it so nice that it must be walked on.

He walked on it.

Hearing the splash, John turned round. 'Oh,' he said quietly. He went white in the face. Rosie looked at Johnnie, and, seeing his face, began to whimper. 'Robbie's valled in,' said John, as the matted curls, covered with sawdust, showed by the plank. Rosie clutched herself and screamed. Her cries echoed back from the sheds of the silent sawmills.

John remembered the whistle with which Daddy called him. So he gave the whistle, hoping that Windles might hear it. But John couldn't whistle very loud. 'Oh,' said John again, for Robbie was screaming as he struggled in the water.

John ran to the plank and caught hold of Robbie's hair. Recently Mother had wanted to cut it, for it fell lower than his shoulders; but Daddy always said, 'No, I love to see it; it is beautiful hair, and I want to see it even longer, right down to his waist, in fact.' This always vexed Mother, for she had to comb it out and brush it when Robbie came home after making mud pies by the river. John clutched the long hair, and tried to pull Robbie out. He was not strong enough. The current was trying to drag Robbie under the plank. Rosie saw Robbie's rubber Wellingtons drawn off his feet, and screamed all the more as she peered into the water. Rosie is shortsighted, and bends down to peer at things.

'Keep away, Rosie,' said John, faintly pink in the face. 'Go on the grass; get away from the water, I tull 'ee!' But Rosie screamed more and more and clutched herself tighter, all drawn up into a knot of fear. John let go Robbie's hair, and, taking her by the hand, he yelled, 'Stand still there, I tell 'ee, wull 'ee?' He knelt on the plank, straining and tugging to get Robbie out of the water. Oh dear! Robbie was too heavy. He was spluttering and choking. 'Help!' cried John, but only the rooks answered, cawing overhead.

Then he remembered what he had been told he must do if a child fell in the river during a heavy spate; he must run downstream to an eddy, in the hope of catching and pulling out the child where the current was checked or even backward-turning. He must never try to pull a child out *against* the power of water. So John let go Robbie's hair, watched him carried under the plank, and, trembling, grabbed the hair again on the other side. Holding on again with all his strength, he pulled Robbie to the side, and after a long time managed to get him out. He staggered with him over the plank, and held his head down while he sicked up a lot of water.

When Robbie was better, but still crying, and Rosie howling, John carried Rosie over, stiff and heavy with fear. He took each by a hand and led them home. He carried Robbie over the muddy places, for Robbie had only his socks on, and they were half off. At home Mother put Robbie into a hot bath, and soon all was well again. And then John told Robbie a story about a salmon that was wearing his Wellingtons, at the bottom of the river.

Perhaps the most remarkable thing is that the chronicler of these little tales never learned of what had happened until he read it, half a year later, in John's book. He was away in London when it happened, and no mention of it was made in any letter from Shallowford. It is never the truth that worries a man; it is lack of truth.

December 1939

TALES OF MY CHILDREN

I

A S THE CHILDREN GREW bigger, the valley became a happy place, although always part of it was in shadow. Ceaselessly the sun rolled over from hill to hill; his work was everlasting. From the gazeless orb of brilliance energy poured down: magnificent to the earth, but a mere dwarf-yellow star of diminishing magnitude in stellar space. It was burning out.

Likewise the human mind, concentrated on one line of thought, was diminishing in energy and light.

Always the river was flowing, by which we walked and watched, and played. Never shall I forget that bright clear water, into which I gazed from Humpy Bridge, pool side, and down from the branches of riverside trees.

One warm spring morning Windles and John watched the trout being turned into the river. How the fish leapt with joy at being free from the confining ice tanks! They were Scottish trout, from Loch Leven. They were greenish-blue, with black and yellow spots; whereas the native trout in the river were a golden-brown with black and red spots.

The first thing I noticed, as I stared through field glasses at the fish below, was that when the Loch Leven trout had been living a few weeks in the pool above Humpy Bridge their yellow spots turned red, and their bluish-green sides became tinged with golden brown as though they were turning into wild Devon trout. Windles and I used to stand on the bridge and look at them as they lay in the clear water below. The summer sun shining down through the water lit every stone and speck of gravel, every wave of fin and curl of tail, every spot, every crimson opening of a gill cover as the fish breathed. Each fish had its regular place; it lay on the gravel, always head to stream, watching the water before and beside it for food floating down. The biggest fish had the best place; the next biggest had the next best place.

The natural food of the trout were the flies which hatched out of the water – not buzzing flies of the kind which bite or sting or are a nuisance in the house, but beautiful, gauzy-winged creatures which lived only a brief while, laid their eggs on the water at evening, and then fell spent, to float away, their brief aerial life over. In time the eggs they dropped out of their long slender triforked tails, or whisks, hatched, and became tiny creatures crawling on the gravel, some building themselves homes of sand-speck and bits of leaf and twig, others hiding in the water mosses and feeding on the little vegetables which grow on the gravel. These vegetables were very small, and looked to our eyes, as we knelt by the riverbank, like a thin brown slime on the stones, but to the creatures they were what a pasture is to grazing cattle. After living about a year underwater, the creatures turn into nymphs, which swim up to the surface, break out of their cases, and arise, very tremulously, as winged flies of the stream. They are frail, delicate, fairy-like things, and live but a few hours. Often in summer we watched them dancing over the water as the sun was setting – they rose and fell as they dropped their eggs, dipping in the water and flying up again – until a ripple broke, and became a ring, and a trout had risen to take one.

I used to feel sad when I thought of these lovely, dreamlike creatures dying in the sunset of their one day of life, but after watching the river for a long time, and seeing how all life renewed itself, how the salmon returned from the sea and laid their eggs in the gravel, and died, and the little salmon hatched and fed on the nymphs, and went down to the sea, and returned again to the river of their ancestors, – spring, summer, autumn, winter, season after season like a wheel turning slowly round, the great stars of heaven wheeling in eternity, – it seemed to me, when I had watched this wheel of life turning, always the same complete turn every year, that all life and death made up the beauty of the river, which had flowed through the valley thousands of centuries before the children and I walked under the hills, holding hands and laughing and peering at the strange life of the river, the beautiful, limpid, shadow-dreaming Bray, the stream which would be flowing a thousand centuries after we were all forgotten.

Summer after summer we stood on Humpy Bridge and threw spoonfuls of food into the pool, and watched the trout coming down like torpedoes, each with its little bow-wave, and saw them slashing round with open mouths to take the food with heads upstream. Always they feed upstream, for the water has to be poured through the gills for a fish to breathe. Therefore a trout faces upstream, not only to watch for its natural food coming down, but for the flow of water to pass through its gills. How they leapt and splashed, under the showers of food! Big trout and little trout, samlet and even eels, all came to the daily banquet. The curious thing was that while this food – which was like broken-up dog-biscuit meal – made the wild brown trout look like the greenish Loch Leven fish, the natural fly-food in the river made the Loch Levens resemble the native brownies! How did that happen? Obviously the color of the spots came from the kind of food the trout ate. Indeed, some of the Loch Levens, which went on upstream and lived entirely wild, looked after a few months exactly like the golden-brown, scarlet-spotted natives! Only by their shape could we tell the difference.

Windles was five when our first tame trout were put into the pool. He used to lead Baby John by the hand across the Deer Park, following me, and Baby John used to stand by the stone coping and always, his eyes wide and solemn, point towards the Railway Viaduct a mile up the valley and lisp, 'Sheed-er-shish? Dad-dad go sheed-er-shish?' He was too small to look over into the river, and one day as we stood there he became very excited, and said, 'Look, sheed-er-shish!' and lo, his idea of feeding the fish was a goods train passing on the viaduct of the Great Western Railway.

The next year John was just big enough to look over the bridge when standing on a special stone placed there for him. The fish remained in the pool during the winter floods, when the water ran too heavy and fast for us to feed them. They became thin, but some fattened again when spring brought nymphs and flies and the showers of food from the familiar figures on the bridge. Sometimes a salmon lived with them awhile, aloof and solitary, never feeding, waiting for the autumn and the spawning season, when its eggs would be laid. I used to see Windles and John creeping over Humpy Bridge, heads down, slowly to peer over into the water below. A fourth pair of eyes was trying to look over when another spring came round – Baby Margaret, led there by John while Windles was at school. John used to grasp Baby Margaret round the middle, and struggle and strain to heave her up on to the stone so that she could see Daddy's Tame Shishes. These trout were now three, four, and even five times as big as they were when we put them in the river. Always we missed one or two when a new spring came and we returned to feed them. New, smaller trout took their place – their children perhaps.

A heron speared the biggest fish one year, and we found it dying in the shallows. Perhaps otters took others. The little fingerlings of one year became the big ones two or three years later. Time flowed away as the water; it was always Now, always the same river, always the trout were there, waiting below for the showers of food during the summer.

Margaret was leading Baby Robert to the bridge to see the fish. Sometimes Rosemary came too; and then there were five small heads peering over as the spoonfuls were cast on the waters.

Afterwards the children would undress in the sunlight, and with shrill cries of joy and excitement would splash about at the edge of the stream, while I lay still in the shallow water, on the golden gravel of the ford, watching the clear cold water foaming over my body, watching it whirling the sand-specks and scooping the stones in little waterfalls and eddies along my length, feeling myself and the children part of the great stream of life, and deeply content for the gift of being alive in the world.

II

But, alas, house life was not so easy as when the sun shone down on us. I was supposed to be growing up; I was now Father, with a capital F. 'Be quiet, babies! Silence, I say! Our Father's thinking!' hissed Windles, frowning terrifically upon them. The cottage, which had seemed so spacious when first we went there, was now too small. The sitting room and the day nursery led one into another through a door with upper panels of glass. Once when I was sitting by the hearth, wondering what to do with myself, I saw five faces peering at me through the glass, two small faces at one end, or rather eyes and foreheads above fingertips pressing there. They vanished! Father must not be disturbed.

But in the open air this strange uneasy difference sometimes fell away, and I was one of them, Arkernoo, a person who provided all kinds of unexpected excitement. Arkernoo was a name originally invented by Rosie, and copied by the other children. Perhaps Windles, and his friend called Sleeboy, son of Farmer Slee, Dolly Ridd, John, and Margy, Harriet Bowden, Rosie, Robbie, and others, would be playing in the Deer Park, and the car would appear with the trailer hitched on behind, to get wood from one of the dumps in the park. 'Come on, get in, everyone!' 'Hurray, Arkernoo's come! Now for some sporty behavior!' cried Windles. 'Coo, I bet we whizz!' said John, pink-cheeked with quiet excitement. 'Yes, us'll whizz now, won't us, Rosie?' echoed Robert. 'Yes, us'll whizz now, won't us, Robbie?'

Across the grass the trailer swayed with its laughing, shouting cargo, and coming to a smooth place, where no ant-hills were, would accelerate, and go round and round faster and faster until all were shrieking with laughter. Or the engine would be stopped and the children chased; or a football match organized, and the wood forgotten. Father, thank God, was forgotten; I was one of them; I had got back, for a while, to the land of enchantment, of unselfconsciousness, to the world of otters, deer, salmon, water, and moonshine – the only world in which perhaps there was consistency, form, integrity. Back again in the house, with letters, bills, typescripts, contracts, the ever-pressing need to turn feelings into words, this world too often faded, and the children were problems of noise, dirt, and even irritation – but never of resentment.

As they grew older, I saw how different the children were. John was the easiest-going. He was seldom put out, always adaptable. At seven years he was long-haired, soft-voiced, wide-eyed, ever ready to help anyone do anything. Solemnly he made cakes in the kitchen – real cakes, not mud pies or mere hardened lumps of dough – or laid the dinner table, helping with the washing up, writing his book of twenty-six chapters (*About my Life*, by Mr. J. Williamson), and tending his garden (about one square yard). He helped make the beds, he took Rosie and Robbie for walks, he knitted a pair of socks for Sleeboy's baby brother, he held the net for me while I threw a fly upstream under the alders. Wouldn't he rather go away and play with the other boys? It must be dull for him waiting about while a water-absorbed fisherman, with catlike intentness, moved so slowly upstream, casting a red gamecock-hackle fly foot by foot higher in the runs and eddies. Oh no, said John, he liked carrying the net; he liked looking in the grass and seeing ants and spiders and 'other fings.' He was quietly happy, enjoying whatsoever he was doing.

Windles was restless, impetuous, imaginative. He came home from school one day in the twilight carrying something carefully in his hands. 'Look!' he cried, with a kind of possessive triumph in his voice. He held out a shoddy bundle of feathers from which depended white legs with clenched claws and lolling head. It was a barn or white owl, dead. Its eyes were glazed and shrunken.

'Did anyone shoot it?'

'I don't know. I found it just like that, in the Deer Park, lying on the grass,' he replied, a little anxiously.

'He wants to know if he can have it stuffed,' said Lœtitia, gently, in my ear.

Taking it in the hand for examination, one noticed first of all its extreme lightness. Although the barn owl in flight looks twice, and, in some lights, thrice the size of a pigeon, its body is no larger than a pigeon's. The pigeon is a fast-flying bird, with tight feathers; the white owl fans slowly over the mice runs in the grass and around the ricks and faggot piles. The pigeon's flight quills are hard and narrow; the owl's broad and soft, fringed with filaments of down which wave in the least breath of air.

They are the silencers of flight; an owl beating down the hedge at sunset is not heard even by mice. It has a mothlike softness, hovering and fanning with large dark eyes in a heart-shaped face peering down; the wings close and the softness becomes a powerful grip of talons. Mice are swallowed whole, after being killed with claw and beak. Later, bones and fur in a casting, or pellet, are ejected from the owl's crop.

Now how had this owl died? It had not been shot; its wings were not broken; its breast was white, although draggled. But how light it was, held in the hand – a few ounces only, a feathered skeleton.

'Look, Windles, at its legs. They're broken.'

The legs were about two and a half inches long, covered with short hairs of incipient feathers like silver wire. One leg appeared to be broken in the thigh. It was withered. The foot of the other leg was maimed; one of the toes was missing. The wound was half healed. The bird had died of starvation, after struggling in and escaping from a rabbit gin.

Standing with my little boy in the lane, the owl between us, I gave him an imaginary picture of its life since it had escaped from the gin. At first, wild fright and freedom: crooked and tottery, perching on an oak branch; falling off; a rest spread-winged in the grass below. Pain, bewilderment, glancing about in the grass for an unknown enemy. An owl's eyes were fixed; it could turn its head a whole circle on its neck. Hunger, and, after a painful take-off, to the air again. A mouse moving below; descent and grip upon the shadow; the mouse escaping. The owl falling over, and flapping upright on useless feet, bewildered.

A very hungry owl, it would seek its barn or hollow tree, there to stare in pain throughout daylight, its great ears, hid under feathers, hearing the movements of wood lice, shrews, even worms in the leaf mould below. At sunset it would climb out laboriously and fly along its regular evening ways.

It would catch no mice. Always it would fall over as it tried to grip them, and flap upright again, and stare about it. There were no beetles or moths in the grass of winter for it to catch. It would begin to feel cold, in spite of its feathers.

At night the flashes of the Dog Star above our valley seem to liquefy in the north wind pouring from the high ground of Exmoor. Perhaps that thin skirling cry we heard coming from the direction of the farmer's haystack a night or two ago, when the constellations were so big and bright, was the death cry of this bird. We saw an owl flying strangely, do you remember, Winny? Wan and irresolute in the wind it passed, a white blur, drifting and swaying; we saw it from your bedroom window, do you remember? The starlight made Farmer Slee's haystack and the hedge very clear. Perhaps the owl did not see the stars, for death is a darkening of the sight, the world fading away. On it flew, tumbling blindly and crying, to fall in the grass, and sleep away from the cold and the pain, until you found it and brought it home, this poor little ghost of a bird. Ah no, boy, it isn't fair to make you cry. Let's all go for a walk on Santon Sands tomorrow! All of us! It's Saturday; no school tomorrow, hurray! Shall we, Windles? John, Margy, how about a walk tomorrow?'

'Shut up,' says Windles. Then, 'I don't want the owl. John can have it.'

'Coo, can I? *Thanks*, Windles.'

'No, Windles ought to get it stuffed,' I said. 'It's our family totem, the owl, and the eldest son shall have it to hang over his bed, with wings in flight. It will keep the rats out of your bed,' I said to Windles.

'Ha, ha, ha,' replied Windles, with hollow laughter.

III

It was amusing to watch how ideas became fixed in their minds. That summer was a brilliant season, with much heat. One morning I took my two-ounce rod from its stand in the hall and went trouting in the river. The air was oppressive. Fishermen had told me that trout were most susceptible to atmospheric pressure; it sent them, dull, to the bottom of the river. I thought I would test this for myself.

Over Exmoor, thunder was rolling. I felt the pressure on my head, on all my body. The river shone with a white grayness that hurt the eyes. The green of pasture and oak leaves had an extraordinary stillness. The valley light was underwater light.

Nothing was happening in air or earth or water. Life was static, stagnant. The heat lifted in bourdons of sound that traveled leagues, and returned to meet new shocks from the skies.

I realized that I was part of the suspended life. I stood at the end of the run, at the edge of the fast water running into the pool.

My split-cane rod lay on the grass. The fly box was open in my hand. There was no energy to select another fly. Nor was there reason; nothing stirred.

For half an hour I had been moving upstream, throwing a hackled fly into all likely places. That was all.

Whiter and whiter the river had gleamed, as though it were oil moving there. The eyes were hurt by it. The sky was a vast slate quarry.

Even the horseflies, which during the past two days of subtropical heat had risen in thousands, were gone. Heavy-winged and burring, they had flown to rest on alder leaf and bramble.

I was wrong; there was movement somewhere. I heard a cry.

A quarter of a mile upriver two small white figures were running on the bank. The children were bathing under the slight summer waterfall. Rod in hand, I walked slowly upstream.

It was now greenly dark. Violet flashes ran down the clouds above the lower slopes of the moor. A pheasant grated wildly in the tenebrous spruce plantations on the hillside.

A young sheepdog appeared along the cart track through the park, fleeing silent and fast, pursued by something we could not see.

Margy, deep brown of leg and arm and pale of body, skipped about in and out of the shallow water with John, whose fair slight body was ripe barley hue. The boy picked up an old brass candlestick lying on the gravel and held it high, laughing gleefully at the idea of a candlestick in the water.

Suddenly that candlestick appeared to be alight; the air crackled; colossal noise fell grayly; the figures were blurred. Everywhere glassy toadstools grew on the river.

175

Cries of terror came from the children. They were getting wet in the rain!

Oh, oh, where were their clothes? Far away in the house! Not even a mackintosh between them! Oh, oh! Cries of despair and misery.

'Quick, *quick*, Daddy! Can't you see we are getting wet?'

'But you're wet already!'

'Quick! Oh! Oh! It's raining.'

No argument or exhortation consoled them. What was the difference between one wet and another? Weren't the large raindrops quite warm, much warmer than the river?

No use. It was raining, they had no mackintoshes, they would be soaked. Margy sobbed. John gibbered with rage because I would not share their plaint, but laughed callously.

While John was crying, I threw off coat and trousers, and splashed into the river. It was a strange feeling, swimming with multitudinous pillars of water arising level with one's eyes, millions of ice-flowers growing instantly and blossoming with white water-drops spilling. It was a delightful feeling, sheltering from the rain in the river. Come in, children, it's fine fun!

'Gitoom, you darned old vool, you!' cried John. 'Us be wet through to the skin, *can't you see*?' He and Margy ran home, weeping – because it hadn't happened before.

January 1940

FROM A NORFOLK FARM

THE DENCHMEN (DANISHMEN) HAVE returned across the North Sea to their pine forests, wherein they make their nests. That is the name they call the Gray or Hoody Crow on the north coast of Norfolk. It shows how slowly things have changed in this small remaining area of Old England. A thousand years and more have passed since the invaders came in their galleys, driving off the local inhabitants, and settling on their farms. One of my neighbors came over (in the blood of his ancestors) about that time and is pure Dane to look at, ruddy of face, fair of hair, with the blue eyes of the northern peoples. His ancestor was a Dane. Flights of gray crows stippled the skies over the pennant of the ship that bore him to the rich isle in the West; every autumn since they have come again – and modern children, clasping cheap chain-store toys which might have been made in Burma, or Japan, look up and say, 'The Denchmen are over in the woods again.' Has there, in all the centuries between, occurred any essential change in the countryside – save for slightly improved housing, clothing, and (doubtfully) food?

The lark still sings as of olden time over the cornfields, the buds break out of the thorn trees, the wind of early spring blows with the very breath of ice from the polar fields beyond the sea. After five months of living in the English woods and fields, the gray crows slip away over the marshes, flying low, and so to the wave-tops and the long flight home again. Almost on the same day they leave, year after year. A week or two after they have gone, the flocks of rock doves, which have picked bare many of the clover fields of the district, follow after them; and the English ringdove, a bigger bird with white collar round his neck, has the woods to itself. On the first warm sunny day of the year the croodling of the male bird is heard from the pine trees; contrast to the passionate cooing of the turtledove which, at the beginning of May, flies here from the valley of the Nile.

The ringdove, or wood pigeon, is a heavy, stolid-looking bird. 'Strong in the arm and thick in the head' is the proverbial saying about the East Anglian laborer, that amalgam of the Nordic invaders with the Saxon, Norman, and Celtic strains; and strong in the wing and thick in the throat and crop might apply also to our native pigeons. I have seen them dragging themselves along the ground, unable to fly, their crops weighted down by a hundred and more acorns, each bird. They are amorous, and in a favorable season (which means food) lay and hatch out as many as six sets of twin white eggs on the rafts of twigs which serve as nests. Their thick feathers resist the charge of shot which the farmer sends after them, as with clover-tight crops they circle the treetops before settling to roost. Their flesh is not easily digested by the human stomach (English variety) unless eaten with stewed prunes.

The Abyssinian turtledove, whose passionate and rapid cooing throb sounds in early summer from the thorn brakes, is the Biblical dove. It is small, and beautifully hued, like the ashes of a mixed wood fire, brown, gray, and spotted white. It is a genuine lover; it travels far in its dream of the English spring, makes its slender nest, brings up its two dovelets, and then away again – before the anticlimax of leaves beginning to rust and the grass losing color. It is a poet, the soul of summer in its keeping. How far back to Solomon? A moment only: the same moment when 'the voice of the turtle is heard in our land.'

June 1940

THE SNIPE'S NEST

MY LONDON FRIENDS TELL me that I, as a farmer, am a fortunate fellow, seeing life in terms of cows grazing in lush meadows, of green corn springing from arable fields, of the wind on the heath and the sun shining over the hill. That is the background, certainly; but it is often no more real to the farmer than the backcloth of a stage play is to the players. The countryside is there, but the farmer seldom sees it plain or clear.

His grazing cows are to him, by necessity, milk-yields involving the filling in of forms for the Milk Marketing Board. His seed corn requires more forms; so do his fertilizers and the yield of his harvest. His tractors require further forms for petrol; so does his car. His men are man-hours, each with its separate income-tax calculation. The barbed wire that keeps his cows from the cornfields means an extra form to be filled in; so does the wood to repair his gates, and coal for threshing. Several sets of certificates are required for the purchase of new implements. Nothing moves in or on British land without many written words and orders preceding action.

In this, the farmer is like any other businessman serving the government and the community. And how he dreads all those details, which are as verbal weeds choking his very life! Even a general in battle has his staffs; and certainly he is not worried by also being his own Quartermaster General.

Ever since he was introduced to the *Atlantic* by John Galsworthy in 1927, HENRY WILLIAMSON has been one of our most valued overseas contributors.

The farmer is all these things, and his battle, continuing day and night for all his life, is visible only to himself.

Such thoughts were with me as I went to see a cow, my best young Ayrshire heifer, which had been shot accidentally by soldiers firing across our meadows. A pair of snipe was nesting somewhere on that meadow, which had a rushy depression which we cannot drain, as the river-bed is higher than the meadow just there. As a small boy, it was my ambition to find a snipe's nest; I searched for years every spring, but was not successful. My boyhood, and the search, closed down in 1914, and though I tried to carry it on in 1919 where I left off, I found that the world of enchantment, in which wild birds were part of a marvelous and thrilling life, was gone, it seemed forever, from my life.

The Ayrshire heifer, such a gentle creature, so docile and shapely, reared by us from a little calf costing only seven shillings in the market, and giving over four gallons of rich milk a day after her first calf, was thrown, and then given an anesthetic on the meadow, before the probing for the bullet began. It was a bad wound: a ricochet had spun into and through the milk bag. I was the more furious because the troops had come on my farm without authority and without notice; bullets had cracked through the woods, smoke bombs had fallen near haystacks, gates had been left open, and even tank-busting grenades had been abandoned, the split pins unsplit and loose, in the grass.

That evening we supped with a grenade on the long refectory table, as a warning to the boys of something that should on no account be touched, should it be found. It remained there after supper, for the youngest boy had not appeared for the meal.

Afterwards, more work, more forms for the farmer to fill in, for a casualty heifer to be transported to where it would become beef quickly. I had thought to take the evening off, but no, work was piling up and must be done. So I sat me down in the little barn converted into a studio, with its unread books and unused fishing rods, its hoes and scythes and paintpots, its little bags of seed and small oaken 'bottles,' or barrels, for cider which we would make 'one day,' when the piles and piles of forms had disappeared.

While I was sitting there, a shadow fell across the open doorway. A small boy came silently into the room. I looked at him as he came slowly towards me: at his large brown eyes and sunburned face, the scratches on his knees and hands, the tears in his old jacket – a hand-me-down jacket from three older brothers and a sister. One of his hands was closed, but not tightly. His eyes glowed with his thoughts. A strange, solitary little boy – quite different from the other children.

He came right up to my table, waiting to see, before speaking, if I were busy. For this little boy is, in his way, an artist; he draws with pencil and crayons on paper, and his concentration while he draws, sometimes for two hours and more at a table, is such that none of us dares to interrupt him while he is at work. He knows, from knowing himself, that it is not good to interrupt others at work. He is not very old; indeed, only last year he told me that his status at the village school was 'First-class Infant.'

'Dad,' he said, very slowly, and by that I knew he was most excited. 'Are you busy?' I shook my head.

At this he drew a deep breath.

'I know,' I said. 'You have been under fire in the woods? You have found a bullet? You have seen the poor heifer being taken away, perhaps?'

'Yes, I did find a bullet,' he replied, 'and I did see the poor heifer being taken away in the lorry, but it's ever so much more than that, Dad.'

I waited while looking at the keen little face of my youngest child: this strange little solitary creature who wandered off alone, for hours, filling his wide and luminous eyes with the mysterious life all about him.

'Look, Dad,' he said. 'I have found a snipe's nest!'

He held out a brown mottled egg in his hand. Outside I heard a cuckoo calling, and the swallows twittering as they dived through the woodshed door, to the rafters where they nested every year. Were they the same birds, year after year, crossing the Libyan desert to return to the place where they were born? Or their children perhaps? Other birds were singing, too; chiffchaff and willow wren, skylark and blackbird. The green valley was filled with bird song. I heard them all suddenly – I saw the faithful English spring – as I looked into the face of the little boy.

January 1945

CLODHOPPER

I

FEELING THE DETERIORATING TREND of European civilized life acutely in 1936, while not being able to determine actually what form or tragic turn events would take, I decided to buy with my small literary savings a farm of 240 acres in East Anglia. Since the last war I had lived in Devon, right at the other side of England, and had been a writer. I knew nothing about farming.

I found the farm by chance. My friend and publisher, Richard de la Mare, the son of the poet, had a country cottage in Norfolk, and one day when I was staying with him he took me to see an old house a few miles along the coast. The house was empty, and had been so for some years. It had been built by Francis Bacon's father in Queen Elizabeth's time, of local flint and brick; it had two decaying towers, the ruins of a banqueting hall in which owls and hawks nested, and it stood picturesquely old and alone among blighted apple trees beside a trout stream. And a chalk stream, moreover, in which trout of three and four pounds had in the past been taken on a dry fly, and sea trout 'ran' up in the summer, fish weighing so much as twelve pounds!

As for the marshes of the flat coast, they were famous for wildfowl of every kind, from jacksnipe to the great geese which flew there in the winter

---

On his demobilization as an infantry officer who had seen three years of fighting in the First World War, HENRY WILLIAMSON took cover in a tiny stone hermitage on the Devon moors, and from that vantage point came his memorable books, *The Old Stag*, *Tarka the Otter*, and *The Village Book*. At the outbreak of the Second World War, Mr. Williamson was in possession of an ancient farm in Norfolk, and there he plowed and harvested with a toil which admitted no time for writing. Now at last he can draw breath and tell his story.

from Spitzbergen and the north. It was wild, deserted country, thinly popu-
lated, on the edge of the arable or corn district of East Anglia – once the
granary of England, but then suffering from the long depression of British
farming.

After several visits to the gloomy old house, said to be haunted, with its
cellars and floors that looked to be dry-rotten, its attics of great oak beams
hung with clusters of pipistrelle bats, – it was winter, and it rained every time
I went to see it, – I decided that it was too big, and probably too costly, for
me. It was for sale with 240 acres of land with hills, valleys, woods, a mile
of trout stream, and wonderful views over the marshes. Woodcock flying
from Scandinavia in the hunter's moon alighted in those woods; teal, mallard, and wigeon flighted to the willow clumps. During one visit I watched
eight 'guns' standing on the meadow below one of the woods, and it seemed
that hundreds of pheasants were flying out before the beaters advancing
though the trees.

What a place to own! It had everything! Half a mile away was the sea,
with many creeks for sailing a small boat, shellfish for the gathering, and
pools for bathing. I visualized ponies for the children, our own hams hanging from the farmhouse beams (only there was no farmhouse with the land!),
and myself with a red fat face, where before I had been thin and pale, myself
a proper John Bull, staring at pigs and corn stacks, slow and easy where
before I had been quick and irritable. In fact, at forty years of age I was
entering the Faustian phase; and I knew it, but avoided the direct realization
by telling myself that in the painful transitional years to come I would be justified in having decided to educate my sons as peasants or yeomen on the
land. The old order was deteriorating; it had been deteriorating since I was
a boy, and a youth in the World War; and now direct action was needed. So
the plow was exchanged for the pen.

I had enough sense to have a professional valuer look over the farm. It
was in a terrible condition. Weeds everywhere: weeds which were excellent
cover for the wild pheasants. The farm was let to a farmer who paid £100
a year rent, and regarded it as a game preserve for the rich sportsmen who
came to stay at the luxury hotel a mile or two away down the coast. It was
burdened by a tithe of £80, to be paid annually out of the rent received by
the landlord; and when taxes and drainage rates had been paid, the landlord
was out of pocket. So he was amazed when someone made his agent an

offer for the land, which no one else had ever wanted. Everyone else had been after that old house, but had shied at the encumbrance of the farm.

But by this time I was entirely transfixed by the immovable idea that I must have that farm. My only hope in life lay in being the farmer of my imagination. I must restore its arable fields to fertility, throw and trim its sprawling hedges, which had overgrown since the end of the last war, drain the bogs in its meadows, make up its roads, erect new gates and gateposts (not one was standing anywhere on the farm), repair the hundreds of square yards of its Elizabethan tiled roofs, remove the thousands of rats which had tunneled the wide flint walls almost hollow, clean its trout stream of the mud which had accumulated there and ruined its fishing, build a farmhouse, teach myself to farm by day and write by night to earn money to pay the bills.

I must at all or any cost to myself or my family restore the land to what it had once been, and in doing so perhaps make of myself what I should have been had there not been a world war and all the mortifying experiences leading up to it. Somehow, scarcely formulated at the back of my mind, somehow I hoped desperately that all these self-imposed difficulties would help in the beginning of a back-to-nature movement which would transform the machine mentality of man and so avert war; and in my own person I trusted that the arduous work would give me the mental and domestic harmony which I had lacked in the years since I went to Devon to become a writer soon after the Armistice of 1918.

II

That was in the winter of 1936. By the summer of that year I had bought the land, against the advice of my valuer, and even against the advice of the lawyers of the old owner, who for six years had been hoping to find a purchaser. I started with a friend in May, 1936, arriving from Devon with a truck and a van. We made a camp in the pine woods overlooking the sea. By the winter of 1937 my friend had quit, unable to stand it all; but meanwhile four old condemned cottages I had bought had been restored and made dry and light, and the family was living in two of them. Our dwelling there was but temporary; for with the land I had bought two better cottages, standing in an acre of garden, and I hoped one day, if I could earn enough money, to alter them and join them into one farmhouse. My friend and I had rebuilt the four cottages with the help of two unemployed laborers in the village, teaching ourselves as we went along. I learned in that time that I would never try to build anything by myself again!

That building job went anything but smoothly. We were racing against time – three of the cottages had to be stripped to the shells of the lower walls – *and also doing other jobs at the same time*. The usual error of the amateur: taking on too much at once! I had hired a gravel pit, and with two other men dug about a thousand tons in three weeks and made up half a mile of potholed roads. After the usual blisters and exhaustion due to unformed muscles, the picking and shoveling was easy; but what I did find hard was the writing at night. We were not having sufficient food, and the differences with my 'partner' (who had neither experience nor capital) were sometimes acute. I am told that our midnight arguments from the hilltop camp among the pine trees were sometimes audible throughout the village.

However, I kept the worst aspects of our disharmony out of the weekly broadcast talks from the BBC in London, and also out of the several articles I wrote each week for the *Daily Express* and other London papers. It meant working to the small hours and rising again at 7.00 a.m., but it was done somehow. At Michaelmas, 1937, the old bankrupt farmer left, and I found I had to pay him, by law, a year's rent for 'disturbing' him! However, I was now the farmer of my own land.

My plan was to plow the hundred acres of the arable and leave them plowed until the luxuriant weeds were high, and then plow them in again to make humus, afterwards cultivating the furrows and killing with harrows every successive generation of weeds that came up. Thus by 1939 my fields would be clean, sweetened by air and sun, and the bare fallow would restore much of the fertility lost by shallow plowings of the past and by cropping with the use of artificial fertilizers only. That was my scheme.

But the men I took on – two, a father and son who had been left entirely to themselves by the old farmer and were spiritually one with the frightful condition the farm was in – persuaded me to grow grain, to 'get something back; otherwise it's pay, pay, pay all the time, guv'nor, and 'twale break you, 'bor.' So instead of remaking the old cow-house, re-laying all the roads, clearing the old overgrown hedges, tiling the fallen roofs, setting new oaken posts and gates, I found myself involved in farming a year before I was ready. Thus I got deeper, as they say in Norfolk, 'in a muddle.'

Oh, those early dawn risings! Taking the truck alone along frosty miles to auction sales of bankrupt and quitting farmers, to buy machinery and implements of whose function or condition I knew absolutely nothing! What was the difference between a one-horse roll, a two-horse roll, and a rib or heavy Cambridge ring roll? What were they *for*, what did they *do*? How dare I find out? Ask the gypsies? But if I did, would they see I was a mug, as the men at home had solemnly assured me, and so 'run me,' making me pay twice or thrice the value of what I had been told I ought to get? I stood there, hollow-feeling, afraid to bid, afraid to lose what was urgently needed.

Time after time I returned home at night with rolls and harrows, barrels and old bedsteads (for concrete work, making future bridges across the meadow dikes), root cutters and scufflers, thill gears and horse collars (to this day I don't know what a thill gear really is), harness and hay knives, old churns for making butter, and Napoleonic wooden machines for dressing the grain, objects like small windmills enclosed in large worm-eaten dog-kennels, bought for a few shillings. I wore overalls and had no time to eat my sandwiches at lunch; rushing home, I unloaded and then, after a wash and a hopeless stare at the fire, set about writing an amusing account of my day's adventures, to pay for what I had acquired that day.

III

A thousand times during that obscure time I said I must give up, for instead of uniting my family on the land, the experience seemed to be breaking it up. No bathroom in the cottages, no plumbing, hardly any furniture. The new roof blew off in a gale. The chimney caught fire; the electric light nearly electrocuted us. But after every depression my spirits rose, and I told the men that one day the farm would be unrecognizable. 'So will you, guv'nor, if you harn't keerful!' warned the old cowman, who refused to wash out the new cow-house with the new hose and piped water I had put up, from the new artesian well bored 76 feet into the chalk. (At least I had the sense not to attempt that boring myself.)

We grew barley that last year of the peace, and it met with the biggest slump for fifteen years. It was the Munich crisis that caused it; the brewers bought of the abundant mid-European grain which came hurriedly to most of the southern and eastern ports of Britain, and when British barley went on the market, the price dropped overnight. So instead of my arable cleaned and restored for the 1939 market, as I had planned, I had about fifty tons of unwanted barley lying in the grain barn. That old barn had beams made out of the spars of sailing ships which had probably carried grain from port to port along the east coast before King Henry VIII dissolved the monasteries. Instead of looking at those beams, so much of an attraction before the buying of the farm, I looked ruefully at the thousands of rats' trails over the heaps of fine malting barley which nobody in the Corn Hall at Norwich wanted. Once again I learned the folly of not trusting to my own ideas.

So the war came, and the land I had bought at a period when British agricultural land had not been so cheap for one hundred and fifty years was immediately an asset. People who only two years before had warned me of my folly now complimented me on my foresight. 'Ah, you're a farmer!' they exclaimed. 'The finest life on earth! Lucky fellow!' adding that they wished they had a farm. What did I think of their chances as farmers, if they 'took the plunge' and did what I had done? Quite sincerely I returned to them the very excellent advice they had given me in the past. In farming, I said, you haven't time to look at the view; farming is all technical problems and often frustrations. Ah, they replied, you farmers are never satisfied!

I don't want to think of those occasions when I gave in to some persuasions and yielded to this or that request from an urban escapist, usually of military age, for a job on the farm. None of them cared about farming, and one and all were a burden in their various ways.

You can't borrow or lend experience; you have to buy it. I bought mine. And somehow I stuck it out. Four derelict cottages made good, and occupied by my men working on the farm; another two cottages made into a habitable farmhouse for the family, *with* plumbing; an old ruinous barn turned into a library-studio, where I sit before a warm open hearth and read my books; a garage built decently of old tiles, natural-edge elm boards sawn on our own bench, and concrete blocks inside plastered white; the acre of garden plowed up and planted with fruit trees; the stream bed cleaned in sections by slanting board-dams (fights with the Drainage Board men over those dams) and the meadows drained; a thousand tons of rich black mud spread over some poor fields, which after two years grew bumper crops; the roads ruined again by an invasion of practice tanks in a wet winter, but made up again a year later; two hundred tons of logs for our open hearths, got from the old thorn hedges cut down; rich leaf mold in the woods plowed out and spread on the arable, to restore fertility; our own game to shoot, and poultry, butter, and eggs. Only one of the original men remains; the others left declaiming there was nothing but work, work, work.

At last I achieved some sort of stability, and began to learn that farming was a whole-time job and a life job at that, if one wanted to become really a first-class yeoman. But the eldest boy, Windles, who was thirteen when war broke out, and was taken away from school in order to learn to be a real worker from that moment, now takes most of the farm work off me. After seven years of it – and the hardest part of it was bringing men grown up in the depression and decay of British farming standards to learn new ways from a 'foreigner' – I am a writer once more, with a zest that is almost equal with that of my beginnings after the World War. Farming taught me my limitations; I am content with a small sphere; the world illusions of the sedentary and the untried are no longer mine.

May 1946

PLOWING THE HOME HILLS

I

WHEN I BOUGHT MY derelict Norfolk farm, and saw its weedy condition, its tired and tufty grass, its boggy roads and overgrown hedges, I determined to begin with it as a farm all over again; as it were, regarding it as virgin land. All the grass must, as soon as practicable, go under the plow. 'Even those steep Home Hills?' asked an old fellow with ragged cap, tattered coat, and hands like roots, who worked on the farm, such as it was, before I bought it. 'Yes, even the Home Hills,' I said. 'But no plow could do it, guv'nor!' he protested. 'You wait and see, Jimmy!'

Two years later, the hills were still unplowed. But the war had broken out, and there was a call for the plowing of a million acres of grassland in Britain. Then another million acres, and again a third. Many of the grass fields plowed up when Napoleon was likely to beat Britain had not been plowed since those times, until they were turned over again in the middle of the Hitlerian war. For over a century they had been grass, fattening grazing bullocks in spring and summer. What more could a man want, asked the inheritors of those pastures, when confronted with plowing-up orders in 1941 or 1942.

The correspondence columns of the *Times* had many letters about the

---

On his demobilization as an infantry officer who had seen three years of fighting in the First World War, HENRY WILLIAMSON took cover in a tiny stone hermitage on the Devon moors, and from that vantage point came those memorable books *The Old Stag*, *Tarka the Otter*, and *The Village Book*. After his marriage he settled down in Devon to farm, to write as a naturalist, and to rear his children. As war approached, he moved to Norfolk to till and transform an ancient farm which had gone to seed since the threat of Napoleon's invasion. It was hard, back-breaking toil which admitted no time for writing. Now at last he can draw breath and tell his story in a pair of essays, the first of which appeared in the *Atlantic* for May.

wisdom or the foolishness of such acts. Modern grasses, such as those bred by Sir George Stapledon in Wales, had more leaf and less stalk than the old; some grew more quickly, others of the same family were bred to grow more slowly, thus providing a 'bite' both early and late in the year. But the opponents of plowing-up declared that their old pastures – carefully grazed and kept almost like lawns – contained herbs (otherwise weeds) which the cattle selected for eating as they felt the need for them; they insisted that a layer of the new improved grasses was too strong, causing indigestion, or 'blowing,' and 'scouring.' To this the new-grass enthusiasts replied that the new layers required as careful grazing as the old pastures, though for different reasons. Once the new technique was understood, they said, the new pasture would be, for its greater grass virility, far superior to the old.

I came from Devon to Norfolk, from a country of lush pastures and frequent rain to an arable country with a small rainfall. Sixty-four inches of rain fell in Devon for twenty-two in Norfolk. The West Country was famous for its cream, the Eastern Counties for their pheasants and partridges. The chicks of game birds survived in the dry East because their tiny feet did not get balled with sticky soil, which in the West caused them to fall behind and die of exposure.

Owing to the rainfall and the warm airs, some of the grazing fields of Devon I used to wander over in my youth earned in rent for six months, between May and September, a sum that would have bought outright twice their acreage of East Anglian arable land. Nearly three times, in fact; for in the depth of the depression of British farming, when Devon grazing let for £5 an acre for the half year, many a Norfolk farm, with an Elizabethan farmhouse and twelve cottages, and 500 acres of land, sold for £1000, or £2 an acre, including the buildings.

Devon is a warm county. The air is soft, and the speech is therefore soft; the rain falls and the sun shines; the Gulf Stream keeps the winters mild. The grass is green in the West when it is gray in the East. Like Ireland, Devon is a country of grazing beasts.

Before the war, I used to get in my open car and cross England from the coast of Norfolk to the coast of Devon in a day, leaving the shining North Sea in the morning as the sun was rising beyond Sweden, and coming to the emerald-green fields of Devon lying under the vast glory of an Atlantic sunset. What a companion, the sun, for the spirit of man, as I followed in its

191

course to Labrador and beyond, to greet it at the door of my hilltop hut next morning after its journey through the Night!

Throughout the journey across England, whenever I stopped, I heard the dialects varying with the soils; from the shrill, hard, clipped North Norfolk of the east winds and sandy soils, to the easy burring voices of the rich-red soils of Somerset. And so to the relaxed life in Devon, served by the slow and easy speech arising from fertile land, soil that was easy to plow, where a seedbed could be made in any season except in heavy rain or frost.

In those pre-war days there was little plowing; half a million visitors in summer wanted half a million pounds and more of Devonshire cream a week, and who was going to bother about growing oats or barley bringing in a gross return of £5 an acre, and costing all but four fifths of that to grow, when an acre of grass by the sea might yield £100 a summer as a caravan site, or £50 in milk and cream? And if you were particularly easygoing, and couldn't be bothered with milk or visitors, your 100-acre farm was looked after by one man, whose job it was to attend fourscore bullocks which would fatten themselves merely by walking about, and lying down to chew the cud. Agricultural depression in Devon? Not likely!

Why bother to cut the thistles, even? Everyone had plenty of money. Missus took in visitors, maybe at four guineas a week, and they were well satisfied, for they returned year after year. The coastal districts were crowded. In the old towns of Barnstaple or Bideford, on market day, the farmers did their business, arriving in smart new cars and sitting hours in the taverns, discussing everything except farming. The grass grew; that was their farming. They had no complaints. Their harrows and their plows rusted in the corners of fields, hidden by nettles, and in the broken-down sheds.

I returned there by train the other day. What a change after five years of war! During the 1944 harvest, which lasted until October, I saw sheaves of corn sprouting six inches out of the ear, still standing in the swampy fields. The year before, I saw hundreds of acres of corn laid flat on the ground: oats and barley, overfed from the rich plowed turf, unable to stand up on the stalks; field upon field of overfed corn which had to be cut with the scythe.

II

Meanwhile we had set about reclaiming the Home Hills. The first thing to do was to clear what Jimmy called the 'great old bull-thorns.' These trees, which wore a mantle of creamy white blossoms in May, were gnarled and black of trunk, their branches growing thick and matted, guarded by long spines which left a blue mark in the hand or leg they pierced. Turtledoves nested in them, when the June air was athrob with their gentle notes. Was I a vandal to think of cutting them all down? I decided to leave one here and there, the shapeliest trees, so that even when the corn was rising green I might also see and smell the flowers of the May.

Sharpening my axe, I went out one morning to start what I knew would be a long job. After I had thrown one – a morning's work, my muscles unused to the seven-pound axehead – I went home, and over a pint of beer I thought that what we needed was one of the bulldozers that were leveling many airfields around us. But such luxuries were not for small farmers – certainly not in wartime; so I thought to telephone the owner of a traction engine which used to travel about threshing the corn stacks of small farmers like myself who could not afford to own one themselves. A few days later the cumbrous fifteen-ton machine, sixty years old, arrived, to chug sideways up the hill and affix a great steel hook, attached to a fifty-ton steel cable, to the first 'great old bull-thorn.' The strain was taken; the smooth flywheel moved round; the cable trembled; there was a shriek and a crack, and the trunk splintered above the root.

He was the first, and obstinate; but the others were more timid; they came with all their roots, dragged out on their sides with two or three tons of soil on the roots, leaving a crater like one made by a small air-bomb, of the kind dropped by Heinkels in 1940. Not all came so easily; the cable snapped nineteen times during the deracination of sixty-four trees. They lay on their sides, for it was then time to drill corn, then to hoe the sugar beet, then to cut and stack the hay; then came the harvest of corn, and after that the dung-carting from the cattle yards – the trodden straw of the last harvest made into muck in the winter – and overtime plowing for winter wheat which made us late for the lifting of the sugar beet. No time that year to attend to the uprooted thorns of the Home Hills.

193

The old thorns lay on their sides during the next twelve months. 'At least,' I said to the boys at our long oak table at supper, 'they will make a grand beacon if the war ends suddenly. The greatest bonfire in Norfolk will blaze from our hill.' But the war did not end that year, or the next; and when at last we came to clear them, the nettles had grown high among them.

After the constant winds sweeping over the hill, the wood was dry and hard for the axe. Bit by bit, however, we got the main branches lopped off, the small branches burned, the limbs and trunks laid in heaps to be carted down to the circular saw. At last the Home Hills were cleared, except for a few trees which the engine-driver, with his ragged lengths of cable tied together, had not dared to tackle. Standing on the slope, the fifteen-ton engine might have got out of control, or even turned over.

When we came to clear the hedges round the hills, we found that they had spread in places as much as twenty yards into the grass, from the original boundary. In one I found the rusty remains of four barbed-wire fences, each several yards from its neighbors. Brambles had covered them, the homes of scores of rabbits, which had spoiled the grass during the neglect of the long agricultural depression between the wars. We cleared the wire and fences, but the roots stayed in the ground, most of them belonging to the hard and sullen blackthorn.

We made fires on the root stubs, but the fires had to be doused every evening, because of the black-out. The fires had to be relit every day. Even so, the roots remained, and when we took the tractor with the deep-digger plow to rip up the worst area by the hedges, for a summer fallow, we had to avoid most of them. The furrows left were very rough, heaps of roots of bramble and lesser thorns. The soil under the turf looked dead and dry, as though neither air nor rain had penetrated there for centuries. We could do no more that spring, for the time was come to drill the corn once more.

Sometimes during the summer I used to walk up the hill, my feet pressing on the springy turf in which grew restharrow, wild thyme, harebells, cowslips, and a strange thistle whose leaves were low on the grasses, in the shape of a star. Its flower was a purple-red, lower than the grasses. Had a thousand generations of sheep taught that thistle its cunning habit of self-protection? In the old days of free wandering over field and moor in Devon

I should have admired it and been glad that it was, as a small unit of life, enduring by its own strength and tenacity; but now, as a farmer dreaming of fine cattle grazing on the hill, I saw the legions of dwarf thistles as enemies that had to be obliterated.

There were other thistles, too, the creeping thistles and the tall annual spear-thistle. The creeping thistles were in colonies; even they found it hard to push their roots through the dense massed and intertwined roots of the ancient turf. Thyme grew on the hill, with eyebright, sulphur-yellow cowslips, pink dove's-foot crane's-bill; and in July the fragile harebells trembled on their slender stalks, azure as summer sky, in the breezes of the uplands. But I had no time or inclination (as I have now in retrospect) to admire or to identify myself with wildflowers or the birds which passed over the hill; I was a farmer, wanting to see corn growing where it had never grown before.

One winter some tanks had come on the hill and cut up the turf with their tracks, and in the following spring I had cultivated those torn places, leaving a loose tilth behind, on which I had broadcast a few handfuls of trefoil and rye grass, before rolling the seeds in and forgetting them. Along these irregular bands of new land the thistles rose, tall and thick, and the trefoil and rye grass grew luxuriantly. That alone told me that I was right in my idea to put the old worn-out turf under the plow.

The fire circles left by the burning of the torn-out thorns remained bare during the summer. Those headlands by the hedges, which had been roughly cleared of the roots of brambles and blackthorns, lay in sullen weathered furrows. Our sheep had been sold a year previously; they had kept the grass down in previous years. I wanted to begin plowing at once, but the hydraulic tractor had broken down and been sent away for repairs; and about this time something broke in me, and I too was sent away for repairs. So the hills were left to the winds and the flowers, to the kestrel that hovered over the plateau for mice and beetles, and the village cats, which prowled on the slopes for rabbits.

III

There were about ten acres of the hills altogether, of varying slopes lying north, west, and south. The official trowel had prodded and scooped and the official bag had carried away for analysis a light sandy soil deficient in phosphate and possibly able to support one crop of rye. This opinion had been given before the thorns had been wrenched out with arboreal cries and groans. It was only when the root craters were visible that I saw to my delight that below the topsoil of sand was a brownish-red medium loam similar to that of the field over the eastern hedge. There were pockets of sand on the hills, for the rabbit burrows were yellow with it; and there was gravel also, for on the western slope lay a saucer-like depression which was obviously an old pit covered by grass; but under most of it, not too deep for our plow, was that brown loam!

It was curious how the soil was light or sandy among the roots of the congested grasses. As I broke it up in my fingers – a blackish sandy mold – it occurred to me that this ancient colony of grasses had, during the centuries, eaten all the heart out of the soil, leaving only indigestible sand. None of the original clay was left; only small grains of rock, called sand, amid the wreckage of centuries of dead roots. Under that layer of compost a fine medium soil was lying, ready to be enlivened by sun and air and rain. Plow and reseed directly on the upturned sod? And have the finest crop of thistles in the district? No; I would plow in the ordinary manner, leave a bare fallow to kill the thistle roots, and drill with corn after a year.

The War Agricultural Committee were, as usual, pleasant and considerate in their attitude toward this idea; and a suggestion was made: Why not utilize the thistles for silage? Young thistles so treated were not unpalatable; and if oats and peas were sown in early spring, they might be cut in early June; after which the seven duck-foot cultivator feet behind the hydraulic tractor would keep the stubble stirred throughout the hot, dry months of July, August, and September, and thus wither the roots and fallow the soil in accordance with my original idea.

Meanwhile, would we be able to plow those steep slopes? The village said no. But the village didn't know the powers of a hydraulic tractor invented by a Belfast engineer; a tractor that he could not sell in Britain, but which, taken to America and shown to Henry Ford, at once found recognition, of one man of genius by another.

The plowing was started on Armistice Day, 1943. The Ferguson tractor, bought in 1937, with one engine-reconditioning, was still as good as new. The plow was a ten-inch double furrow. I opened the first furrow along the plateau, running from east to west, and returning west to east. I was on top of the world; the village lay below, with its trees, flint walls, and red-tiled roofs. Afar was the blue line of the North Sea, the sand hills, and on the horizon sailed a convoy of small ships.

I felt an extraordinary exaltation as the bright breasts of the plows turned up the sod and cast it over. It was sandy soil just there; it was level; it was easy. Nevertheless, I had begun what I had waited seven long years to do. My eyes felt clear, the world looked fresh and good, filled with color. A cock pheasant flew over me with rocketing wings, and I turned to watch him glide into my wood behind, thinking of the pigeon-shooting there in the coming months. I had a hide against one of the oak trees, made of boughs and interlaced with branches; this year would be the first I had shot since 1938. There had been no time in the interval.

The wild and ancient grasses certainly were tough. I was on the easiest part of the hill; yet even in low gear the engine needed all its compression. The little fifteen-hundredweight tractor was Gulliver among the Lilliputians: hundreds of roots were protesting and holding against the shear and lift of share and breast. Sometimes the furrow wheel with its iron spuds turned thumpingly, as the resistance of an extraordinarily strong clump of roots held the plow shudderingly still. Jumping off, I found they were the roots, long, thick, and dark, of restharrow; and immediately I thought that this was how the wildflower – I did not like to call it weed to myself – with its pink pea-like blooms, had got its name in olden time. Rest harrow, or stop harrow.

The tractor did not rest. A slight lift of the lever, and the hydraulic oil-pump lifted the plows; it went forward again, another touch of the lever setting the points deeper once more. All the way, we were held up by the roots of restharrow, which went deep into the loamy subsoil.

I saw that I could not hope to penetrate to the rich brown loam at the first plowing. It took the engine all of its multiple synthetic horses to cut two furrows each seven inches deep. The furrow slices, too, were by no means tractable; I longed for moldboards or plow-breasts of the Old Norfolk 'Olland' shape, by which the slices would have been screwed over nearly 180 degrees and laid flat. My furrow slices often wavered behind the tractor, before deciding to sit upright, the grassy edge at right angles to the earth from which they had been torn. Never mind, I thought; snow and frost will subdue those obstinate furrows, and in the spring our new disk harrows will chop them to bits and press them down. So I went on with my task, easy in mind.

It was a warm day. The convoy on the sea-horizon proceeded without the bomb-rolls we were used to; for now the tide of war had changed, and along the far coast of North Africa the German armies were in retreat, passing over the sand which once had been the cornfields of a great Empire long ago gone to ruin: to ruin, some said, because Rome in its urban pride had forgotten that the strength and virtue of a race are based not on its art, or culture, or civic pride – but on its soil.

IV

In the days that followed, as I plowed the thick turf of the hill, I wondered whether Dr. Johnson, had he been with me, would have discovered an original and ironic meaning in a phrase often used among farmers and laborers to describe a stubborn object which temporarily frustrates their strength and ingenuity. Restharrow might, on account of roots like tarred ropes, cause a pair of horses to rest, and the plowman with them, in sympathy; but as any plowman of virgin soil will tell you, an old sod is liable to do more things than merely arrest the forward movement of a plow.

Toiling up a slope of one-in-four, I heard a report like a rifle shot, followed by a grating noise. The two-inch steel axle had broken suddenly. Six years of arduous work on the other hilly fields, often gouging twenty-pound flints out of a sea-laid chalky subsoil never disturbed during the millions of years since the waves had receded, had crystallized the steel – broken its heart – killed it – so that in dying it had gone back to its ancestral crystals. Fortunately we had a spare half-axle, and my dejection was equaled by the confidence of my son, who came up the hill with the new Ford-Ferguson tractor drawing a trailer with jack, tool roll and spare axle. I left him and one of our men to it, and strolled away, feeling myself to be a coward, yet arguing that as the doctor had ordered me to go easy after my return from hospital, I would obey, and spend an hour or two as a naturalist.

What a hope! The farm was in my blood; and after all, the boy was only seventeen and had no experience except that picked up from me. To my delight when I returned, the new axle was fitted, and almost at once I was going slowly up the steep slope again, in low gear, peering backwards over my right shoulder for the pleasure of watching the turf rising up and flopping over. Always my hand was on the hydraulic lever, to raise the plows should the furrow wheel begin to 'scrap,' or race in the furrow, when the pull of the turf was greater than the 2400-pound pull of the tractor.

Once the furrow seemed to scream. My heart jumped; but it was only a stone caught between rear furrow wheel and scraper. At other times the furrow would smolder; a dull-red spark glowered there; smoke fumed out of the damp earth. This was when a flint-and-steel spark had ignited dry roots. Sometimes, for a reason I could not account for, a strip of turf reared up behind the plow in contortion; it hesitated, and then with the aid of gravity unrolled along its length, yard after yard, sometimes as much as fifteen yards, settling itself as it had lain originally, grassy side up once again.

While I was plowing up and down the hill, old Jimmy walked slowly from where he had been milking the cows. He stared slowly about him. I got off, throttled back the tractor, and gave him a cigarette.

'Well, Jimmy, what do you think of it?'

'Humph,' said Jimmy.

'What does that "Humph" mean, Jimmy?'

He puffed at the cigarette.

'Yew bruk its back, di'n you?' he said presently.

'Yes,' I said, 'but that axle was already strained by the flints on Hilly Piece, two years ago.'

'It was an' all, guv'nor.'

'Shall we get a crop off the Home Hills, d'you think, Jimmy?'

'Yew might, guv'nor.'

'I might?'

'An' yew might break your neck, too, I'm thinking, 'bor. Fare you well.' And with this encouragement, the old fellow walked away. I knew Jimmy did not approve of pulling out the old hawthorns; and as I clambered into the sack-covered iron seat again, I thought of W. H. Hudson's story, 'The Old Thorn,' and the Wiltshire legend that only harm could come to one who hurt a May tree.

It was suddenly cold on the hill; the Arctic Circle air that usually stole over the land about five o'clock all at once struck through my clothes. I walked to the sullen furrow, trying to heave it over with my arms, knowing that if it lay like that it would not rot, but live to grow with greater exuberance in the spring, stimulated by the nitrogen of the coming snow and the cutting of the old roots. Kneeling down, I soon found it was vain to try to heave over the dull resistance of many hundredweights. There the furrow slice lay, ten inches by seven inches by fifty feet, a strip unbroken, marked by two parallel lines showing where the disk colters had cut the turf.

The gulls which had been following the plowing, soaring and sweeping down on white narrow wings, with open red mouths screaming for lugworm and wireworm, now were drifting disconsolately in the upper air. They were finished for the day; their brethren had already flown away in silent V-formations to their roost in the distant sand hills. I felt suddenly hopeless, and getting on the tractor, took it downhill to the hovel or cart shed where it stood during the night.

Then I went home, slowly, thinking of the dead in the sands of Africa, in the snows of Russia, in the gray wastes of the Atlantic, among the far islands of the East. I recalled the young pilot of the Luftwaffe lying in hospital with broken legs and bullet wounds, and how he had thrust his knuckles into his mouth to stop any cry in his throat. Having refused a blood transfusion, he had died two days later, with hardly a sound.

I passed Jimmy in the village street, coming back with his week's rations and his weekly ounce of tobacco, for it was pay night. He was a queer old fellow: a year before, when a mine had exploded a mile away on the coast, with a terrific reverberation and a column of smoke above the woods, Jimmy had come running to where I had been plowing, gasping out that he had heard it, and thought it was the tractor blowing up. Jimmy felt the land through his whole body, as his forefathers had for a dozen centuries; he did not trust machinery. 'What's it all lead to, guv'nor? Why that!' And he pointed to the bombers, hundreds of them in the height of the sky, going east over the darkening sea.

V

I could do nothing with those stubborn furrows. They beat me. I tried to replow them, running down the steep slopes in reverse gear, then stopping, dropping the plow again, and going uphill again. In vain; the wheel sank in and revolved impotently; or the slices curled up, reared, doubled, and broke, choking colter, moldboard, and frame until I had to stop, dismount, and then shove, kick, heave, and push the heap apart. What a mess, I thought, and remembered the injunction of the War Agricultural Committee to 'plow in a husbandlike manner.' Well, some husbands kicked, pushed, and swore; so perhaps after all I was carrying out the order literally.

Yet on the whole it was not a bad job. I do not think any other tractor, even a crawler, could have tackled those slopes. Certainly not horses with an ordinary plow, though a special match-plow, of the kind used in competition, might have turned a few nice furrows, till its share was blunted and 'wrung.' Some parts of the hill had to be plowed sideways; these were the most difficult, for the tractor was often leaning over at an angle that made me wonder if it would topple and I fall underneath it. It was then that I longed for a Devon one-way plow and a pair of strong horses. I had in the past watched a man with such a team plowing the side of a hill which rose at an angle of 45 degrees. He began at the bottom, and at the end of the field turned round, threw over the other plow-breast, and plowed back along his furrow, creeping slowly up the hill, parallel all the way up.

While I was going slowly round the headland, to finish the job, the intermediate strips having been plowed, the gulls which had been accompanying me suddenly flew up, and I saw six small boys on the skyline above me. One explained that they had been trying to reverse the sullen furrows; and might they follow behind the tractor and push back any furrow slice before it made up its mind to fall the wrong way?

'You are like Blücher at the battle of Waterloo,' I said. 'You come when the work is over.'

'We didn't know,' said the leader, who was Richard, my youngest son.

They fell on the obstinate turf with the eagerness of starlings, dropping on knees and pushing and heaving with teeth clenched, a picture of Man wrestling with brute Nature. After a while this became somewhat arduous, so they turned it into a game, under a leader whose job it was, apparently, to stand above and with a wave of a stick, which was also a tommy gun, to lead his men down to the assault of the backsliding furrows.

It was not long before small hands and knees were grubby with soil, and their minds had invented other rules of the game, which took them from the wake of the tractor to the inside of a distant henhouse, their headquarters. The gulls, which had been waiting above, swept down once more and the scream and scramble for worms, mice, and insects restarted behind me.

There were a few more 'rounds' of the headland to be done, then the hills would be finished. The sun was disappearing in the west, small and smoky, when I began the final round. Frost in the shade by the lower hedge began to look whiter. The engine seemed to be noisier. I began to feel that probably I had been foolish to think of plowing the hill, and how much more sensible it would have been to remain a writer, to sit by a fire and be my own master of time, instead of having a farm as my master. But at least I knew these thoughts for what they were worth: they were end-of-the-day thoughts. One more round and I would leave the tractor by the hedge, water drained from the radiator into that old can left by the Army, the cloth tied over the aluminium body. Only one more round.

The flights of starlings had gone across the sky; the gulls had flown away to the sand hills. Well, it was nearly over: let the mind stop thinking, running back upon itself, canceling out its hopes maintained despite the war; switch off end-of-day thoughts. Go home, take off boots and puttees, wash properly, change, and relax before the fire. To relax is not to be idle. Don't animals and birds relax? Are they then idle or lazy? Take a drink of whiskey; that is not indulgence, it is food. Wasn't there some still in that bottle bought before the war, the only one in the house for seven years? Whiskey made from barley; you grow barley, so why not drink whiskey when you are tired? That puritan complex, driving the body to do things beyond its capacity, comes only from early inhibitions. So, in the twilight and the thunder of the bombers, in the midst of my own veering thoughts I came towards the end of the last furrow.

In front of me, where a long snake of green turf had curled back, something white lay; and stopping the tractor, I got off and walked stiffly forward, to pause above a pair of delicate gray wings spread motionless on the frosting grass. One of the black-headed gulls, alighting and dipping for a worm, had been caught by the back-curling furrow of my penultimate round, and its head was pressed under. It must surely be suffocated, after lying like that for twenty minutes, I thought as I knelt to heave back the strip of turf.

It was very heavy, and I felt tired, but at last I got it free, expecting the head to be limp and crushed. I held the fragile bird in my open hands. After a while it raised its head, turned to look at me, and a feeble scream came from its red mouth. Then it elbowed itself lightly into the air and with slow strokes of those slender gray wings flew slowly away. And slowly I went down the plowed hills to my fireside, to sit and rest among my children, to think of nothing, while slowly a feeling of contentment came upon me.

June 1946

HOOLY

I

ONE APRIL EVENING, COMING home to tea from the farm, I stopped by the kitchen door on my way to wash, and spoke to my wife, who was kneading a whole-wheat loaf on the table. I noticed a wicker basket on the kitchen floor, and what appeared to be a small kneaded piece of dough in it. I was about to ask why the two small boys, Robert and Richard, were allowed to play with food in wartime, when something about the dough made me look closer. It seemed already to be covered with mildew. Going closer, I saw it was a nestling owl.

Richard, our youngest, came in at that moment and explained that it was 'lost,' and had been brought to the door by a 'little old boy.' Apparently this 'little old boy' (aged about five years) had found the object under a bramble-berry bush in the lane. 'His father and mother,' explained Richard (also five years old), pointing at the object, 'lost it – so the little old boy brought it to here, because you like owls.'

'But it is warm and comfortably covered in flesh,' I replied, kneeling by the basket, 'so it could not have been lost very long. I expect its parents knew it was there, and will miss it tonight.'

'They do so want to keep it, and have a tame owl,' said Rikky's mother. Rikky and Robby looked anxiously at me.

The owlet raised its long thin head and chirruped. It was the hunger

One of England's most talented naturalists, who made a notable record as an infantry officer in the First World War, HENRY WILLIAMSON revived a rugged old farm in Norfolk which had gone to seed since the threat of Napoleon's invasion. It was back-breaking labor which left little time for writing, but now he can catch breath and remember.

noise. I remembered it from the tame owls of my own boyhood. Its beak opened and it tried to swallow my finger as I stroked the back of its head with my finger tip.

There was an air rifle in the cupboard, and some sparrows on the ridge tiles of the farmhouse roof. Richard and I went out to stalk them. Not long afterwards we returned, and one of the sparrows went, piece by piece, into the owlet's crop. When I went back for more, the sparrows, who had meanwhile re-formed a row on the ridge tile, took immediate evasive action (to use current flying jargon) into the lane beyond. Thereafter they were never about in their old haunts more than half a second after the barrel of the rifle had appeared, though many a small lead-splash was left on the tiles just after legs and tail-feathers had vanished from view. 'Huh, wise guys,' murmured Richard, regarding several such evasions. He waited with a catapult round the gateway, but the small piece of chalk flipped from his feeble engine sped even more harmlessly through the air. We returned to the farmhouse parlor to talk it over.

Our house is in the valley, facing south. An acre of garden slopes gradually to a river, and across this narrow stream is a small paddock of an acre or so, beyond which are the farm road and the Home Hills rising steeply to the skyline. On the hills are many rabbits, which tunnel and make their deep buries in the sandy southern slopes. I do not like rabbits; they are vermin; they pare the grasses and corn with their rodent teeth, and their urine poisons the soil. Whereas sheep will improve a pasture, rabbits will slowly destroy it. So I had no compunction in shooting them – only a vague resentment that after a long working day I should have to go out with a gun and bring one of the wretched little beasts back for the owlet, whose chirrupings were sharper with its hunger. So fitting together my light Gallyon 20-bore shotgun, I set out to get one of the hopping gray animals.

It was easy on the first night, but on succeeding occasions the rabbits grew warier, and sometimes it was dusk before I returned. Apparently it was my job to procure food for the growing Hooly, as we now called our owl. After working and scheming all day (for writing books and working 240 acres of difficult and hilly land require much energy), I had to force my reluctance aside and go shoot a rabbit every night. However, it was nice to be greeted by the fluffy little bird, and also by the enthusiasm of the youngest child, Richard.

Hooly grew rapidly; and as the spring advanced, and the bombers began to roar in the sky as they flew out over the North Sea, I was accustomed to find Hooly, on my return, waiting for me on the roof. If I walked up the path quietly, I could observe him before he saw me – he was a small monkey-like object walking on the roof ridge, setting one clawed foot before the other, carefully – until suddenly turning his dark eyes upon me, he slithered down the pantiles, to jump on my shoulder and flap and scream for food.

By this time Hooly had explored most of the lower rooms of the house. For a while he had slept happily in the hot-cupboard in the kitchen, always in his basket. From the first he had accepted all he saw; he never showed any fear. When tired of playing in the flower beds outside in the garden, he would walk into the kitchen, cross the floor, climb into his basket, and, stretching his legs out behind his body, lie flat, his head bowed and his face hidden. If one or other of our children touched the gray feathers of his head, beside the large cavities of the ears, he would not look up, but give a sleepy chirrup, and then go to sleep – a feathered kitten.

As he grew bigger his range of traveling extended all over the house. A favorite perching place was among the caps and gloves of the oak tallboy standing in the parlor. He flapped and hauled his way to the top, and there squatted in an attitude of complete relaxation. I have never seen another bird sleep like that; he reminded me of my old spaniel in Devon, who, after a walk through the fields to the sea, used to scratch himself a hole in the summer sands, and collapse into it suddenly, shooting his hind legs out seal-like, the pads of each foot turned uppermost.

Sometimes the owl played with an old green-and-red glove, relic of skiing in the snows of New Hampshire eleven years before; he was indeed a feathered kitten, throwing up the glove and catching it with his mouth. Hooly was a nice little owl, and only once tried to swallow my ear lobe when I was somewhat slow in offering him portions of rabbit.

As his flight feathers grew, he took to climbing up the vines and creepers of the jasmine to the roof, and there he stayed after being fed – beside the chimney stack. He grew into a wild-looking bird, his big eyes as dark as grapes with the bloom on them. He accepted the tokens of affection – food and poll-scratching – but gave no affection back. Nor did the children expect it, being wild, in the natural sense, themselves. Not 'wild' in the civilized meaning of the word, for they were calm and self-contained: it was never necessary to complain of their behavior towards others.

II

One night, as I was standing in the garden looking at the converging streams of hundreds of four-engined black bombers, flying slow and heavy and droning eastwards in the height of the wan and starry sky, a strange owl flew a few feet over my head and braked suddenly with its wide, soft wings. It startled me; and it startled Hooly as it alighted beside him. Seeing the apparition Hooly snapped his beak in alarm. At the same moment the big owl turned its head to take in any movement – the quick retinal stare of a wild creature, whose life is one calculation in motion after another. I kept quite still. The glance was of a second's duration before the bird turned to Hooly, revealing that it carried a sparrow in its beak. With a swift movement the sparrow was transferred to a foot. With a sideway striking motion Hooly snatched it, and at once the old bird flapped up and away.

It was most exciting, even exhilarating. I wished young Rikky had been with me. Hooly stood there, the dead sparrow in his foot. He took the best part of half an hour to break it up with plucking and pullings; first one wing was swallowed, then another, and at last the skull was gulped down. After which he flapped and walked to the chimney stack at the other end of the roof ridge, and settled down to a rest. The night was silent; a few search-lights moved bleakly across the horizon; in the western sky the evening star was shining serenely, to be watched awhile with a sigh. Thoughts about the war were vain thoughts, and I went to my room, drew the blackout curtains, lit the lamp, and tried to read in order to be able to sleep before 5.00 a.m., when I got up to water and feed the farm horses.

In the morning I told the children about the strange owl. Robert, the imaginative, said it might have been Hooly's mother or father. Then why, I suggested, did Hooly snap his beak in sudden fear when he saw the old bird? Perhaps, suggested Margaret, the mother owl had known all along that her nestling had been in the hot-cupboard, and had waited her chance to get to it. John added that the old owl had probably heard Hooly chirruping to himself at night in the basket, and had bided her time to take him away. 'Shall we catch the old owl and then we'll have two?' I asked, to see the effect. 'NO!' cried the children with one voice.

The next night Hooly was on the ridge when the big owl came again, this time with a young rat. Hooly thereupon dropped the stale rabbit pelt he was playing with and clumped and scratched his way to the chimney stack with the rat. Soon afterwards the tail of the rat was sticking out of his mouth as he huddled himself to doze among the blackened chimney pots. During the following day he was missing from his accustomed place, but at evening time, as the sun was sinking and once again the sky was thundering with the passage of the great nocturnal airfleets, we heard his chissicking cries. I crossed the road to the tall trees behind the wooden Village Institute hut, where dances and whist-drives and other social occasions took place, and he saw me and flew down and sat on my shoulder. I walked with him across the road and fed him as he perched on the old draw-well frame above the well outside the kitchen door. As soon as he was fed he flew up to the roof, flapping and clawing, to his favorite ridge.

The following evening when I called him he sailed on brown broad wings over the iron-sheet Institute roof to my shoulder. Two soldiers passed, walking up and down the village street to find something interesting, but though I was standing still in the road, and they saw us, they took no notice of an owl flying to alight on a man's shoulder. Perhaps they were townsmen and saw nothing interesting in such a sight; perhaps they were anxious to find the fish-and-chip hut. It was said that the food in the camp was scanty and poor. And when the fish shop opened, once a week, on Friday, which was also payday in the farming week, the fried fish and potatoes were very soon sold out. Even so, I have often wondered why the two soldiers on that occasion did not give the owl a second glance; at the time there was always present in my mind an ironic connection between the dulled observation of the town mind and the dulling of life by war, which is never made by countrymen.

III

The tall green trees of sycamore and ash, growing out of the old marlpit under which the Village Institute hut stood, became our tame owl's day-hide and roost. Every evening I went out to call him; every evening, after chissicking cries to get me to fly to him, he was forced to fly to me: he glided down to my shoulder, a brown-and-yellow feathered face set with two dark eyes looming larger and larger until, with a flapping and a screaming of open beak, Hooly was clutching the shoulder of my old Mackinaw jacket. This happened for several nights, until one time I went to call him, he was not there.

It was a Friday night. I knew it was Friday by the smell of frying fat wafted on the western breeze from the middle of the village. Nor did he return the next day. I wondered if the events of the previous night had affected Hooly, for later in the Thursday night – the last night I had seen him – a wounded pilot had fallen on a parachute in the woods; there had been a running fight with a Heinkel bomber, during which the German pilot had jettisoned the two 2000-pound land mines he carried. Suddenly, while I slept, a stupendous and pale blue flash had seemed to split the universe. Immediately afterwards, another flash and stunning reverberation, but not so metallic-hard. I thought my cottage was collapsing. Tiles showered into the road, and the ceiling of the adjoining empty bedroom collapsed. The first land mine had fallen on the edge of the chalk ridge above the village; the second on the clay of the marshes.

Later, I wondered if the explosions had killed Hooly, or broken his eardrums. He, with the other living creatures of the district, was probably used to the bumps and shakings of odd bombs falling here and there, and of the blue-white stars of incendiaries which sometimes broke out of the darkness on the Home Hills across the valley at night. We felt the vibration through the earth of these distant bombs before we heard them in the air; so did the wild pheasants roosting in the woods, for the cocks always uttered their cucketting cries a split second before the heavy bomb-roll made to quiver slightly the very earth under our feet.

Well, I thought, at least I will not have to go shooting wretched rabbits any more. But in this I was mistaken; for on the Sunday morning I was awakened by a screaking in my bedroom, and there on the window sill was a little grayish monkey face and body, staring with misery in its eyes, its feet shifting as with pain. Seeing one of my gray woolen socks on a chair, Hooly flew to it, and standing on it, made a distracted pretense of swallowing it.

It was five o'clock in the morning; it was Sunday; it was the farmer's day of rest; but how could one relax while those famished eyes stared with such anguish? Getting out of bed, I put on dressing gown and slippers and went downstairs to get Hooly's Friday rabbit. But a cat had apparently taken it from where I had hung it on the outer brick casing of the circular draw-well. Meanwhile Hooly was facing me, perching on one of the disused iron-bound buckets which until recently had drawn the water for the farmhouse. He flew down from the rickety bucket, and screeched into my face. I went to the larder, but found only some bacon and the remains of a potato pasty. Bacon, a ration of two ounces weekly each person, was far too good for him; so I stood still, considering what I should do.

Sunday, the day of rest! No matter, the truant must be fed. Ah, the air rifle, and perhaps a sparrow on the roof! But the sparrows, who had been chittering their comments in a row a moment before, were abruptly absent. Perhaps they had organized themselves into an Avian Home Guard, for when I returned round the corner to the well, there were a dozen or more around Hooly, mobbing him, and one old cock was actually pulling a feather from the back of his head. Seeing me, they scattered, and chittered in the lilac bushes, while the air rifle phutted towards one or another in vain.

So I walked down to the bridge and across the river and so to the cartshed which faced the chalk quarry. Sparrows chirped in their nests under the tiles of the 'hovel,' – the Norfolk name of the shed, which, according to rough numerals in red brick let into the flint walls, was rebuilt in 1667, – but I would not take a fledgling sparrow from a nest, even for a starving owlet. Fortunately for my peace of mind a starling flew to a branch of an ash, and fell down as the little waisted pellet of lead spun through its chest. Starlings,

I suspected, were rank-tasting, for the hawks and owls I had kept as a boy never ate them; but Hooly found this more palatable than a woolen sock.

IV

Thereafter he took to being absent at twilight and came instead to my open window at dawn, crying and flapping his brown mottled wings for food and walking over the blanket to yell in my ear if I did not awake, Sometimes he visited other cottage windows; and from one cottage at least, occupied by a queer-tempered old soldier who worked on our farm – we called him Jack the Jackdaw among ourselves – Hooly departed hurriedly, accompanied by oaths and the slamming of the window.

There used to be a one-winged jackdaw about the farm premises, which climbed trees and fed alone on the meadows and generally looked an odd, lonely creature, with which I could not make friends. The wounded jackdaw looked like our Jack, who was dark, with a beaky nose; a wound from the Somme a quarter of a century before had made one arm and shoulder almost useless. Jack was a good worker, tidier than the other men, and always punctual; but in addition to his wound he came of a nervous family. During the farming depression of the thirties, he did not have regular employment, and when as a newcomer I took him on I soon saw why. I have seen him, with tears of impotence in his eyes, jerking the bridle of a cart horse with rage, and hitting the animal, though not dangerously, about the head.

At other times he would address inanimate objects, such as heavy harrows which, on a weedy field, constantly needed lifting to be cleaned, with puny cries of rage, swearing at them, kicking the iron frame, making a speech of misery and frustration to the wind in the middle of the field, while the horses stood patiently by, awaiting his word to go forward again. Jack was hard to talk to: he moved away, he could not listen. Once or twice I was the recipient of his speeches; usually a dour fellow, when he got going his arm waved, he yelled at the top of his voice, froth on his lips, until his hoarse voice grew feeble, and he was near sobbing.

At heart poor Jack the Jackdaw was a kindly man, living with two sisters who were normally as subdued and apart from what little village communal life existed, as he was. I understood Jack the Jackdaw, because I knew what it was to feel one's resistance to life overcome by the tasks confronting a man. I knew how he felt when the last of his nerve power was running out in those frenzied monologues, accompanied by waving arm and his ragged cap dashed to the earth; I knew, even as I knew myself, how much of his life had left him in sweat and fear and blood on the Somme battlefields. I had heard those tones, or overtones, coming from my jittery self; I had heard those tones, though with deeper penetration and cutting power, on the radio, coming from the east where now the bombers were nightly flying; so I thought I understood our Jack, and his nervous curses when he had been awakened by an owl standing on his pillow.

Other people in the village, who had been casually amused by the sight of Hooly in the past taking food on my shoulder, tried to feed him, offering him pieces of bread or even fragments of wood or stones, to get him to fly down to them, for amusement. The singleness of the bird's mind towards human beings was in disintegration, and he flew now to anyone and into any open window.

Robert, who was seven, once woke up and found Hooly pulling at his hair. Both Robert and Richard liked Hooly, of course, and welcomed him in their bedroom at any hour of the day or night; but not so their mother, who had to rise at six every morning, to give Windles, the eldest boy who worked on the farm, his breakfast. For in her bedroom Hooly always behaved very badly. He saw himself in a mirror, and at once began to fight his own image. Lœtitia had to turn the mirror round, lest the owl hurt himself. His beak-snapping rages kept her awake; and so I was not altogether unrelieved when Hooly disappeared for the second time.

We said perhaps he had been shot; but no, Hooly returned within a week, flying down unexpectedly one sunset to the weathered oak frame of the draw-well. He screaked down at my face, but when I offered my shoulder, and went near him, he edged away. Obviously someone else had tried to handle him, instead of letting him perch in freedom on head or shoulder.

While he perched on the well three two-engined bombers with dark crosses on their fuselage flew in at roof-top height from over the marshes. They had come at wave-top height across the North Sea and with a flick of the stick had lifted over the cottages and the trees and dipped again, to climb over the wood on the hill-line across the valley. I saw the red points of tracers leaving them, as they banked to shoot up the camp beyond. Children were calling in the village with excited cries, but in a moment it was over; the Heinkels were gone, flying into a cloud which hung like a great quarry in the western sky. Soon three Spitfires were screaming around that dark cloud, circling like falcons.

Now a most extraordinary coincidence happened as I stood by the well. Nine swallows, with ringing cries, began to circle above and around the brick well, on the oak frame of which the owl was perched. First one, then another, peeled off and dived at the figure of the owl, swishing by within an inch or two of his amazed and jerky eyes, to zoom again and join the rotating ring six feet or so above the well. One after another they came down, sweeping up again and taking their turn to dive once more. They cut at Hooly from in front and from behind, and Hooly did not like it. He flew away.

It was then that I heard from the upper air the terrible grumbling roll of a Spit's 8-gun squirt – the bullets cutting through fabric and metal and flesh and bone like a thunderous circular saw; and then a second shuddering, rolling roar; and after an interval, and more distantly, a third. Breathing quickly, and conscious that I was quivering within, I was about to run into the farmhouse to call the children, when an owl hooted from the roof, and, turning, I saw a large bird perching on the chimney rim of my writing room stack, twenty yards away in the garden.

That, then, was the secret of the truant! The wild owl was hunting for and feeding our tame bird. It called Hooly with a sharp *ker-jick, ker-jick!* and flew away abruptly, followed by Hooly.

Meanwhile three Spitfires, with superchargers whining, followed by another section of three a thousand feet above them, hurtled across the sky. They flew towards the vast gold-lined cumulus cloud towering in the west, and up its craggy precipices they seemed to climb almost perpendicularly, to open formation like a shamrock, and, turning just before stalling point, to rave down again in separate arcs of three great circles, engines full on, to zoom up again as they waited for the remaining 'bandit' to come out of the cloud. After three such circles they disappeared, and a moment later I heard again the heart-chilling, sullen roar of multiple machine guns in the unseen distance. The bursts were repeated, growing duller and far away – one-second bursts – and then came a long metallic roll which was the end.

*

To my surprise, Hooly came to the well on the following evening, and while the old bird perched in a damson tree, he flew down to my shoulder. He came by habit, that was all; he cried to me by habit, for he was not hungry. He came because of what a scientist would call an association of ideas; but what I would call friendship. The old owl had accepted the fact that Hooly had human friends and waited quietly until Hooly was ready to fly off again. I was relieved; it was one less thing to think about. I wondered if the old owl was Hooly's mother after all.

About a week later we heard that a brown or tawny owl had been shot in a neighboring village for 'attacking soldiers.' Was this the end of our little tame bird that had never known fear of any human being? I dreaded so; but the very next evening down by the duckpond on the farm I saw Hooly perched on a willow branch. He allowed me to stroke his head, while closing his large-grape-like eyes with pleasure; and, just as does a cat, he liked being scratched about the ears. Hooly looked very handsome in his new browns and blacks and whites, and the eyes had that full authentic keenness of perfect natural form. 'Hooly,' I whispered, 'Hooly.' He gave me a long stare; a baby chirrup came from the scarce-open beak; then, without a cry, Hooly flew into the twilight, following a dark and silent winged form – and so out of our lives. And in the years that followed, I liked to think that the white splashes on the asphalt floor of our corn barn – revealing where owls waited on the great ship's-timber beams above for the rats below on the barley heaps – signified that Hooly, or Hooly's children, were still our friends.

July 1947

BOTH SIDES OF THE WATER

HENRY WILLIAMSON'S ASSOCIATION WITH
THE ATLANTIC MONTHLY

B Y A STRANGE QUIRK of serendipity *The Atlantic Monthly* celebrates its 150th anniversary in November 2007, so it is particularly apposite that this volume of Henry Williamson's writings, which appeared in its pages during its 'middle' period as it were, should be published this same year. To celebrate that anniversary and this publication, a little background to the magazine and HW's part in it seems an appropriate toast. Interesting in its own right, some understanding of the background of this prestigious journal illuminates the reason why HW was sought out as a contributor.

The Atlantic Monthly was founded by a handful of men – the cream of the writers and thinkers that made up the intellectual society of Boston, Massachusetts – including such luminaries as Ralph Waldo Emerson, Henry Wadsworth Longfellow, James Russell Lowell, and Oliver Wendell Holmes, who met over dinner in a Boston hotel in April 1857.

To set the scene historically, the inaugural date of 1857 predates publication of Darwin's *On the Origin of Species* by two years and the American Civil War (1861-1865) by four years. (I was amazed to find that the *Atlantic*'s dispatches from the battlefields were written by Nathaniel Hawthorne.) Reading through the various sources of information and looking at copies of the actual journal is a trawl through the history of American literature and philosophy, and indeed the history of world literature and philosophy.

Ralph Waldo Emerson (together with his protégé Henry David Thoreau) was the leading light of Transcendentalism, a literary and philosophical movement set up in New England at this time. Its followers were critical of formal religion and believed every created being was linked directly to the divine and that all creative activity was a direct expression of the divine spirit.

Possibly originally set up as an organ in which to publish the writings and ideas of the founding members – thus as a mouthpiece for Transcendentalism – *The Atlantic Monthly* also set out to encourage and stimulate Boston as a centre of intellectual and philosophical thought, and to encourage young aspiring writers. The first issue, 'a journal of literature, politics, science, and the arts', appeared in November 1857 with James Russell Lowell as the first editor. Its stated Declaration of Purpose encompassed the idea of 'Freedom, National Progress and Honor'. Avowing no actual political affiliation, it was to encompass the 'American idea'.

The *Atlantic* thrived and within two years the circulation was over 30,000. Today, according to information gleaned from its website, sales (via subscription and news-stands) equal roughly half a million. However by the 1890s circulation had dropped to 15,000 and it was running at a $5000 annual deficit. This fall in sales and popularity was apparently in some measure due to Harriet Beecher Stowe who, in writing an article about the private life of Lord Byron (whose wife had become a friend when Stowe visited England), seems to have offended the sensibilities of a large part of the readership. It was not until the advent of Ellery Sedgwick[1] as editor in 1909 that the journal once more became a thriving concern, and by 1928 its circulation had grown to 137,000.

The Atlantic Monthly has always had a high reputation for its literary content and many great names of American – and indeed European and British – literature can be found within its pages over the years: for example, the earlier issues with Emerson and Longfellow, and later Mark Twain, Henry James, Edith Wharton, and, with the advent of Ellery Sedgwick, Ernest Hemingway and Gertrude Stein. It is proud of having published Julia Ward Howe's poem 'The Battle Hymn of the Republic' in its issue for February 1862. On the other hand, unfortunately Sedgwick turned down the earliest poetical offerings from Robert Frost prior to his sojourn in England in 1912 – although this was rectified once the (now established) poet returned to the United States in 1915.

It is Ellery Sedgwick and his successor Edward Weeks[2] that concern us in relation to HW, for in 1925 Sedgwick approached the young English writer, still in the earliest stages of his writing career, and well before he was famous. The genesis of this approach is interesting. Sedgwick's first letter to Henry Williamson is dated 9 November:

Dear Mr. Williamson:–

My friend, Mr. Galsworthy, has been kind enough to write me of his interest in your work. He mentions that he does not know you personally, but believes that what you have to give would be of real interest to Atlantic readers, and I am writing to say how glad I should be if you would send me your manuscript personally.

Yours sincerely,
[signed] Ellery Sedgwick

Henry Williamson, Esquire
Skirr Cottage [etc.]

Thus it was John Galsworthy that HW has to thank for an introduction to this prestigious literary magazine. It is not known what Galsworthy actually said about HW's writing – but he would have been aware of the ethos governing *The Atlantic Monthly*. And I think it is obvious that the content of *The Lone Swallows* and *The Peregrine's Saga*, and indeed the early volumes of *The Flax of Dream*, would have been of suitable content to fit into that original background of Transcendentalism philosophy – virtually a back-to-nature movement – which would have still governed the ethos of the magazine to some extent. We know that HW was aware of Galsworthy from his attendance immediately after the First World War at The Tomorrow Club (later PEN) and that he had certainly attended a talk by Galsworthy there.[3] We know also that the two men actually met face to face on 29 November 1926,[4] for later that day Galsworthy wrote to Edward Garnett, drawing his attention to HW's writing, with far reaching consequences; but this instance of Galsworthy's help antedates that occasion by a whole year. Galsworthy does seem to have felt a close empathy for HW, which may stem from the fact that – unknown to either – they were actually related through a common great-great-grandfather.[5] It was certainly a very kind and thoughtful action on Galsworthy's part to promote HW in this way.

However, it would appear that nothing came of this first approach from Sedgwick, for no article by HW was printed at that time. One wonders why, for HW was very hungry for outlets for his work and his agent, Andrew Dakers,[6] was working diligently on his behalf.

The next letter from Sedgwick is dated 28 April 1927:

> Dear Mr. Williamson,
>
> You will remember our former correspondence, and will realize how pleasant it is for me to make amends for missing the last opportunity by accepting the next which came along. Through the Putnam Syndicate, three tiny but very pretty essays have come my way, and I plan to group them in an early issue of the Atlantic. Even the three of them make a brief contribution, but the quality is charming.
>
> Good luck to you!
>
> Yours sincerely,
>
> [signed] Ellery Sedgwick

The Putnam Syndicate was a part of G. P. Putnam & Sons Ltd, and HW would appear to have been using it to place his articles in various publications (although it is not clear what Dakers' position would have been in this arrangement). An accounts statement from the Putnam Syndicate, made up to 31 July 1928, shows these three 'tiny but very pretty essays' – which appeared in *The Atlantic Monthly* for August 1927 as 'English Idylls' and are the first item in this present volume – earned HW £18.10.4d, more or less twice as much as their individual placings in various English newspapers, which totalled only nine guineas.

On 16 June 1927, Sedgwick wrote to say he had read HW's story of the otter (sent by Putnam's) and liked it, but could not serialise such a story, which he felt should be read at one sitting: writing for serialisation was an art in itself. But he continued that he had taken 'two other little sketches. Besides the three tiny ones we accepted the other day.' He ended: 'Don't think then, that you have no friends in America.'

Constant Huntington of Putnam's (HW's publisher for *The Old Stag* and *Tarka the Otter*) wrote to HW on 16 November 1927, addressed to his parents' home at 11 Eastern Road, Brockley, stating that he had sent Ellery Sedgwick a copy of *Tarka* and that Sedgwick was currently in London, suggesting that HW telephone him to arrange a meeting the next day. HW had obviously been grumbling, for Huntington states: 'I shall not run your novels down to him or anyone else. I don't even seem to feel any desire to do so, but if I should have any criticism I should not tell anyone but you.' To date I have not found any evidence that a meeting between HW and Ellery Sedgwick did take place at that time – though that does not necessarily mean it didn't.

On 1 December 1927 there was a letter from O. E. Oliver of the Putnam Syndicate stating that 'the New York office of the Syndicate is trying to secure $175 for "THE HELLER" which is as much as the *Atlantic Monthly* ever pay for any story.'

The account statement from Putnam's shows that 'The Linhay on the Downs' (Oct 1927) and 'Muggy, the Rabbit Agent' (Nov 1927) earned £22.16.8d between them, and 'The Heller' (May 1928) a princely £32.7.3d. (these sums would be net, after the deduction of costs for exchanging dollars into sterling and commission; using the exchange rate current in 1928, $175 equated to £35.19.6d).

The next letter from Sedgwick is dated 20 December 1933 and shows that there has been a problem: 'It seems a tragic thing that a magazine like the Atlantic cannot make use of stories full of the best descriptions now written . . .' The problem was that Sedgwick felt the 'sketches' were too English to appeal to an American readership. He mentions 'A Tale of a Trout' and 'Whatever has Happened?' He is obviously very sad to have to write in such a manner about work he considers of very high quality.

Then, towards the end of 1934, the situation was resolved and 'Christmas' appeared in the December issue (vol. 154, no. 6),[7] along with its accompanying note in 'The Contributors' column: 'Henry Williamson appeared last in the *Atlantic* more than six years ago, but "Christmas" will recall his delightful nature pieces and such books as *The Pathway* and *Tarka the Otter*, which have won for him a high and special place in modern literature.' HW's diary entry for 11 February 1935 records: 'Rec'd from Atlantic Monthly, English sale of "Christmas" £5/5/-.' This seems a decided drop in the rate of remuneration but I am fairly sure this represents a 'second rights' sale – not the amount for the actual *Atlantic Monthly* printing.

The February 1935 issue printed 'A Night on Salisbury Plain', accompanied by the editorial note, 'continues the delightful series of English sketches by Henry Williamson, novelist, essayist, naturalist'. HW's essay was followed by 'The Revolt against Reason' by Bertrand Russell. Russell's editorial note – 'his name is token of what awaits the reader' – would seem to denote that Sedgwick found its content somewhat baffling!

HW's diary entry for Tuesday, 19 March 1935 states: 'Heard from Edward Weeks of Boston that he wants to be my American publisher. Hurray!' This was balm to his psyche and in contrast to two weeks previously, when he had written: 'Farrar & Rinehart do not want to make any further commitments of publishing, so they write today. They will be sorry.' It should be explained here that The Atlantic Monthly Press ran both the journal and an actual publishing house, that of Little, Brown, and Company.

On 29 March 1935 Sedgwick wrote an encouraging letter having received 'your little essay "Tales of my children"'. As a gloss . . . your letter is a thing of infinite zest.'[8] Sedgwick states that he will be glad to print the first chapter, and indeed, to make a little series of such pieces. He continues that he will show Weeks HW's letter and discuss the book with him, ending, 'be of good courage . . . you will win through.' 'The Dear One' appeared in May 1935 but 'Tales of My Children' proper was not to appear until after the Second World War had started. Some of these essays had first appeared in the magazine *Family* in 1935.

Edward Weeks was involved in The Atlantic Monthly Press Inc., which published books as well as the celebrated journal. Sedgwick's proposed discussion brought an immediate response from Weeks in the form of a 'Post Office Telegraph':

SEND ME YOUR MANUSCRIPTS RESERVE AMERICAN BOOK RIGHTS FOR ATLANTIC MONTHLY PRESS IMMENSELY ENCOURAGED YOUR ACCOUNT OF CHILDRENS DEVON HOLIDAY AND SALMON

Weeks followed this telegram up immediately with a long appreciative letter, which opens: 'Your last letter to Mr. Sedgwick brought with it information which I have been hoping to hear for many a moon.' Then he gives a most interesting piece of information: HW and Weeks had already met when HW was in the United States in 1931, and had given his lecture 'Hamlet and Modern Life' first at Dartmouth college in Hanover, New Hampshire, and then at Harvard (and apparently Yale), for Weeks states:

You will remember some friendly conversation we had at the time of your visit to Boston when, following your memorable lecture at Widener

Library, we retired to my apartment with some good Scotch whiskey between us and the world to talk over.

Weeks recalls Galsworthy's friendliness in alerting them to the quality of HW's writing, continuing: 'The Atlantic has always regarded you as one of its most distinctive and responsive contributors and I can think of no association more congenial than the opportunity of being able to publish your manuscripts both in magazine and book form.' Weeks shows that HW has obviously outlined a 'quartet' of *Linhay*, *Salar*, *Devon Holiday*, and *Tales of My Children*. 'The Salmon of course should be your magnum opus!' and he asks HW, as soon as he has time to spare, to let them have a synopsis which would appeal to American readers. *The Atlantic Monthly* with its 105,000 loyal readers will secure for HW 'a hearing such as you have long deserved'. Weeks indicates that he is reading V. M. Yeates's *Winged Victory*, calling it 'unquestionably the best picture of flying ever written'.

Ellery Sedgwick also sent a letter on 4 April 1935, ostensibly to add his voice to that of Weeks – but I think really to stake the claim of *The Atlantic Monthly* to serialise 'Tales of My Children'.

That HW was encouraged – indeed delighted – by this is shown by his diary entry for Friday, 12 April 1935: 'Another enthusiastic letter from Weeks, reinforced by one from Sedgwick, editor of <u>Atlantic Monthly</u>. They are keen on <u>Tales of My children</u>.'

HW answered Weeks's letter on 18 April 1935, a copy or version of which he kept in his own files:

Shallowford, Filleigh, N. Devon   England   18 April 1935

Dear Weeks

  Many thanks indeed for your letter of 4 April, and will you please give some of them to Ellery Sedgwick? He is the only Editor I know who seems to be what every writer hopes an Editor will be. He has divination, and a sense of direction for it. Apart from that one Editor, one had given up hope of any such contacts in the magazine world. So you can see how WELCOME your letters were.

  Now for information. You have received I hope LINHAY ON DOWNS. Bits, scraps, hardly a book? Here is DEVON HOLIDAY. [inserted above in red ms ink: 'separate cover'] The end of a period;

221

superficial sophistication; fatigue; the beginning of a new lease of life, or wind. The Maiden Salmon story at end gives this suggestion? You will see I realise now what these books are. But is it amusing? Has it a strain of harshness? It was slung together (between ourselves) to end a long option with a publisher: to enable me to start clear with SALAR THE LEAPER, a real book about a group of salmon. Shortly I shall send you part One, and I hope you will see it instantly as something REAL. I would be very glad if you could serialise it in the ATLANTIC right away, as it is due for publication in England in the Fall 1935. It takes all my life, energy (decreasing) and thought now; how I hate, fear, and dread the writing of it. It drags out my life.

Therefore, I feel I cant give much time now to TALES OF MY CHILDREN. If the Editor has already began [*sic*] to print the first chunk I sent, then I will write a few instalments. It will be easy. But at present things do seem rather too much for an overworked brain. My wife informs me, on her return after 3 months absence (she too was exhausted by events arising perhaps primarily out of a growing fear of poverty)[9] (coupled with a growing family) that in August she will present me with a fifth child. Splendid; but surely the last. This small cottage echoes with cries, yells, laughter; the children seem like weights on the base of the skull. Devon is said to be 100 years behind the times, I often feel. So it is sort of lonely. However, don't heed this sort of stuff; when the salmon is done, I shall breathe again. Faber is very excited about it. He saved my life, or rather Dick de la Mare, by offering me £750 advance for it. Since the Linhay sold through Cape only about 2000, this was marvellous. I feel I cant work with Cape any more as from that house come objections, objections, all the time. It snaps the gossamers. They said the three parts of the Flax of Dream, preceding Pathway, were bad. They said this was bad, that was bad. But Faber seems to be an easier air to breathe.

Yes, Tales of my Children will be good and readable. I perceive the way to move and interest people in the classical manner; as opposed to the romantic or sentimental.

But ATLANTIC SALMON is a masterpiece. Or will be. There are very few localisms: it is already for easy translation. After the children book and this, I want to write a real novel; been in me for 20 years; The Flax of Dream (Pathway etc) is trial work. This will be my old wives tale [a reference to Arnold Bennett's bestselling book]. Then a book of travel-fishing in Devon, Scotland, Florida, Canada. Perhaps elsewhere, if I get some money to have a holiday: and settle the family. You have printed at least one of the stories in DEVON HOLIDAY – the white stoat crossing field. The girl in the book is imaginary. The Assistant Professor is H. West of Dartmouth. (Caricature of course.) MFH Zeale is SPB Mais, the 'modern columbus' of the Columbia Broadcasting Company and our BBC. Thanks awfully, thanks a lot, for your letter. I must go now and throw a fly for a salmon; spate on. Count on me. I can write.

      Best woshes [the 'o' corrected in red ink to 'i']

      [signed in red ink] Henry Williamson

Well, as is frequently the case, one can only feel cross with HW for some of the things he writes, the continual 'doing of himself down' syndrome – especially to a publisher he was trying to impress. One only hopes that the letter that was sent had been carefully edited, but I doubt it! But such letters are of great interest to students of his psyche and working methods.

The river was indeed in spate. HW's diary (containing very few entries at this time) had recorded a few days earlier that the river was extraordinarily high for the time of year, and it was just after this that he caught, with the help of John Heygate, the 9lb 'fresh-run salmon . . . in pool between water-fall and Viaduct . . . Suddenly a weight on my line, and half a tail breaking the water.' There are photographs of HW and John Heygate holding this salmon triumphantly outside Shallowford.

The next communication was a telegram from Weeks, dated 9 May 1935.

LET NOTHING INTERFERE WITH SALAR SEND ME
INSTALMENTS FOR POSSIBLE SUMMER SERIALIZATION
ATLANTIC WE WANT BOOK TOO

HW's diary records two points at this time. On Wednesday, 8 May 1935: 'Rec'd £20 from Atlantic Monthly for first instalment of <u>Children</u>.' (This was 'The Dear One', printed in the issue for May 1935, vol. 155, no. 5.) And on Friday, 10 May 1935 a euphoric: 'Cable from Weeks of <u>Atlantic Monthly</u> Press asking for Salmon Tss for serial. The first time someone has wanted my stuff in real earnest.' (That is not strictly true of course, but it reflects the mood of the moment!)

The next few days were caught up in the drama of T. E. Lawrence's motorcycle accident and subsequent death. HW heard the news of the accident over the wireless on Tuesday, 14 May, presumably at breakfast time, for he would have been preparing to leave for Cloud's Hill in time to arrive for lunch, as arranged by the previous day's telegram from Lawrence, sent by him only minutes before the accident occurred. Later that same day HW received a telegram from Ellery Sedgwick (a fact not recorded in his personal papers anywhere, and thus not previously noted by myself), stamped 14 May 1935, timed 8.29 p.m.

SYMPATHETIC AND ENTIRELY PERSONAL SKETCH OF LAWRENCE COULD BE HIGHLY INTERESTING COULD YOU WRITE IT   SEDGWICK

A subsequent letter dated 29 May 1935 shows that HW had sent some answer to this, for Sedgwick states that he is glad HW is going to send them 'the paper which you will write with the candor he would have desired . . . any letters . . . would give it added poignancy'.

And tucked away in an obscure business file is the carbon copy of HW's letter accompanying that article, which ties up with the previously cryptic entry in his diary for Thursday, 13 June 1935 in Ann Thomas's handwriting: 'Lawrence article posted to Atlantic Monthly.' How quickly had HW dashed off what surely has to be the eventual *Genius of Friendship*, published by Faber and Faber in 1941. This clears up what had previously been a slight mystery as I noted in my biography.[10]

Shallowford, Filleigh, North Devon, England.   12th June, 1935

Dear Mr. Sedgwick,

Here is the Lawrence article. I have put all my eggs in one basket and refused several other suggestions to write about him. This article will not be published in England. At least, not by my arrangement. Do you think it is worth a thousand dollars? I hope it will add distinction to your already distinguished magazine.

Would the Atlantic Monthly Press care to publish it as soon after it appears in your magazine as you or they wish? The Seven Pillars of Wisdom will be out in August, and this as a little book, a memoir and appreciation would then be very timely. If so, perhaps they will let me know immediately it is convenient.

I am now rushing on with Salar the Salmon, which I have sworn to finish by 30 June. As soon as typed a copy will be dispatched to Edward Weeks. Then I shall finish Tales of my Children. Then I have an immense novel at the peak of my writing career to do.

I suppose Weeks is still keen to publish my books – at any rate I will not begin to make other arrangements until he has had time to write to me.

Yours sincerely,

P.S. I feel Lawrence would like this bit of writing about him. It is on the lines of my shorter article about Yeates, of which his opinion is contained in this article.

Weeks would not have received this letter before he sent the following telegram on 14 June:

WILL SERIALIZE PORTIONS SALAR DELAY ENGLISH
PUBLICATION UNTIL LATE AUTUMN SEND SPECIMEN
ILLUSTRATIONS   WEEKS

Apart from the fact that HW's English publishers, Faber and Faber, would (had they known) hardly have taken very kindly to being asked so peremptorily to delay publication, Weeks would have had no idea of HW's situation at this time. We know the state he was in, as he frantically tried to get the book written under extremely difficult circumstances.[11] A letter from Ann Thomas to Edward Weeks dated 22 June gives more background to the proposed *Salar* extracts. Things were moving apace.

Shallowford, Filleigh, North Devon, England.   22 June, 1935

Dear Sir,

I am sending you herewith chapters 13 and 14 of SALAR THE SALMON, which concludes the second section of the book.

I am also enclosing revised pages 57, 58, 108, 109, which, if it is not too late, could you please substitute for the original pages with these numbers in the typescript sent to you previously. Henry Williamson has decided to call the second section of the book, commencing with chapter Seven, page 59, SPRING SPATE, instead of "Summer river", so that I am sending you this alteration as well, in the hope there will be time to make this adjustment in print.

    With many thanks,
        Yours faithfully,
            [not signed as duplicate, but as from Ann Thomas]

Edward Weeks, Esq.,
[address included]

On 27 June Weeks sent a letter beginning: 'It is not my habit to talk with my friends in the clipped utterance of the cable. You have deserved a full and friendly letter long before this.' He goes on to discuss SALAR (his capitals), about which he is very enthusiastic, but he is really very tactfully setting out his own stall – an iron fist in a velvet glove comes to mind: 'these pages show you at the very top of your power, writing with an imagination and an accuracy which no present student of nature could surpass.'

Weeks continues that he wants to serialise as much of the book as possible in three or even four successive issues of the *Atlantic* and reiterates the point about Faber holding off publication until the autumn. But then 'there came the Lawrence catastrophe', and Weeks states that he had urged Sedgwick to cable HW to ask for 'whatever memorial you wished to write'. This manuscript has now arrived and has presented a problem as it is so long as to need serialising in itself and, as Weeks points out, they could not run two serials by the same author at the same time. However, if HW would agree to it being edited and cut down to a single unit 'without destroying any of its spirit' (one can imagine HW's reaction to that), then he could prepare it for the forthcoming September issue, and follow with the SALAR extracts in October, November, and December. He asks for decisions quickly so he can plan the editorial schedules, both for the Press and the magazine. A postscript suggests that there would be no objection if the Lawrence memorial were published in an English periodical after 15 September.

But on 10 July HW had to send the following Western Union Cablegram:

LAWRENCE EXECUTORS BAN QUOTATION LETTERS UNTIL
AD 2000 AM IMMEDIATELY TRANSMUTING ABBREVIATED
REVISED ARTICLE SUGGEST SERIALISATION SALMON
BOOK 70000 ONLY   WILLIAMSON

Weeks's reply – 'A Night Cable' – is dated 9 July (which threw me momentarily – but of course it is due to the difference in time zones) in which he agrees to begin *Salar* serialisation in September, which was the original plan anyway, and ends 'DROP LAWRENCE'. Obviously Weeks can foresee further copyright problems arising and that his editorial schedules are likely to be put out again. He wrote a further long letter on 2 August 1935 pointing out he was waiting for an answer to his 27 June letter. He offers $250 for each instalment of *Salar* – 3 or possibly 4 of them – and encloses a 'check' for the first two, which are already set up, and says that he has used all the typescript so far received from HW's secretary. The first part is to appear in the September issue, due out on 20 August, and the second and longer 'Spring Spate' in the October *Atlantic*, but he urgently needs further typescript to meet the planned schedules, as it is very important there is no gap in the serialisation. Weeks then goes on to praise the work which, like Thoreau's prose, makes him feel:

> as though I had just been given a new pair of antennae which make me sensitive to realms of experience which I had never previously even dreamed of. Your under-water world is a scene of freshness, beauty, and agitation, and you contrive by your skilful interludes with the poachers and fishermen to sustain and to quicken our interest in the strange realm without ever allowing our imagination to pall. It is an extraordinary undertaking . . .

They plan to publish the book under their imprint as soon as the serialisation is completed, and once the full typescript is to hand they can send a contract. Weeks wants illustrations, 'a competent artist – preferably, I believe, a man on your side of the water', stating that remuneration for this artist is to be in mutual agreement with Faber – that is, to share the cost. (Again, a rather arrogant assumption of Faber's acquiescence in his plans.)

HW's reply (typed, of which two copies, with slight variations, are in the file) explains his thoughts on the situation. I will indicate the main differences between the two versions.

Shallowford, Filleigh, N. Devon, England.   17 August, 1935

Dear Weeks,

I have, with thanks, your letter and cheque of 2 August.

For your queries:–

Part 3 of SALAR, called "Summer River", was sent off 5 weeks ago [crossed out and '29 July' inserted in version b)].   A duplicate followed by next mail [crossed out for 'on Aug 1']

Part 4, "Winter Star-stream" went off 10 August. Duplicate followed 14 August.

Meantime I sent a letter stating that Faber was hoping for English Book society for November. He had scheduled publication for October; but had postponed until November at my request. Later, would prejudice its chances. He has paid £750 for the book, and wants to get the first wave in good time for it to settle before the Xmas wave. His campaign was built around it, for the Fall. I suggested that as serial publication had been delayed by your requests for a T. E. Lawrence article, with letter-quotations, which you asked me to drop by cable; and further, as your December numbers would be on the stand by 20 November, it would have a clear way before any stray copies got into the U.S. I know your rule to have virgin print; but suggest that the circumstances might justify this small lapse.

Now about the book contract.

I confess I was a little bit disappointed by the suggested serial payments. They seemed out of proportion to the previous cheques from the ATLANTIC; 40,000 words for 500 dollars. But I realise that Mr. Sedgwick is away, and this may be a preliminary payment, to tide me over. I estimated [some text crossed out in version a) and not appearing in version b) which is a complicated calculation about what payment he should be getting] that I would get at least £100 for each instalment, reckoning four instalments. [more calculations deleted] You say in your letter that you hope to set up SALAR in type for book publication as soon as you receive the whole copy. I feel this may be expensive, for I have revised parts of the book since, with additions and alterations; and also, [some text deleted in version a)] I think it would be more generally satisfactory to agree on terms first, to avoid any misunderstanding. I am of course hoping that nothing will interfere with the publication of the book in

America by your house; it would be a keen disappointment, after our friendly feelings. Faber tells me the success of the book is assured in England, and there will be some enquiries from the American side fairly soon. You say you can estimate better when you have read all the book. So meanwhile, I will say only that since The Pathway I have had a 15% royalty from Dutton; but for the successor to Tarka, I think 17½% after 10,000 sold, is merited. And I realise that an advance will be mooted after discussion with Mr. Sedgwick. I would consider giving three options on my next three books to be written after Salar, to give the publisher some security for any plans of campaign.

Illustrations. Faber is not having an illustrated edition until later. Most of them are done, the equal if not superior of the text; done by my side, on the very places. Marvellous things!

Yours in haste,

H. Williamson [typed but also signed in green ink]

[In version a) there is added a postscript, ms in green ink, along the side of the first page thus: 'I am going to Germany to meet Hitler & look around on 5 Sept. next, & shall be away 3 weeks.' This is typed as a postscript on version b).]

The *Salar* extracts duly appeared as indicated. The following fulsome tributes were printed in the 'Contributor's Column':

For September 1935 (Vol 156, No 3):
In the direct literary tradition of White of Selborne, Richard Jefferies, and W. H. Hudson, Henry Williamson fills a place unique in English letters today. A protégé of John Galsworthy, he has long owned a latchkey to our columns. Unfortunates who do not know his work should begin with *The Old Stag and Other Stories* and then pass on to *Tarka the Otter*, which won the Hawthornden Prize in 1927.

For October 1935 (Vol 156, No 4):
On his return from the war, Henry Williamson withdrew to a tiny stone hut on the Devon Moors, and from that hermitage began his exploration of Nature and his study of lives hidden to most men.

For November 1935 (Vol 156, No 5):
Whether in his novels, his essays, or his short stories, Henry Williamson

is at his best when he writes of nature. His studies of the Devon moors, his stories of the little-seen denizens of the British Isles, have brought him an increasing number of devoted readers, among whom were to be numbered John Galsworthy and the late T. E. Lawrence. The *Atlantic* considers itself fortunate to print in this and in earlier issues three panels from Mr. Williamson's most recent work *Salar the Salmon*. This story of undersea life will be published in book form early in the spring of 1936.

Weeks wrote on 19 September 1935 with an embracing 'Dear Friend Williamson' and encouragement oozing out of every line. He reveals he has already had comments from readers 'alert to the splendid prose and the unbelievably acute observation' on the first instalment of *Salar*, and sets out the format for the following, regretting that due to Faber's publication dates, he has had to confine the serialisation to three issues, and to justify the editing, but he thinks he has succeeded in reproducing the 'main narrative in miniature … [with] sufficient beauty, color and continuity to preserve the pulse and vitality of your story'. Weeks goes on to state that they have published no more than 24,000 words and that therefore the rate of payment was actually fairer than it had appeared to HW.

Weeks then sets out a proposal for royalties for the actual book of $500 advance (half on signing contract, half on publication, or one lump sum if preferred) with a royalty of 15% on the publisher's price on all US sales. He points out that sales on HW's recent books in the United States have been poor (this must refer to *The Gold Falcon* in particular) and that they will have to convince booksellers 'that in our hands you are making a new start'. He emphasises the known integrity of The Atlantic Monthly house and that Little, Brown and Company and the *Atlantic* will do all that is possible to promote the book, but they can only afford to do this if HW will agree to the 15% royalty only (and not rising to 17½% after 10,000 as suggested by HW in his previous letter). He adds that they are planning to publish a straightforward trade edition (not a limited one) round about the following February, but are needing information about the illustrations and any arrangements with Faber. The final paragraph makes encouraging (perhaps placatory) comments on options for following books, but a handwritten postscript points out that *Devon Holiday* is not suitable for the American market.

The October 1935 issue in particular included articles by other writers that are interesting to note, for HW was appearing in very good company: including Erskine Caldwell, Havelock Ellis (an excellent essay on Proust), Leon Trotsky, John Foster Dulles, and 'The Meaning of Literary Prizes' by Edward Weeks. 'Prizes are a phenomenon of our time.' After discussing the Nobel and Pulitzer, and highlighting Sinclair Lewis's rejection of the latter for his novel *Arrowsmith* (which must have caused a great stir), and the James Tait Black, Weeks turns to 'lesser prizes':

> More partisan in their intent, more contemporary in their choice . . . they single out an author who might otherwise be neglected; . . . there's a man whose book you can't afford to miss. Few bookmen in England had heard of Henry Williamson until the Hawthornden Prize helped to illuminate the value of his *Tarka the Otter*.

Well, that is a bit of a back-handed compliment – but one must assume it was meant in good faith. But it is evident that the relationship is beginning to wear a bit thin. HW's next letter, dated 8 October 1935, shows a certain weariness, an ennui, with the whole *Salar* business, and, really, not how to impress one's publisher with either optimism or enthusiasm for the work in hand.

Shallowford, Filleigh, N. Devon, England   8 October 1935

Dear Weeks

I am sending by this mail a complete final copy of SALAR THE SALMON with endpaper map disfigured by one excision. If you want to reproduce it in the book (and it is very helpful I guess) Faber will send a new clean proof to you ON REQUEST.

Regarding the terms you offer, will you please try and get me 1000 dollars advance for the book against a 15% royalty. You say the royalty on 'publishers price'; I presume this means the published price, or retail price, round about 2.50 dollars? If so, please go ahead with the contract and try and persuade the chaps to give 1000 advance.

Fabers copy is a beautiful production. The wrapper, which I think you should use, is particularly good. It is enclosed. [This was the coloured Tunnicliffe wrap-around painting.]

About options, I do not want any in the contract. At one time an

American publisher was claiming from me, on an original novel contract with 3 options,

3 new novels

3 new books like Tarka

3 new books of short stories

3 village books

3 rambling books

3 war books

In fact three of every kind of book he had published for me and this after he had printed 11 books on the original contract. Or it may have been 12 or even 13.

You know my feelings about my new U.S. publishers. I do not want, or intend, to consider any offers, following on a success, from other publishers, providing that everything is oke, as you say on Broadway. If I had wanted to, I could have waited 14 days from now and possible have gotten a good advance from someone in London for Salar, for it will have a good press at once; but I know you are good people, and feel intuitively that you are the right people for me. I never felt at ease with any other publisher, except one, and not for long with him; entirely my fault or lack. So rest assured that in saying no options I am at the same time fully hopeful that our publishing contact will last during my writing life. [It had been, of course, HW's own suggestion to offer options on future books in his previous letter!]

You mention the Book of the month. H'm. As an old hand at the game, I have my doubts about their choosing it.[12] But they might, in America. They do queer things there. But my book to me now looks like a thin, dry, tour de force, or attempt at such. In fact, I feel rather mournful about it. Tired. Also got neurisis in one leg. But it will get better. Champagne in Germany following prolongued exhaustion, I think. I see clear sky ahead now.

Yours faithfully,

Henry Williamson

There is then a large gap in this archive file: although rather, there is a large gap in what I have currently unearthed. There may well be further material on this matter, tucked away in other files, or even hidden in unexpected places (there are many such instances – and I often find strange coincidences, when blocked for want of a particular item, of opening a book or a journal and finding what I need is tucked inside – all of which is quite shiver-making at times!) but to actually search further in the hope of finding more is, at this time, too daunting a task. I think what is here more than adequately covers the task in hand, and it leaves that little expectancy that, one day, an assiduous student may still be able to shed further light.

Salar the Salmon was published by Little, Brown, and Company in June 1936 – a delay from what we know was envisaged. They had taken Charles Tunnicliffe's black and white illustrations, which greatly enhance the text. It was reprinted that same June, and again in October and December (it would be interesting to know what the print numbers were), in October 1938, and again in 1950. It was a very nice looking volume, though the cover – a composite of various items – was surpassed by Faber's editions, both the first (October 1935) and the subsequent 'illustrated' one (October 1936), which carried superb coloured plates by Tunnicliffe.

The Atlantic Monthly continued to print HW's articles – including the incomparable 'A Crown of Life' in the January 1936 issue, about which the editorial comment was: 'There is a Franciscan flavor about Henry Williamson's story which makes it appropriate for the holiday season. [The issue would have come out before Christmas.] For those in doubt, we can say that the parson certainly had a dog biscuit in his pocket.' That remark would seem to show a certain reservation about the reaction of an American readership to the content of the tale. It also kills the atmosphere of this very beautiful story (one of my personal favourites of HW's work). Like the end of *Tarka*, there is a deliberate nuance here which gives the reader an opportunity to insert his own ideas: there are those of us who like to think, as HW subtly suggests, that the rector may have secreted a piece of communion bread for such a faithful dog to enjoy. Incidentally, the story has been cut out of the copy of the *Atlantic* in the archive with a very sharp knife. Henry probably used it to send off elsewhere!

Other articles followed at a steady trickle with extracts, as you will have seen, from 'Tales of My Children' and 'The Norfolk Farm'. The May 1937 'East Wind' gains the note, worth repeating here:

Nature writer and essayist in direct descent from Gilbert White and Richard Jefferies, Henry Williamson has made illuminating contributions to our understanding of the land and its creatures. His novel, *Tarka the Otter*, was awarded the Hawthornden Prize in 1930 [*sic*] and of his more recent book *Salar the Salmon*, chapters of which first appeared in the *Atlantic*, Lewis Gannett, the critic, had this to say: 'Of all English books of the year 1936, my warmest thanks to Henry Williamson for *Salar the Salmon*, which I think will be remembered when the year's best selling, well tailored English fiction is all forgotten.

On the following page of this issue is a letter from Lowell Thomas, writing from the Rockefeller Centre, New York City, commenting on a recent article by Eric Kennington on T. E. Lawrence[13] (a copy is not in HW's archive). It is headed: 'Shortly after the war, all London was flocking to the Albert Hall for Lowell Thomas's illustrated lectures on Lawrence of Arabia. Concerning Eric Kennington's portrait of Lawrence, in the April *Atlantic*, Mr Thomas writes: . . .' So *The Atlantic Monthly* had its TEL appreciation after all! HW probably (almost certainly) would have felt upset that he had been usurped. A letter from Kennington to HW dated 28 July 1954 shows that HW had referred to the article in an earlier letter, for he states: 'Reviewers wrote quite a lot of only praise. The Atlantic Monthly selected it from the rest.'

Edward Weeks took over as official editor in 1938, at which time Sedgwick sold up, I think due to ill health. The next several journal volumes are not in the archive. But Little, Brown, and Company published *Goodbye West Country* in 1938, slightly edited for the US market.

At some point after June 1940 (which is the last volume in the archive in the original format) the format of *The Atlantic Monthly* changed, for the next issue in the archive, for January 1945 (vol. 175, no. 1), is in quarto size with a better designed cover. I doubt such a luxury could have occurred in England at that time, even if the war was approaching its end. Towards the end of that issue, in a section called 'Accent on Living' is HW's contribution 'The Snipe's Nest': the lad with spring in his face was of course Rikky – as Richard was called by his family.

The last article by HW that appeared in *The Atlantic Monthly* was 'Hooly', in July 1947. (Interestingly, it is followed by an article by Sergei Prokofiev[14] on his early years at the St Petersburg Conservatory.) There are three copies of that issue in the files, and in one of them I found actually stuck in with glue two further letters from Edward Weeks. The first is dated 17 March 1947. Weeks praises 'Hooly': 'That essay of yours on Hooley the Owl [*sic*] is a true beauty. It finds you at your very best . . .' HW's diary records on 23 April 1947 that he received 'Atlantic Monthly payment . . . $300 £74.4.4.' (for 'Hooly').

That there has been some discussion about a new book, possibly over several previous letters, is obvious. Weeks points out that he has already told HW's New York agent, Bernice Baumgarten, and HW himself previously, that it would be a mistake to resume post-war publication in the US 'with a collection of your bucolic papers'. This statement would seem to refer to pieces about the Norfolk Farm and Devon: I doubt if HW took very kindly, however, to the use of the word 'bucolic', which on this side of the water tends to be somewhat derogatory, rather than 'pastoral'. The letter ends 'Affectionately as ever'. (Little, Brown, and Company published *The Phasian Bird* in 1950.)[15]

Before addressing the content of the second letter that was pasted in front of the 'Hooly' article, there is an oddity that occurred in HW's affairs at this time that needs some small explanation, namely: 'food parcels'. Food parcels as such were quite a common occurrence towards the end, and after the end, of the Second World War. They were sent from abroad – America, Canada, and Australia – by relatives and other kind people to help out war-stricken families in Britain, and tended to contain such things as dried fruit, jam, and tinned comestibles unobtainable in Britain at that time due to rationing. But in HW's case, these parcels seem to have represented some, if not all, of the payment due for articles printed in these countries. There were of course, strict regulations in place about the amount of money that could be transferred in and out of the country, and it must be due to such regulations that this arrangement was instigated.

A few extracts from HW's 1947 diary (all in Ann Thomas's handwriting) will illustrate this point, and including here other pertinent details:

Friday 12 Sept. 1947: Request from "Australian Journal" to reprint "Hooly" (from Atlantic Monthly) at fee of 10gns. Replied Yes – fee to be sent in food parcels to H.W. & I.L.W.
Wed. 19 Nov. '47: [HW & AT are at Ox's Cross field after time spent at Botesdale and in London]
Food parcel received from Atlantic Monthly [also one privately sent from

Australia – AT's note states 'presumably Alister Kershaw' – but he was in France at this time]

Thurs. 20 Nov. '47: Sent to "Atlantic Monthly" by airmail 5000 words from "Lucifer" beginning at New Years' Eve 1942.

Sat. 22 Nov. '47: Sent copy of "The Alternative" to Edward Weeks of "Atlantic Monthly"

Sun. 23 Nov. '47: A revised version of 'A Chronicle Writ in Darkness' superseding that posted on 20.11.47 sent by air Mail to "Atlantic Monthly", with note to E. Weeks to destroy previous copy.

Wed 3 Dec. '47: Letter in HW's hand to Edward Weeks saying 'if he lives' the MS will be with The Atlantic Monthly in January 1948, for publication in Sept. 1948 [This must refer to *The Phasian Bird*, though it was not published until 1950, with significant revisions from the Faber text, to cater for the US reader.]

Sat. 20 Dec. '47: 2 parcels received from Atlantic monthly – Ham dried fruit & rice. [also] 1 parcel received from "Australian Journal".

Wed. 31 Dec. '47: Ack'd parcels (2 each to H.W. & I.L.W.) to Australian Journal. Letter from them today accepting "The Heller" for 10gns to be paid in 5 food parcels each to H.W. & I.L.W. as before.

So to return to the second letter from Edward Weeks, dated 10 July 1947, found pasted into the July 1947 issue of *The Atlantic Monthly*: Weeks is alerting HW to the fact that November 1947 will be the 90th anniversary of the Atlantic, and that he is striving to bring together

the most distinguished and well beloved writers on your side of the water and ours. I have made a reservation in your name in the Table of Contents, and it would delight me to know that I could count on receiving from you by the first week in September either a fresh essay or perhaps a chapter of the new book which might stand effectively by itself. …

Affectionately as ever,
[signed] Edward Weeks

The November 1947 Anniversary issue contained articles by many well-known writers: Albert Einstein, Robert Frost, W. H. Auden, Mark Twain, Somerset Maugham, Sir Osbert Sitwell, Anne Morrow Lindbergh, Henry

James, Ellery Sedgwick, and George Bernard Shaw are among the names. But there is nothing by Henry Williamson. There is nothing in the 1947 diary to indicate the why or wherefore of this – in fact the diary is singularly blank altogether – the entries I have quoted being among the very few for the whole year. It is rather strange. That communication continued between the two men is obvious, and one would have thought that HW would have wanted to have something in such a particularly prestigious issue – especially as he would be relying on good will for the forthcoming publication of *The Phasian Bird*. And 60 years later, on the 150th anniversary of *The Atlantic Monthly*, like so many little mysteries in HW's affairs, that one for the moment must remain unresolved.

Anne Williamson

NOTES

I am grateful to Ellie Smith, of the permissions staff at *Atlantic*, for her enthusiastic encouragement, and for her valuable help in tracing Ellery Sedgwick's grandson (Ellery Sedgwick III), who kindly has given unreserved permission for use of quoted excerpts from letters. Despite all efforts, at the time of going to print we have been unable to trace a descendent of Edward Weeks.

1. Ellery Sedgwick (1872-1960), American editor, from a leading literary Massachusetts' family. Editor of *The Atlantic Monthly* 1909-38, and President of the Atlantic Monthly Company. Held Conservative (right-wing) views and defended Franco, the Spanish dictator, in the Atlantic in 1930s.
2. Edward A. Weeks, editor of *The Atlantic Monthly* 1938-66, was considered to hold more liberal views than Ellery Sedgwick.
3. The Tomorrow Club, founded by Mrs C. A. Dawson Scott (Mrs Sappho) in 1917 to help aspiring young writers. Later this became PEN, the renowned international society for 'Poets, Essayists, & Novelists' – whose first President was John Galsworthy.
4. See Anne Williamson, *Henry Williamson: Tarka and the Last Romantic*, Sutton, 1995, p. 109; note 13 on p. 339.
5. See Anne Williamson, 'Biographical Matters', sub-section 'Frankley-Hagley: an examination of the relationship between John Galsworthy and Henry Williamson', *Henry Williamson Society Journal*, no. 32, Sept. 1996, pp. 50-55;

also Editorial, ibid, p. 4.

6. Andrew Dakers, on the staff of Curtis Brown Ltd, International Publishing Bureau, became HW's agent in 1920. Dakers subsequently set up his own agency. His support of HW went far beyond the call of duty as the many letters and documents in HW's archive show. (See references in Anne Williamson, *Henry Williamson: Tarka and the Last Romantic*.)

7. The following Christmas an American couple, Mr and Mrs Frederic Main from Massachusetts, decided to print 'Christmas' as a Christmas greeting pamphlet for their friends. They sought and were granted permission from *The Atlantic Monthly* – but not from HW himself.

8. This is the letter in which Sedgwick mentions Hitler – see Anne Williamson, *Henry Williamson: Tarka and the Last Romantic*, p. 190.

9. HW's wife, Ida Loetitia Williamson (Gipsy) had left Shallowford on 15 Jan 1935 to exchange places with Ann Thomas, the latter coming to live and work with HW while ILW lived at AT's home in Tenterden, Kent, to look after things there, including keeping an eye on AT's neurotic sister, Bronwen. The Williamson children stayed at Shallowford, (as presumably did AT's daughter, Rosemary) where they would have been looked after by Annie Rawle.

10. Anne Williamson, *Henry Williamson: Tarka and the Last Romantic*, p. 183.

11. ibid, p. 186.

12. HW will be thinking here of the controversy that surrounded *The Pathway* in the United States in 1930, when it was expected to be 'Book of the Month' but was outvoted by a conspiracy. See Anne Williamson, 'The amazing storm that attended *The Pathway* in the USA', *Henry Williamson Society Journal*, no. 20, Sept. 1989, pp. 34-7; also the pages reproducing the full page advertisement in the *New York Herald Tribune*, full of praises for *The Pathway*, ibid. p. 28-9. Weeks (and Sedgwick) would certainly have known all about this furore – both the praise and the debacle.

13. Eric H. Kennington, 'Lawrence: an unofficial portrait', *The Atlantic Monthly*, April 1937, pp. 406-415. The text is exactly as Kennington's essay in *T. E. Lawrence by his Friends*, ed. A. W. Lawrence (Cape, 1937). Kennington (1888-1960), painter and sculptor, official war artist, illustrator for TEL's *Seven Pillars of Wisdom*, sculpted the effigy of TEL in St Martin's church, Wareham, Dorset, and the Tate Gallery, and the bust of TEL in St. Paul's Cathedral, and All Soul's, Oxford.

14. Sergei Prokofiev (1891-1953), Russian pianist and composer, who lived for

many years in exile due to strictures of the Soviet regime. Died on the same day as Stalin. HW is known to have stated that Prokofiev had wanted to compose music based on *Salar*. If this is true, then the juxtaposition of these two in the *Atlantic* may have provided the contact point.

15. A two-and-a half page letter from Edward Weeks dated 28 November 1949 was a pre-publication critique/analysis of *The Phasian Bird* indicating his thoughts about the book and the amendments he would need to make for the American market: 'It is a remarkable book: the finest passages, those having to do with Chee-kai, find you in the full power of your maturity . . . I rate the book as one of your big three [with *Tarka* and *Salar*].'

Weeks went on to analyse three themes in the novel: the life of Chee-kai – his attachment to Petris and Perdix, and his fight for survival in a merciless environment; conservation, and the woeful condition of English farming during the Depression; and the story of the idealist farmer (although he wanted to cut the accusation of spying and its consequences).

Editor's Note and Acknowledgements

Sixty years after the last of Henry Williamson's contributions to *The Atlantic Monthly* was published, these various essays and stories are collected now for the first time in this latest collection of Williamson's writings to be published by The Henry Williamson Society. While some small errors have been corrected, the *Atlantic*'s American spelling and punctuation has been retained; although unfamiliar to the eye of the modern British reader, they add considerably to the transatlantic flavour and period atmosphere of the pieces.

The edited version of *Salar the Salmon* which is included here was something of a coup for the *Atlantic*, the first part predating by a month the publication of the book in Britain. The book was an immediate bestseller; and indeed the condensed version – skilfully done, and subsequently used twice by the *Reader's Digest* – created much interest in its own right in the United States prior to the book's publication there in June 1936. Perhaps its presence here will encourage demand for a reprint of the book, long overdue.

My thanks must go to the following: to the Trustees of the Henry Williamson Literary Estate for their kind permission to reprint the texts; to Richard and Anne Williamson for their valuable contributions and – as always – their encouragement; to *The Atlantic Monthly* for allowing the use of the brief, if not entirely accurate, author portraits; to Tony Evans and Walker Burns for their help during the production of the book; and particular thanks to Mick Loates for his striking illustration of a leaping salmon, painted especially for *Atlantic Tales*.

I am most grateful to the Estate of C. F. Tunnicliffe for permission to use the superb drawings and woodcuts by Charles Tunnicliffe. Most of them are taken from the first British illustrated edition of *Salar the Salmon*, published in October 1936; those from other works are: p. 15, Henry Williamson, *The Lone Swallows*, 1933; p. 19, E. L. Grant Watson, *The Leaves Return*, 1947; p. 31, Charles S. Bane, *Exploring England*, 1944; p. 124, H. E. Bates, *In the Heart of the Country*, 1942; p. 130, C. F. Tunnicliffe, *Shorelands Summer Diary*, 1952; p. 178, C. F. Tunnicliffe, *My Country Book*, 1942; p. 189, Sidney Rogerson, *Both Sides of the Road*, 1949; p. 203, C. F. Tunnicliffe, *Bird Portraiture*, 1945; and p. 207, Ian Niall, *Portrait of a Country Artist: C. F. Tunnicliffe RA, 1901-1979*, 1980.

The illustrations on pp. 56 and 110 are provided courtesy of University of Exeter Information Services Special Collections, and are from collection MS 126: 'Henry Williamson: correspondence with Charles Tunnicliffe, 1932-1977'.

John Gregory

240